Optical Mineralogy

OPTICAL MINERALOGY

Paul F. Kerr, Ph.D.

PROFESSOR OF MINERALOGY, COLUMBIA UNIVERSITY

THIRD EDITION

*Previous Editions
by Austin F. Rogers
and Paul F. Kerr*

McGRAW-HILL BOOK COMPANY, INC.

New York   Toronto   London

1959

OPTICAL MINERALOGY

Library of Congress Catalog Card Number 58-13880

THE MAPLE PRESS COMPANY, YORK, PA.

To
the Memory of
LEA MCILVAINE LUQUER
1864–1930

Preface

Austin F. Rogers, the senior author of the first two editions of this text and professor emeritus in mineralogy at Stanford University, passed away at Berkeley, California, in April, 1957. His wise counsel as a former professor and his judgment as a mineralogist have been greatly missed during this revision. On the other hand, many readers, particularly those most familiar with Professor Rogers and his work, will recognize the influence of his teaching and will remember portions of the text which remain unchanged in the third edition.

Sixteen years have elapsed since the second edition of this text appeared. The fidelity of the readers who have maintained a steady demand over this period indicates that the general features of the second edition have been found useful and consequently they are retained.

The first objective in this revision has been concern over the student who has found difficulty with the phraseology or explanations of previous editions. Within the limitations of space every effort has been made to prepare a text which could be used with a minimum of supervision and a maximum of self-instruction. Optical mineralogy is acquired by the student with greatest facility with a good set of illustrative material under competent classroom instruction. On the other hand, experience has shown that a considerable number, lacking classroom facilities and desirous of learning the techniques described, have made considerable progress with representative thin sections and the text alone.

The format of mineral description has been retained. The length of the text is essentially the same. However, each mineral description has been reviewed, many have been revised, a few have been added. Descriptions of opaque minerals have been reduced in order to make space for other material. Selected references have been added in an attempt to extend the scope of the text without undue enlargement.

The polarizing microscope has undergone considerable evolution in recent years. New illustrations have been substituted to call attention to improved equipment now available. Phase microscopy is illustrated. The chapter intended to guide the student in the selection of methods of grinding thin sections has been revised. A chapter is included to serve as an outline in acquiring a working knowledge of the universal stage. The identification tables have been revised in an attempt to make them more useful in the solution of the problem of identifying unknown minerals.

The text is intended primarily for thin-section study, but both the descriptions and the tables will be found useful for work with mineral fragments. The feldspars have been the subject of considerable revision in the light of recent studies. Other mineral groups have not been so extensively revised, although frequent revision will be noted throughout. This applies to the pyroxenes, amphiboles, chlorite, serpentine, the clays, and evaporites.

The writer is particularly indebted to colleagues and research associates at Columbia University who have offered suggestions. Professors Arie Poldervaart, Brian Mason, and Ralph J. Holmes; Miss P. K. Hamilton, Research Associate; Mr. Martin Molloy, Mr. William Bassett, and Mr. Davis M. Lapham, Graduate Assistants, have all provided assistance in various ways. The manufacturers of optical equipment have cooperated in furnishing a number of illustrations. Mr. E. O. Rowland, Laboratory Technician, Kings College, London, has advised on thin-section methods. Numerous conversations with instructors who have used previous editions have been particularly helpful.

Paul F. Kerr

Contents

Indicatrix)—The Axial Angles $2E$ and $2V$—Variation in Axial Angle—Determination of the Optic Sign of a Biaxial Mineral—The Optic-axis Figure—Dispersion in Biaxial Interference Figures.

Purpose—Stage Assembly—Graduated Circles—The Stereographic Plot—Adjustment—Orientation with the Universal Stage—Location of the Uniaxial Optic Axis—Optical Directions in Biaxial Crystals—Illustrative Mounts—Illustrative Exercises—Stereographic Net.

Color and Pleochroism—Form or Aggregation—Natural Crystal Form in Thin Section—Cleavage, Parting, and Fracture as an Aid in Distinguishing Minerals—Orientation.

Crushed Fragments—Methods of Mounting—Immersion Method—Index Determinations by Immersion—Form of Mineral Fragments—Immersion Media—Standardization and Care of Liquids.

Tables—Opaque Minerals (Table 10-1)—Transparent Minerals (Tables 10-2 to 10-10)—Isotropic Minerals (Table 10-6)—Birefringent Minerals (Table 10-7)—Optical Character (Tables 10-8, 10-9, and 10-10)—Conclusion.

PART TWO. MINERAL DESCRIPTIONS

Mineral Groups

Elements: Graphite.
Sulfides: Sphalerite—Pyrite—Pyrrhotite—Chalcopyrite.
Halides: Halite—Fluorite.
Oxides: Periclase—Corundum—Hematite—Ilmenite—Rutile—Cassiterite.
Multiple Oxides: Spinel—Magnetite—Chromite—Perovskite.
Hydroxides: Diaspore—Brucite—Boehmite—Gibbsite—Cliachite—Limonite.

Carbonates: Calcite—Dolomite—Magnesite—Siderite—Aragonite.
Sulfates: Barite—Celestite—Anhydrite—Gypsum—Polyhalite—Alunite—Jarosite.
Phosphates: Monazite—Apatite—Dahllite—Collophane—Lazulite.

Silica Group: Quartz—Chalcedony—Opal—Tridymite—Cristobalite—Lechatelierite—Coesite.
Feldspars: Orthoclase—Adularia—Sanidine—Microcline—Anorthoclase—Albite—Oligoclase—Andesine—Labradorite—Bytownite—Anorthite.
Feldspathoids: Leucite—Nepheline—Cancrinite—Sodalite—Haüyne—Melilite.

Abbreviations

Mineral type to which index symbol applies	Symbols used in this text	Symbols used by Dana, Johannsen, Larsen and Berman	Symbols used by Winchell
Isotropic.....................	n	n	N
Uniaxial			
Extraordinary ray............	n_ϵ	ϵ	Ne
Ordinary ray................	n_ω	ω	No
Biaxial			
Least value................	n_α	α	Np
Intermediate value............	n_β	β	Nm
Greatest value................	n_γ	γ	Ng

n = index of refraction.

n_α(alpha) = the index of the fast ray in biaxial minerals. The least index of refraction.

n_β(beta) = the index of the ray at right angles to n_α and n_γ.

n_γ(gamma) = the index of the slow ray in biaxial minerals. The greatest index of refraction.

n_ϵ(epsilon) = the maximum (in positive) and the minimum (in negative) index of refraction of the extraordinary ray in uniaxial minerals.

n_ω(omega) = the index of refraction of the ordinary ray in uniaxial minerals. If $n_\omega < n_\epsilon$, the mineral is positive. If $n_\omega > n_\epsilon$, the mineral is negative. n_ω is constant in a given uniaxial mineral, whereas the index of the extraordinary ray varies from n_ω to n_ϵ.

n_1 and n_2 = the lesser and greater indices of refraction of the two rays in any crystal section at random orientation.

X = the axis of greatest ease of vibration. Light vibrating parallel to X travels with maximum velocity (also indicated by α).

Z = the axis of least ease of vibration. Light vibrating parallel to Z travels with minimum velocity (also indicated by γ).

Y = the intermediate axis at right angles to the plane of X and Z (also indicated by β).

ϵ = the axis of vibration of the extraordinary ray.

ω = the axis of vibration of the ordinary ray (in a plane at right angles to ϵ).

r = the dispersion for red.

v = the dispersion for violet.

$2V$ = the axial angle within the mineral.

$2E$ = the axial angle observed in air.

Bx_a = acute bisectrix.

Bx_o = obtuse bisectrix.

Ax. pl. = the plane of the optic axes.

μ = micron, thousandth of a millimeter (0.001 mm.).

$m\mu$ = millimicron, millionth of a millimeter (0.000001 mm.).

A = angstrom unit, tenth of a millimicron (0.0000001 mm.).

Δ = retardation in $m\mu$ (millimicrons).

t = thickness of a thin section. Usually given in hundredths of a millimeter (0.01 mm.).

a, b, and c = the crystallographic axes.

$\angle\alpha$, β, γ = angles between the crystallographic axes.

$(n_\gamma - n_\alpha)$ = double refraction for biaxial minerals.

$(n_\omega - n_\epsilon)$; $(n_\epsilon - n_\omega)$ = double refraction for uniaxial minerals.

H_1 = the slow ray of the Berek compensator.

H_2 = the fast ray of the Berek compensator.

e = the extraordinary ray.

o = the ordinary ray.

Length-fast (or negative elongation) = elongation parallel to the vibration direction of the fast ray.

Length-slow (or positive elongation) = elongation parallel to the vibration direction of the slow ray.

ca. = circa (about).

PART ONE

Mineral Optics

CHAPTER 1

Mineral Preparations for Microscopic Study

Types of Preparations. The preparation of minerals for microscopic study depends largely upon the microscope used. If only surficial features are to be examined as with a binocular microscope, little preparation is required. In this case small crystals, mineral grains, or even specimens several inches across, either opaque or transparent, may be examined unmounted, under a range of magnifications up to about 100 times.

In other studies the microscope used differs for opaque and transparent materials. Opaque minerals are often sawed to produce a flat surface, mounted for convenience in handling, and polished until a brilliantly reflecting surface is developed. Such surfaces are examined with the reflecting microscope. Transparent minerals are usually cemented to glass slides with Canada balsam or a similar transparent mounting material. Small crystals, grains, or fragments are often scattered over the central portion of the slide and mounted without further preparation. Sands and mineral concentrates are particularly suitable for such treatment. When mounted, the preparations are examined in transmitted light with the polarizing microscope.

A common form of microscopic examination employed for transparent materials involves the use of thin sections. This text is mainly concerned with such study. Thin sections are ordinarily about 0.03 mm thick and measure about an inch square.

Many mineral materials may be studied to advantage in thin sections with the polarizing microscope. Probably the most widely employed application lies in the examination of igneous, metamorphic, and sedimentary rocks. The technique, however, is capable of wider application. With suitable impregnation, soils, clays, and many forms of loosely consolidated materials may be mounted for this form of study. Mineral fragments may also be cemented into a briquette and ground thin.

Crystals of minerals or artificial chemical compounds are often oriented and sliced at desired angles in order to emphasize certain optical properties. Frequently rock specimens are carefully marked with respect to their position in the outcrop when it is desired to correlate the position

3

of individual crystals in a thin section with the rock mass from which the section has been cut.

Materials for Thin Sections. Few students of mineralogy prepare their own thin sections, but it is desirable for all to know how thin sections are made. With natural manual dexterity and patience students have learned to make sections equal to those ground by professional section makers.[1] The speed may not equal that of the professional, but with a little care the section cut may be equally satisfactory.

The technique employed varies with the nature of the material. Grinding sections of compact igneous, sedimentary, and metamorphic rocks is a routine process. Friable or fractured rocks and unconsolidated materials should be firmly cemented with a penetrating binding substance before

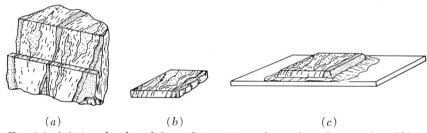

(a)   (b)   (c)

FIG. 1-1. (a) A rock selected for a thin section and sawed to obtain a chip. (b) A sawed chip of proper dimensions for a thin section (bottom surface smooth). (c) The chip mounted on a glass slide with Canada balsam ready for the first stage of grinding.

being mounted on a glass slide. One method involves a preliminary heating with the mineral specimen immersed in Canada balsam either in an open dish or under a vacuum bell jar. Methyl methacrylate "lucite" has been used by Bell (1939) to impregnate friable material under a vacuum. Exley (1956) has impregnated friable kaolin specimens with a synthetic resin supplied by Bakelite, Ltd. A friable specimen is cemented with a mixture of (1) resin, (2) a modifying agent, (3) a catalyst, and (4) an accelerator. The four materials (with corresponding trade numbers) are mixed in order as follows: resin, 100 g (SR 17431); modifying agent, 10 to 15 g (Z 17453); catalyst, 1 g (Q 17447); and an accelerator, 2 g (Q 17448). The mixture is said to gel in 2 hours at 25°C. It will harden

[1] The following list is furnished for the convenience of readers who wish the names of technicians making thin sections:

D. M. Organist, Box 176, Newark, Del.
George Rév, 324 Schermerhorn Hall, 119 St. and Amsterdam Ave., New York 27, N.Y.
Fred Roberts, 1106 W. Newark Ave., Monterey Park, Calif.
Alexander Tihonravov, 954 Russel Ave., Los Altos, Calif.
Rudolph von Huene, 865 N. Mentor Ave., Pasadena, Calif.

in 6 hours at 50°C or in 1 hour at 100°C. Thin sections cut from decomposed granite in which kaolinite has replaced feldspar retain sharp crystal boundaries with this treatment.

The earlier stages in the preparation of an ordinary rock section are illustrated in Figure 1-1. The first problem involves the choice of material and a decision concerning the direction of the cut. A specimen suitable for effective study with the microscope is selected. Such a specimen may contain fine-grained materials not easily studied by the unaided eye, structures that yield readily to examination with the microscope, or any one of those numerous minor features so effectively revealed by microscopic examination. The direction in which the section is to be cut should be clearly marked on the specimen.

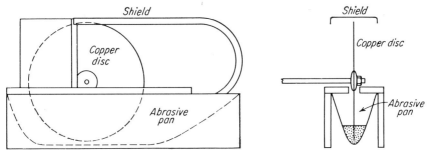

FIG. 1-2. A mineralogical saw consisting of a hard rolled copper disk used with carborundum.

The Mineral Chip. The first step in the manufacture of a thin section involves the preparation of a mineral chip with a smooth surface suitable for mounting on a glass slide. The chip may be broken from a specimen and ground flat on one side, or a slice of suitable dimensions may be sawed directly from a specimen. An ideal chip is about 1 inch square and ⅛ inch thick.

Where it is desired to cut chips, several types of saws are available. In each case, however, the cutting action is actually grinding along a groove rather than sawing in the ordinary sense of the word. The grinding action is accomplished with an abrasive powder. The saw itself is usually a metal disk. The abrasive may be fed against the disk in loose particles, or it may be imbedded in the outer rim. Abrasives may be either carborundum or diamond powders.

Figure 1-2 illustrates an ordinary mineralogical saw. It may be a hard-rolled copper disk that operates over a trough filled with carborundum and sludge. The edge of the rotating disk picks up carborundum and rubs it against the specimen. If a proper mixture of mud, carborundum, and water is maintained, it is possible to grind a narrow channel completely through an inch of solid quartz in a few minutes.

When a chip is ready, a smooth surface is polished on one side by utilizing successively 100, FFF, and 600 carborundum and finishing with 302½ American Optical Company's emery. In case the rock is fairly soft, the first grinding with 100 carborundum is omitted. The 100 carborundum is coarse and tends to destroy soft material.

The smoothly ground but unpolished surface of the chip is cleaned and dried. It is then mounted on a glass object slide, employing Canada balsam or Lakeside 70 as a cementing material. Balsam should be cooked about 2 minutes at 160°C until a bead is tenacious and solid. The chip may then be warmed at 120°C for mounting. Balsam should not be overcooked, since it then becomes too brittle and may even turn brown. While the balsam is still warm and liquid, the flat surface of the warmed chip is placed upon a slide containing a cooked smear of Canada balsam. On cooling, the chip will be firmly cemented to the glass slide. The bond should be an even layer of balsam unbroken by air bubbles. If air bubbles are present, the chip should be warmed, removed, and remounted. The problem of properly cooking Canada balsam may be solved by using a hot plate with thermostat control, or a glycerin plate as shown in Figure 1-3. Lakeside 70, heated at 140°C, may be used to cement directly without cooking. The index of refraction, $n = 1.540$, is close to but slightly higher than that for balsam (1.537). Air pockets are less likely to form between the glass slide and the chip than with balsam.

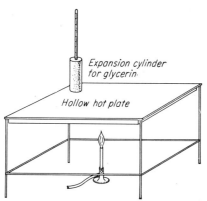

Expansion cylinder for glycerin

Hollow hot plate

FIG. 1-3. A hot plate containing a glycerin chamber and thermometer well for control in cooking Canada balsam. (*Developed by Paul H. Bird.*)

Cutting the Chip to a Thin Section. Much attention has been devoted to the problem of producing a thin uniform slice 0.03 mm thick from a chip several millimeters thick. In general, this may be accomplished in two ways. In one method the chip is ground in successive stages with carborundum and emery on laps, in a sequence similar to that used to produce a smooth surface on the chip. In another, a carefully adjusted saw is used to cut the chip to about 0.06 mm and it is then completed to 0.03 mm on a lap.

Mechanical grinding of mounted chips usually takes place on flat metal laps faced to a plane flat surface. The laps should be at least 12 inches in diameter and should rotate at a speed of about 600 rpm. Bearings must be shielded against abrasive powder. The lap for fine grinding should be made of copper or brass and grooved. A helical groove pattern is effective. Where precision diamond saws are used to cut initial slices 0.06 to 0.08 mm thick, many sections may be completed by hand on a glass plate with abrasive powder, or in some instances with abrasive papers.

Great precautions concerning cleanliness are necessary throughout the entire process. A single grain of coarse grit rubbed against the slide at the wrong time will often destroy a thin section.

The exposed side of the mounted chip is ground in turn with medium carborundum, fine carborundum, and alundum. Alundum is utilized when the chip has been reduced to a thickness of about 0.1 mm. The specimen may be ground on a rotating grooved lap or finished by hand on a smooth glass plate. A fine alundum or emery paste is used for the final grinding. Water is ordinarily employed to make the paste, but kerosene or glycol are required for water-soluble materials. This last stage demands considerable manual dexterity. The thin slice should be kept uniform in thickness during grinding and the grinding continued until a thickness of about 0.03 mm is attained. The thickness of the slide is controlled through the final stage by micro-

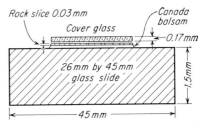

FIG. 1-4. A cross section of the mounted rock slice (vertical scale exaggerated).

scopic observation of the interference colors given by some known mineral in the section when covered with a film of water. Quartz is frequently present, in which case the resulting interference colors should be almost entirely white or gray. Some prefer large sections for which the thickness may be about 0.04 mm. A thin section properly ground shows a remarkable degree of transparency.

Small holders are useful for holding the mounted chips during grinding. Such holders keep the opposite surfaces of the slide parallel and facilitate the process of fine grinding. Holders also permit the operator to grind several sections at the same time until the final stage is reached. Three holders form a useful combination. One, holding six slides, may be used to grind the chip to a thickness of about 0.5 mm; the second, arranged for two slides, to carry the grinding to 0.1 mm; and the third, holding a single slide, to complete the sections. In case a holder is not available, a small cork may be connected to the back of the slide with balsam.

When the section is ground to the proper thickness, it is washed free from grinding powder and dried. Fresh balsam is then smeared over the surface of the slice. It is cooked, and faced with a cover glass (thickness about 0.17 mm or less). The preparation is then cooled, and excess balsam around the edge of the cover glass is dissolved with xylol, followed by a wash with kerosene. The thin section is now covered and ready for use (Figure 1-4).

In case the slice is composed of substantial and compact material, it may be transferred from the glass slide on which it has been ground to another slide free from scratches. To effect the transfer, the slide holding the slice is smeared with balsam and heated on a hot plate as in covering.

FIG. 1-5. A diamond saw designed to cut slices of rocks to about 0.06 mm, by E. O. Rowland. (*Cutrock Engineering Co., Ltd., Dollis Mews, Dollis Park, Finchley, London, N. 3, England.*)

A clean slide smeared with balsam is placed on the hot plate next to the ground slide containing the chip, and the balsam cooked at the same time.[2] When both smears of balsam are cooked the slice is worked free from the ground slide with the aid of a toothpick and floated to the clean side. It is then covered with a cover glass in the usual way.

Rapid and precise cuts may be made with metal saws which contain diamond powder[3] imbedded in the metal of the rim (Meyer, 1946). The smooth chip is cemented to a glass slide with Lakeside 70 as a cementing material. A well-balanced diamond saw then cuts the precisely held chip to a thickness of about 0.06 mm in a single operation. The slice is then reduced to standard thickness on a finishing lap.

Rowland (1953) has described a saw as shown in Figure 1-5. The saw is mounted vertically above a platform. The latter is free to move up or down or horizontally with machine precision. A special holder mounted on the platform holds the material to be sectioned. Equipment of this sort has been called a *petrotome* by Isachsen (1951).

Special Thin Sections. Thin "peeled" films removed from the smooth surface of clays may be mounted in balsam on glass slides and examined as ordinary thin sections. The mounted films are for the most part exceed-

[2] Precooked balsam may be heated to 100°C for mounting.
[3] A 6-inch blade charged with powdered diamonds is made by the Consolidated Diamond Tool Corporation, Yonkers, N.Y.

ingly thin, although coarse particles may be plucked from the clay mass and will protrude from the balance of the film.

A smooth surface is carefully prepared by polishing on dry ground-glass plates. While still moist, the surface is covered with amyl acetate and pyroxylin. After the preparation is dried for from 5 to 6 hours, the dry film formed by the pyroxylin is peeled from the clay surface with a knife blade. The film is then mounted with Canada balsam on a glass slide and covered with a cover glass.

Special thin sections are occasionally made in which the area of the section may measure as much as 3 inches by 4 inches although the thickness is usually greater than normal. Such sections may provide a survey of textural relations which extends beyond the area ordinarily covered by a thin section. They have also been used in a limited manner for lantern projection either directly or with polarized light derived from superimposed polaroid sheets.

Specimens are frequently examined which contain both transparent and opaque minerals. The technique of polishing metallic minerals and the methods of examination employed are beyond the scope of this text, but it should be pointed out that a number of laboratories have found it advantageous to prepare dual-purpose thin sections. These sections are not only ground to the conventional thickness, but one surface is polished to allow examination of metallic constituents in reflected light in addition to the customary study with transmitted polarized light (Rankama, 1941; Kennedy, 1945).

REFERENCES

Bell, James F.: Notes on the Uses of Methyl Methacrylate "Lucite" in a Geological Laboratory, *Econ. Geol.*, vol. 34, pp. 804–811, 1939.

Exley, C. S.: A Method of Impregnating Friable Rocks for the Cutting of Thin Sections, *Mineral. Mag.*, vol. 31, pp. 347–349, 1956.

Isachsen, Y. William: A Petrotome Modification for Cutting Extremely Thin Rock Sections, *Proc. Penn. Acad. Sci.*, vol. 25, pp. 109–112, 1951.

Kennedy, George C.: The Preparation of Polished Thin Sections, *Econ. Geol.*, vol. 40, pp. 353–360, 1945.

Keyes, Mary G.: Making Thin Sections of Rocks, *Am. J. Sci.*, 5th ser., vol. 10, pp. 538–550, 1925.

Meyer, Charles: Notes on the Cutting and Polishing of Thin Sections, *Econ. Geol.*, vol. 41, pp. 166–172, 1946.

Rankama, K.: An Improved Technique for the Making of Thinned Polished Sections, *Econ. Geol.*, vol. 36, pp. 561–563, 1941.

Ross, C. S.: Methods of Preparation of Sedimentary Materials for Study, *Econ. Geol.*, vol. 21, pp. 454–468, 1926. See also *Am. J. Sci.*, 5th ser., vol. 7, pp. 483–485, 1924.

Rowland, E. O.: A Rapid Method for the Preparation of Thin Rock Sections, *Mineral. Mag.*, vol. 30, pp. 254–258, 1953.

Weatherhead, A. V.: A New Method for the Preparation of Thin Sections of Clays, *Mineral. Mag.*, vol. 25, pp. 529–533, 1940.

Weymouth, A. Allen: Simple Methods for Making Thin Sections, *Econ. Geol.*, vol. 23, pp. 323–330, 1928.

Wilson, D. A. P., and V. L. Bosazza: A Rock Cutting Machine for the Preparation of Specimens for Microscopic Examination, *Can. Mining J.*, vol. 59, no. 10, pp. 549–550, 1938.

CHAPTER 2

The Polarizing Microscope

General Features. The polarizing microscope is widely employed to examine transparent minerals although other types are used for special forms of mineral work, such as (1) the phase microscope, (2) the reflecting microscope, and (3) the binocular microscope. The phase microscope is useful in distinguishing minute obscure particles. The reflecting microscope serves for polished surfaces of metallic minerals. The binocular microscope is used mainly to observe surface features.

Aside from minor reference to other microscopes the discussion in this text is confined to the polarizing microscope since it applies to such a broad range of study.[1] It is extensively used to examine mineral fragments, grains, and small crystals, as well as thin sections of minerals, rocks, and other crystals. It is particularly useful in the determination of the optical properties of individual crystals or aggregates, and in the interpretation of textures, patterns, and various relationships of natural or artificial substances as shown in thin sections. Several polarizing microscopes have been selected for illustration in Figures 2-1 to 2-6 from a considerable number of models available. These range from serviceable instruments suitable for most work to more advanced types specially designed for research.

The lens system of the polarizing microscope corresponds in many respects to the lens system of the usual compound microscope, but contains several modifications which greatly increase its range of usefulness in work with minerals. The most distinctive features are the polarizing and analyzing devices, both below and above the stage. The rotating stage, the Amici-Bertrand lens, and several accessories such as the mica

---

[1] A list of firms that manufacture or distribute polarizing microscopes is given here:

American Optical Company (Scientific Instrument Division), Buffalo 11, N.Y.
Bausch and Lomb Optical Co., Rochester 2, N.Y.
Cooke, Troughton and Simms, York, England.
E. Leitz, Inc., 468 Fourth Ave., New York 16, N.Y.
Reichert, William J. Hacker & Co., Inc., 82 Beaver St., New York 5, N.Y.
Unitron, United Scientific Co., 204–6 Milk St., Boston, Mass.
Zeiss-Winkel (Gottingen), Carl Zeiss, Inc., 485 Fifth Ave., New York 17, N.Y.

plate, the gypsum plate, the quartz wedge, and the compensator are also distinctive.

The polarizing microscope as employed for the examination of minerals utilizes both plane-polarized light and light with the polarized planes crossed. For ordinary inspection a lower polarizing device is left in place below the condenser, and the upper polarizing device remains at one side. For examination between crossed planes, opposed polarizing plates, or nicol prisms[2] fit in the optical train at right angles.

A serviceable polarizing microscope for general use equipped with polarizing plates (polaroid) is illustrated in Figure 2-1. A rotating stage with spring clamps holds the thin section. Special high-quality polaroid used for such microscopes furnishes sharp, black extinction and yields well-developed interference figures.

A polarizing microscope with a deviating prism and inclined tube for convenient observation is shown in Figure 2-2. The names used for the several parts are given at either side of the photograph. A thin section appears in position on the stage. The stage not only rotates but may be raised and lowered. The analyzing nicol prism and the Amici-Bertrand lens are enclosed in the tube between the objective and the eyepiece.

FIG. 2-1. A student model polarizing microscope equipped with polarizing plates (*Bausch and Lomb Optical Co.*). Both the analyzer plate and the Amici-Bertrand lens are sealed in the tube and flip in or out of the optical path as the proper knob is turned. The stage may be rotated and also raised and lowered.

Both sectional and complete views of a polarizing microscope with polarizing prisms are shown in Figures 2-3 and 2-4. As illustrated, the optical train from the mirror upward consists of the polarizer (Ahrens type), lower fixed lenses of the condenser, removable upper lenses of the condenser, object in position on the stage, objective,

---

[2] The term *nicol* is often used to indicate the polarizing device used in the microscope. It is derived from the prism originally designed by William Nicol. The prisms now used are the *Ahrens* or a similar more efficient type. Polarizing plates may also be substituted.

analyzer (Ahrens type), Amici-Bertrand lens, and the eyepiece. In this alignment the instrument yields conoscopic observation as used for interference figures. With the removal of the Amici-Bertrand lens the instrument yields orthoscopic observation.

Both sectional and complete views of a more elaborate polarizing microscope of a combined research and operational type are shown in Figures 2-5 and 2-6. Here the optical train consists of a polarizer plate, lower fixed lenses of the condenser, removable upper lenses of the condenser, object in position on the stage, objective, analyzer plate, deviating

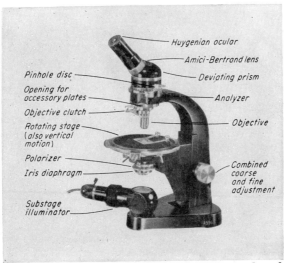

FIG. 2-2. A polarizing microscope with polarizing plates and a deviating prism (*E. Leitz, Inc.*). The features shown are suitable for most microscopic work. The eyepiece tube is inclined to permit observation at a convenient angle, the analyzer and polarizer are polarizing plates, and either a mirror or substage illuminator may be employed.

prism, and eyepiece. As aligned, the instrument would yield orthoscopic observation. The deviating prism and inclined tube replace the inclination joint and tilting arrangement of Figure 2-4, while the stage remains horizontal at all times. Plates are used for both the polarizer and the analyzer. The analyzer and the Amici-Bertrand lens are turned in and out of the train as a substitute for the sliding motion in the previous instrument.

Optical System. The polarizing microscope may be assembled either for orthoscopic or conoscopic observation. The orthoscopic arrangement provides the eye with a realistic virtual image with a flat field showing the object on the microscope stage. Minerals may be observed with a single polarizing device or with crossed nicols. Conoscopic observation

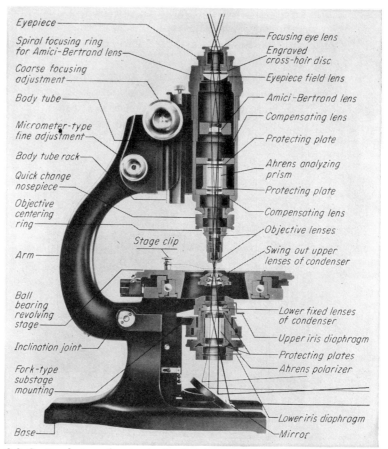

Eyepiece
Spiral focusing ring
for Amici-Bertrand lens
Coarse focusing
adjustment
Body tube
Micrometer-type
fine adjustment
Body tube rack
Quick change
nosepiece
Objective
centering
ring
Stage clip
Arm
Ball
bearing
revolving
stage
Inclination joint
Fork-type
substage
mounting
Base

Focusing eye lens
Engraved
cross-hair disc
Eyepiece field lens
Amici-Bertrand lens
Compensating lens
Protecting plate
Ahrens analyzing
prism
Protecting plate
Compensating lens
Objective lenses
Swing out upper
lenses of condenser
Lower fixed lenses
of condenser
Upper iris diaphragm
Protecting plates
Ahrens polarizer
Lower iris diaphragm
Mirror

Fig. 2-3. Sectional view of a standard polarizing microscope (*American Optical Co.*). The instrument is equipped with nicol prisms (Ahrens type), with a continuous vertical optical system, and is suitable for either orthoscopic or conoscopic observation. The names of the different parts are indicated on the two sides.

yields interference figures which represent an optical effect caused by the behavior of light in individual crystals. The figures are formed in the back focal plane of the objective, where they may be observed with the eye alone if the eyepiece and Amici-Bertrand lens are removed, or as an enlarged image with the eyepiece in place, and the Amici-Bertrand lens inserted. The paths of rays for conoscopic and orthoscopic observation are compared in the sectional diagrams of Figure 2-7*a,b*. Aside from polarizing devices, the optical arrangement in orthoscopic observation involves an illuminating source, a concentrating light system, a substage condenser, the object to be observed on the stage, the objective with the objective circle, the eyepiece with the image field, and the eyepiece circle.

If the best results are to be achieved, regardless of the source of illumination employed, it is important to regulate the light entering the microscope with respect to the optical system. In order to accomplish this result, suitable filters should be available for the source of illumination, the illuminator used should be equipped with an iris diaphragm,

and the condenser system should contain a suitable diaphragm. The field of view in the microscope should be carefully bounded by these diaphragms and the proper filter system employed to reduce the illumination to suitable intensity. Proper resolution for each magnification may be secured in this way.

Three important fields are involved: the image, the object, and the source. The circular field of view seen by the observer when he looks through the microscope is bounded primarily by the diaphragm of the eyepiece. This diaphragm is fixed and also contains the crosshairs. The magnified diaphragm image bounds the *image field* as seen through the eyepiece. The object field is a field of view equal in diameter to the diameter of the image field divided by the total magnification. It measures the area of the thin section or other object under observation at a particular instant. The *source field* is

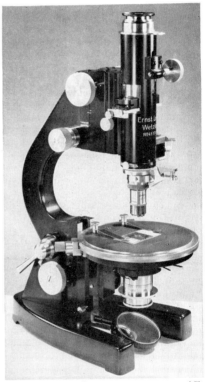

Fig. 2-4. A polarizing microscope (*E. Leitz, Inc.*). Both the stage and the tube may be adjusted vertically. The instrument is equipped with nicol prisms.

the field of view at the glass filter of the illuminator (Figure 2-8). The diameter of the source field is equal to the product of the diameter of the object field and the reciprocal of the reduction caused by the condenser. In the control of illumination, the area of the light from the illuminator is cut by the condenser to equal the source field. When the light entering the microscope is limited in this way, only the circle of the object that is observed becomes illuminated, and glare due to the interference of marginal light is eliminated.

When the condenser is in focus, the iris diaphragm determines the used aperture of the condenser. It is important that this aperture be filled with uniform illumination. If the objective is placed in focus and the eye-piece removed, the used aperture of the condenser may be observed by looking down the tube of the microscope. This may be termed the *condenser circle*. It is a bright circular area encircled by a dimly lighted band

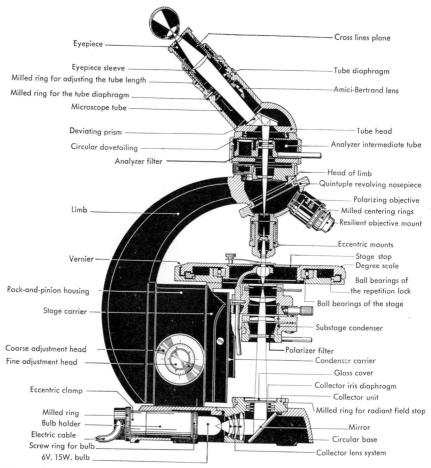

Eyepiece

Eyepiece sleeve
Milled ring for adjusting the tube length
Milled ring for the tube diaphragm
Microscope tube

Deviating prism
Circular dovetailing
Analyzer filter

Limb

Vernier

Rack-and-pinion housing

Stage carrier

Coarse adjustment head
Fine adjustment head

Eccentric clamp

Milled ring
Bulb holder
Electric cable
Screw ring for bulb
6V. 15W. bulb

Cross lines plane

Tube diaphragm

Amici-Bertrand lens

Tube head
Analyzer intermediate tube

Head of limb
Quintuple revolving nosepiece
Polarizing objective
Milled centering rings
Resilient objective mount

Eccentric mounts
Stage stop
Degree scale
Ball bearings of the repetition lock
Ball bearings of the stage

Substage condenser

Polarizer filter
Condenser carrier
Glass cover
Collector iris diaphragm
Collector unit
Milled ring for radiant field stop
Mirror
Circular base
Collector lens system

FIG. 2-5. Sectional view of a research polarizing microscope (*Carl Zeiss, Gottingen, West Germany*). The instrument is constructed with an inclined tube, deviating prism, polarizing plates, internal illumination, and eccentric centering objectives.

or ring. The latter is sometimes termed the objective circle. The objective circle is not bounded by a diaphragm but is limited by the margin of the objective lenses. In microscopic adjustment, it has been found that the condenser circle should be as nearly equal to the objective circle in diameter as possible, without causing glare. This is particularly important in using objectives yielding high initial magnification with correspondingly high numerical apertures. Oil-immersion objectives usually require the use of immersion condensers in order to avoid the loss of useful magnification from glare. Either corrected water or oil-immersion condensers may be used. The numerical aperture of the condenser should be less than the numerical aperture of the objective by a small amount.

Conoscopic Observation. The arrangement of the image-forming and illuminating beams in conoscopic observation differs in part from the orthoscopic assemblage.

The object may be considered as an originating source for the observation of interference images which appear in the objective circle. The light rays which pass through the condenser diaphragm have passed through the polarizer and are polarized. The rays are parallel to each other on emerging from the condenser front lens, but then become convergent to an extent which depends on the aperture of the substage. The convergent rays penetrate the object, which modifies the light transmitted and develops unusual optical effects.

The rays diverge above the objective circle and pass through a polarizing device with a plane at right angles to the polarizer (the analyzer). They merge in the plane of the field stop in the eyepiece to produce an image of the objective aperture stop. The field-stop image

Fig. 2-6. A polarizing microscope previously illustrated in section (Fig. 2-5) (*Carl Zeiss, Gottingen, West Germany*). Features of this microscope are polarizing plates, eccentric centered objectives, a rotating nose piece, built-in illumination, inclined tube, and vertical as well as horizontal stage adjustment.

is seen in the eyepiece and forms an image on the retina of the eye.

The position of the exit pupil depends upon the objective employed. The distance of the image in the field stop from the Bertrand lens will also differ. The position of the eyepiece must be adjusted to permit a focus at the field stop.

The image of the object, which simulates a light source, is brought by the Amici-Bertrand lens to the plane of the diaphragm in the microscope tube. The eyepiece then operates to bring the image into the plane of the

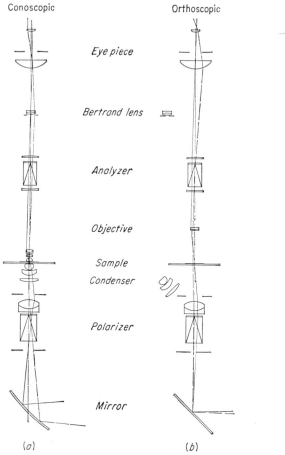

Conoscopic   Orthoscopic

Eye piece

Bertrand lens

Analyzer

Objective

Sample

Condenser

Polarizer

Mirror

(a)   (b)

FIG. 2-7. A diagram showing the path of light through the microscope. (a) Conoscopic observation, high magnification, Huygenian ocular, Amici-Bertrand lens, polarizing prisms, crossed nicols, and an auxiliary condenser immediately below the object are illustrated. An optical pattern is observed in the eye. (b) Orthoscopic observation, crossed nicols, intermediate magnification, Huygenian ocular, and polarizing prisms are illustrated. A realistic flat picture of the object is formed in the eye. (American Optical Co.)

exit pupil of the microscope. The pupil of the eye is placed at this level to observe the interference figure.

Parts of the Microscope. The parts of a polarizing microscope equipped either with polarizing plates or nicols are indicated in Figures 2-2, 2-3, and 2-5. The names of the mechanical features are largely self-explanatory, but a number of the optical items will receive further comment.

Oculars. The ocular consists of a tube which fits snugly into the tube of the microscope, ordinarily with a small set screw to hold it in a fixed

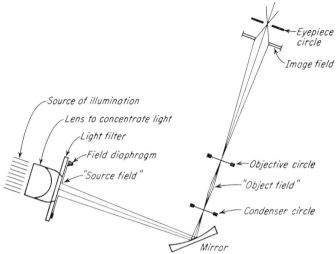

FIG. 2-8. Diagram showing the relative dimensions of the different fields in the microscope and their relation to the illumination. (*After Belling.*)

position with crosshairs north-south and east-west in the field of view. An eye lens is located above and a field lens below. A visual field stop with crosshairs, cross lines, or a field micrometer lies above the field lens in the Huygenian ocular (Figure 2-9*a*). The field stop lies below the field lens in the Ramsden-type ocular (Figure 2-9*b*). The image plane and the plane of the crosshairs should coincide.

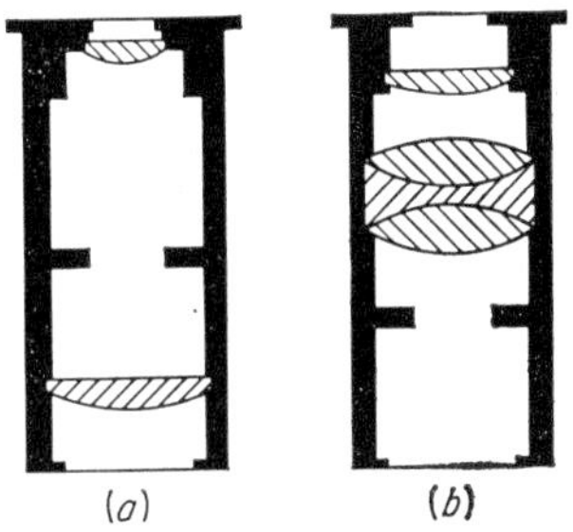

Oculars used in modern petrographic microscopes are ordinarily of the Huygenian type or a simple modification. These are usually used in combination with 40 mm or 16 mm or corresponding objectives. Where combinations giving higher magnifications are desired, the ocular is similar to the Huygenian ocular but contains a specially corrected eye-lens arrangement giving a flat field. Such correction is particularly important for photomicrography.

The Huygenian ocular is frequently called

FIG. 2-9. Sections of positive and negative oculars. (*a*) The Huygenian ocular (a negative ocular). (*b*) The Ramsden ocular (a positive ocular).

a *negative ocular.* The eyepiece as a whole has no external focal plane on the field-lens side. The Ramsden ocular is described as a *positive ocular.* The focal plane lies below the field lens and the object image is formed by the objective in this plane.

Compensating oculars are constructed to accompany apochromatic objectives. In order to secure the best results, oculars magnifying more than ten times should be of this type. Ordinary 5× and 10× oculars are satisfactory for most work with the polarizing microscope.

The Filar micrometer eyepiece (Figure 2-10) is designed for accurate horizontal measurement across the field of view. A small crossline is

moved to and fro. The movement is recorded on a drum at the side of the eyepiece. A fine line through the center of the field parallel to the screw axis serves as a guide in orienting the object with reference to the direction of movement of the crossline. In the lower section of the field, a scale ruled in 0.5 mm with every second interval numbered serves for counting screw revolutions.

Fig. 2-10. The filar micrometer. The drum records the movement of a crossline which traverses the field of view. (*Bausch and Lomb Optical Co.*)

Micrometer eyepieces are also utilized when the dimensions of particular objects in the field of view are desired (Figure 2-11*a*). The Huygenian eyepiece contains a scale divided into 0.1 mm movable by means of a screw at the side. The eye lens is focused on the scale. Such eyepieces are useful in determining the axial angle of interference figures with the microscope. The eyepieces should be calibrated with the aid of the stage

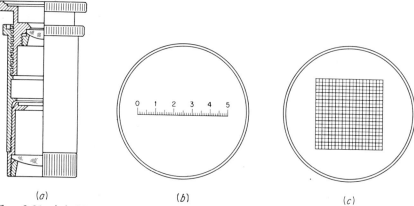

(*a*)   (*b*)   (*c*)

Fig. 2-11. (*a*) Micrometer ocular; (*b*) scale in a micrometer ocular; (*c*) grating micrometer. (*Carl Zeiss, Gottingen, West Germany.*)

micrometers for various objectives. The dimensions represented by the divisions in the micrometer ocular (Figure 2-11*b*) as observed at the eye are governed by relations between the objective, the eyepiece, the tube length, and by the presence or absence in the optical train of the analyzer.

Micrometer eyepieces of the grating type (Figure 2-11c) are employed to measure the areas of grains or fragments in the microscope field. These are also calibrated for different lens combinations with a stage micrometer.

Objectives. Views of several cut objectives appear in Figure 2-12. Achromatic objectives are ordinarily used for thin-section or fragment studies. Manufacturers usually supply as standard equipment 40-, 32-, 16- and 4-mm achromatic objectives, which serve for most purposes. In the case of achromatic objectives correction of aberrations of the image becomes more difficult with high eyepiece magnification, and only the

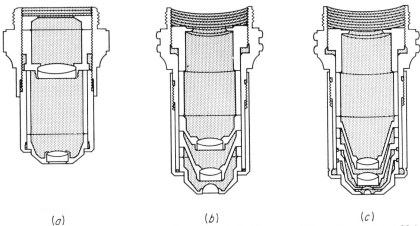

(*a*)   (*b*)   (*c*)

FIG. 2-12. Sectional views of objectives. (*a*) Objective 10×, 16 mm, 0.25 N.A. divisible achromatic. (*b*) Achromatic objective 43X, 4 mm, 0.65 N.A. (*c*) Achromatic objective 97×, 1.8 mm, 1.25 N.A. oil immersion. (*Bausch and Lomb Optical Co.*)

best achromatic objectives will give satisfactory results with an eyepiece magnification of 12× or greater.

Apochromatic objectives are constructed to provide additional color correction beyond that usually given by achromatic objectives. In this objective practically all the images produced by the different colors of the spectrum lie in the same plane and are equally sharp. The lenses are made of combinations of fluorite and glass. The problems of securing good fluorite and the practical difficulties in their manufacture are considerable; consequently the cost is greater than the cost of ordinary achromatic objectives. These objectives are only occasionally used for microscopic study of minerals.

The principal features of an objective that are of interest to the student are the initial magnification, the numerical aperture, the focal length, and the working distance.

The optical tube length divided by the focal length equals the initial magnification. Several manufacturers stamp the initial magnification for a standard mechanical tube length[3] on the objective. This figure multiplied by the power of the eyepiece gives the magnification for a standard tube length. This should be corrected, however, when the analyzing prism is inserted (unless the prism mount contains a correcting lens). Corrections may be determined by using stage and eyepiece micrometers.

The working distance is the distance between the objective and the top of the cover glass of the microscope slide when the objective is in focus.

The numerical aperture (N.A.) of an objective is a measure of the largest cone of light that it covers from an object point at the principal focus. N.A. equals $n \sin \mu$, where n is the index of refraction of the

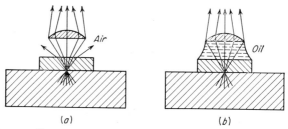

Fig. 2-13. Diagram illustrating the convergence of light by means of cedar oil placed in front of the lens of an oil-immersion objective. (a) Air alone without cedar oil; (b) with cedar oil.

medium between the object under examination and the objective[4] and μ is one-half the angle of the cone of light entering the lens. The numerical aperture furnishes a criterion of the quality of an objective. Other things being equal, at any magnification, the intensity of the image depends upon N.A.; the resolving power is directly proportional to N.A.; the depth of focus is inversely proportional to N.A. In two objectives having the same focal distance and therefore the same magnification, the one with the greater N.A. will take a larger cone of light from the object and will yield a brighter image. In general, with ordinary lighting, the limit of useful magnification for an average observer lies between 500 and 1000 times the N.A.

Oil-immersion objectives are used for high magnifications where a high degree of resolving power and correction are required. The oil should agree in both dispersive power and index of refraction with the front lens of the objective. The effect of oil immersion on the cone of light entering the front lens of an oil-immersion objective is shown in Figure 2-13.

[3] Bausch and Lomb Optical Co. and Spencer Lens Co. $= 160$ mm, Leitz $= 170$ mm, Zeiss $= 170$ mm.
[4] Air ($n = 1$) in the case of a dry objective and specially prepared cedar oil ($n = 1.515$) in an oil-immersion objective.

A considerable advantage is also gained by placing a drop of oil between the auxiliary condenser lens and the microscope slide. The working distance of an oil-immersion objective is very short; the lenses are difficult to manufacture and are consequently expensive. A good oil-immersion objective, however, gives a beautiful field with high magnification. The objective should be handled carefully, especially in focusing. After use the oil should be removed by the use of lens paper moistened with xylol or benzine.

Magnification. The microscope is primarily an instrument for magnification. It is worthwhile, therefore, to form an idea of the enlargement of the field of view with the lens systems available. The following table outlines the magnifications at the eye for different combinations of objectives with an equivalent focus of 40, 32, 16, 8, 4, and 2 mm (oil immersion) and also oculars magnifying five, ten, and fifteen times, respectively.

MAGNIFICATIONS

Type of objective	Equivalent focus, millimeters	Magnification number	Magnifications with oculars			Working distance, millimeters	N.A.
			5×	10×	15×		
Achromatic...............	40	3.2	16	32	48	34.5	0.12
Achromatic...............	32	4.3	22	43	65	27.0	0.15
Achromatic...............	16	10	50	100	150	5.8	0.25
Apochromatic............	8	23	115	230	345	0.85	0.65
Apochromatic...........	4	46	230	460	690	0.20	0.95
Apochromatic (oil immersion)	2	92	460	920	1380	0.11	1.32

Tube length: 170 mm
Image distance: 250 mm
SOURCE: After Leitz.

There are limits to the resolving power of the microscope, even with the best lens systems available. As long as the increase in magnification results in better vision of an object and more definite separation of detail, the magnification may be said to be "useful." When the object merely becomes larger without any increase in resolving power, the magnification is "empty." So-called *empty* magnifications of great magnitude are possible.

For practical purposes the upper limit of "useful" magnification with the polarizing microscope is about 1800:1.[5] Larger magnifications, as

[5] An oil-immersion objective (Carl Zeiss) primary magnification 120, N.A. 1.3, free working distance 0.08 mm, in combination with a 15× ocular, should yield a magnification ratio of 1800:1.

usually reported, are the result of some form of projection or special equipment in which the exact limits of useful magnification are not clearly known. A common form of projection is the enlargement employed in taking photomicrographs. Photomicrographs taken with a camera having a long bellows may increase the magnification ratio given by the microscope several times. Thus magnification ratios of 3000:1, 4000:1, or even considerably higher may be obtained. Such increase in magnification above the magnification of the microscope is essentially enlargement and does not result in increase in resolution. From the standpoint of increase in resolution or detail, it is "empty" magnification. Enlarged photomicrographs of this type, however, may have value for purposes of demonstration.

The limit of resolution for green light with a lens of N.A. 1.40 is said to be approximately 0.18μ. This might be described as the distance apart of two object points in the field of view of the microscope whose disk images would just touch as projected to the eye. It has been shown mathematically that the limit of resolution equals the wavelength divided by twice the numerical aperture. From this relationship it is possible to compute the number of lines per inch that can be separated by different numerical apertures. Several may be given as follows for blue light wavelength 486:

N.A.	Lines per inch separated
1.30	136,000
0.85	89,000
0.65	68,000
0.30	31,000

An accurate check of the magnification of the field of view in the microscope may be obtained by using a stage micrometer. The stage micrometer is a glass slide carefully ruled into hundredths of a millimeter or 0.001 inch. It not only serves as a comparison object for determining the magnification of the microscope but also may be used to give the magnification of micro drawings, of micro projections, and of photomicrographs.

Analyzer. The nicol prism or polarizing plate mounted in the tube of the microscope above the objective is known as the *analyzer.* The nicol is carried on a sliding mount (Figure 2-4) while in some models the plate (Figure 2-1) flips downward into the optical path. Either may be inserted or withdrawn from the optical path at will. The plane of vibration is normal to the plane of the polarizer and is usually either perpendicular or horizontal in the field of view. More elaborate microscopes (Figure 2-6) are fitted with a means for rotating the analyzer.

Polarizer. The prism or polaroid plate mounted in the substage system (Figure 2-14) is known as the *polarizer*. It may be set at any angle through 360° but is usually kept adjusted to a plane at right angles to the plane of the analyzer. The crosshairs in the eyepiece are set parallel to the two planes. A polarizing plate mounted in the substage assembly is shown in Figure 2-5.

Amici-Bertrand Lens. This lens is inserted in the tube of the microscope between the ocular and the analyzer (Figure 2-3). It serves to

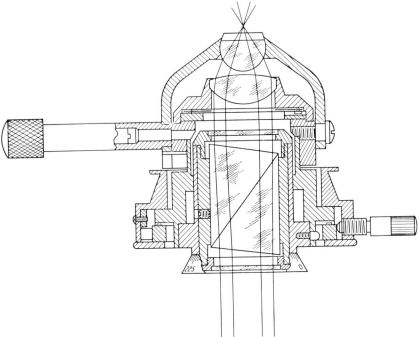

FIG. 2-14. A sectional view showing a prism in position in the substage assembly. A section of a substage assembly containing a polarizing plate (filter) is shown in Fig. 2-4. (*American Optical Co.*)

bring the image of an interference figure into the focal plane of the ocular. The device was originally used by Amici (1844) and was later adapted by Bertrand (1878).

Interference figures may be observed without the Amici-Bertrand lens if the ocular is removed. For superior results, an Amici-Bertrand lens with a focusing diaphragm and an auxiliary magnifier to fit over the eyepiece is used.

Condenser. Three components may be present in a condenser system of the type selected for illustration. In ordinary examination with low-power objectives a lens component with an illuminating aperture of about 0.22 is used. In working with high power or in obtaining interference figures, another condenser on a movable mounting (Figure 2-15) swings across the axis. This suffices for all objectives of N.A. up to 1.0. In the case of higher numerical apertures a special lens is inserted in place of the condenser in the movable mounting. This is more effective if used with oil immersion.

The arrangement of the condenser, together with the various adjustments for the polarizer, is shown in Figure 2-14.

Iris Diaphragm. The iris diaphragm is attached to the lower side of the tube that holds the polarizer. It serves to reduce the cone of light, lessening the illumination of the field of view, and causes objects to stand out with increased relief. The diaphragm is useful in the application of various tests when determining indices of refraction with the microscope.

Mirror. The mirror is usually reversible, with one surface plane and the other concave. The plane mirror surface is suitable for low-power microscopic work. The concave mirror converges the light upon the object. It is especially useful in high-power examination. It should also be used for low power when the illuminator produces a convergent beam.

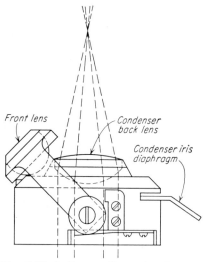

Fig. 2-15. A diagram illustrating the construction of the condenser system. (*American Optical Co.*)

Fine Adjustment. It is advantageous to have the finest adjustment graduated so as to permit the measurement of the displacement of the tube to within 2.5μ (thousandths of a millimeter). The adjustment is used both for measuring depth and for focusing on objects at high magnifications. The relationship between a coarse and fine adjustment and the detail of the fine adjustment for one type of microscope are illustrated in Figure 2-16.

Microscope Accessories. The accessories provided with the microscope generally include a quartz wedge, gypsum plate, and mica plate. These are marked with arrows indicating the fast- and slow-ray vibration directions and are mounted in frames to fit the opening in the tube of the microscope between the objective and the analyzer.

The quartz wedge is ground to produce interference colors from the beginning of the first to the end of the third or fourth order. It is marked and mounted as shown in Figure 2-17.

The mica plate and gypsum plate (German—*Glimmer* and *Gips*), together with a centering pin, are illustrated in Figure 2-18. The slow-ray directions in both the mica and gypsum plates are indicated.

Berek Compensator. The compensator is designed to fit the tube slit above the objective in the same opening used for the gypsum and the mica plates. It is employed in the determination of the order of interference colors between crossed nicols.

A calcite plate with the *c*-axis vertical is inserted in the accessory slot of the microscope. The plate forms a window in the compensator and is rotated by turning a graduated drum. The compensator (Figure 2-19) is rotated until the color of the mineral is neutralized (becomes gray). The rotation of the compensator necessary to bring this about is a measure of the retardation.

A compensator to measure small differences in retardation is shown in Figure 2-20. A mica plate with a retardation of $\frac{1}{30}\lambda$ red is tilted by turning a horizontal graduated drum.

Object Slide. Various lengths and widths of object slides may be used, but the thickness is of greater importance. Immersion condensers are made to work to best advantage with slides from 0.9 to 1.0 mm thick. Thus slides intended for study at high magnifications should conform to this thickness if the most satisfactory results are to be secured.

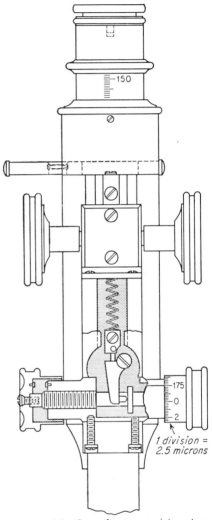

FIG. 2-16. The fine adjustment. (*American Optical Co.*)

Slides 26 mm wide by 45 mm long are generally used for mounting thin sections of minerals and rocks. Such slides fit easily on the rotating stage of the polarizing microscope yet are large enough to contain a good-sized slice and also a label of suitable dimensions. Long slides usually employed in biological investigations may be quite inconvenient on a rotating stage.

Cover Glass. Objectives usually employed for thin-section work are corrected by the manufacturers for a cover-glass thickness of from 0.15 to 0.17 mm. It is assumed that the top of the slice is pressed

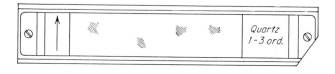

Fig. 2-17. The quartz wedge mounted on a glass plate and in a metal frame. The arrow marks the slow-ray direction. Ordinarily a wedge covers four orders from the thin edge to the thickest portion. (*American Optical Co.*)

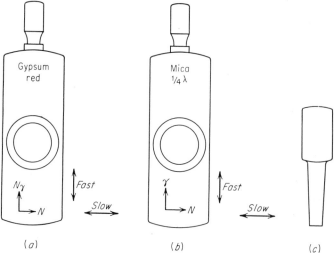

Fig. 2-18. The gypsum plate (*a*), mica plate (*b*), and a centering pin (*c*). (*E. Leitz, Inc.*)

directly against the bottom of the cover glass. In case the slide is poorly mounted and a space intervenes between the top of the slice and the bottom of the cover glass, the extra distance should be considered as so much additional thickness of cover glass. In order to obtain the best results with objectives, cover glasses of standard thickness should be employed.

Precautions to Be Observed in the Use of the Microscope. Even under the best conditions microscope work produces a certain amount of strain upon the eyes. It is essential, therefore, to employ the best possible conditions of work in order to reduce such strain to a minimum.

The student should assume an erect but not too rigid position. Such a position with the microscope tube inclined allows him to work with maximum comfort.

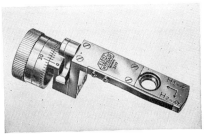

FIG. 2-19. The Berek Compensator. (E. Leitz, Inc.)

Both eyes should be kept open while looking through the instrument. If it is difficult to do this at first, a shield should be placed over the eye not in use. It is also a good plan to learn to observe equally well with either eye and not to develop the so-called *microscope eye*.

Care of the Instrument. A polarizing microscope is expensive. Properly used, it should last a lifetime. Otherwise, it may become useless with little real service. Most of the precautions to be observed in the use of the instrument are such as should be applied to any piece of fine apparatus. A few, however, are of special nature and should be specially mentioned.

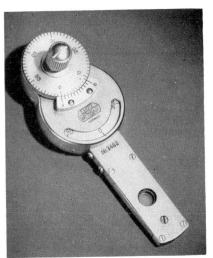

FIG. 2-20. A compensator to measure small differences in retardation. Mica forms a window in the accessory plate. It may be tilted by turning the drum. The retardation is $\frac{1}{30}$ red. (E. Leitz, Inc.)

Fine-textured lens paper or, still better, a camel's-hair brush should be used for cleaning all optical parts. This applies to the ocular, the objectives, the substage system, the mirror, and the two nicols.

Objectives should be brought into focus by moving the tube of the microscope upward rather than downward. Possibility of contact between the lower lens of the objective and the thin section is thus avoided. High-power or oil-immersion objectives should be cleaned with lens paper and xylol or benzine (not alcohol).

Chemicals should not be used on the stage unless special precautions are taken to protect the objective. Objectives may be protected by the use of cover glasses fastened to the lower lens. Occasionally an old objective is reserved for chemical work alone.

Illuminators. At ordinary magnifications a good north light with a broad, clear sky forms an excellent source of illumination for the polarizing microscope.

In case such illumination is not available, artificial daylight lights may be successfully employed. These consist of various types of electric bulbs mounted in cases with a special blue-glass light filter in the path of the illumination. Three types are illustrated in Figure 2-21a,b,c. A low-voltage bulb with a condensing lens and diaphragm, as illustrated in Figure 2-21c, provides suitable illumination for a wide variety of magnifications.

FIG. 2-21. Various types of artificial illumination for the microscope: (a) small substage lamp. (*Bausch and Lomb Optical Co.*)

At high magnifications and for photomicrographic work a mechanical-feed arc lamp is sometimes used. The beam from the arc is very warm and should always be passed through a cooling cell of water in order to avoid injuring the cement in the prisms of the microscope (unless special prisms are employed).

Phase Microscopy. The technique of phase microscopy has found considerable application in biological science where specimens lacking in contrast may be illuminated in such a way that structures become visible without using stains. In the examination of minerals the technique of late has received some attention. In case the refractive index of a mineral less than about 10μ thick differs but slightly from the refractive index of the mounting medium, phase microscopy may offer a significant method of examination.

The theory and application of phase microscopy have been reviewed at some length by Bennett et al. (1951). Phase differences between light waves passing through points in the mineral and in the surround are utilized to bring out contrast at the eye. An annulus at the level of the condenser diaphragm and a diffraction plate at the back focal plane of the objective are utilized to produce phase differences (Figure 2-22). Minerals with extremely low relief in balsam may be made to stand out more distinctly with this arrangement.

The use of annular diaphragms develops a change in optical path, or phase relation, in light entering the objective directly from an object and light diffracted from an object. A phase-shifting element may be mounted at the rear focal plane of the objective. Such elements may be made by the deposition of films of predetermined thickness by high-vacuum thermal-evaporation processes. Patterns of annular shape which introduce a phase shift of one-quarter wavelength of green light have been found effective. An annular aperture diaphragm is placed at the front focal plane of the substage condenser. When illuminated it furnishes a light

FIG. 2-21b. A strong lamp for general utility. (*American Optical Co.*)

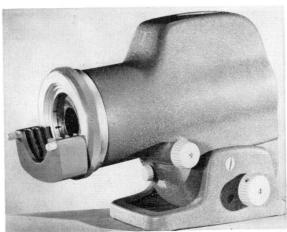

FIG. 2-21c. A low-voltage lamp with V-slots for filters. (*Bausch and Lomb Optical Co.*)

source at infinity with respect to the object plane. The two annuli when exactly concentric and superimposed produce a phase difference of one-quarter wavelength.

Both "dark" contrast and "bright" contrast may be produced by control of the film thickness which contributes to the phase shift. Where the directly transmitted light is effectively accelerated over the diffracted light, the regions of greater optical path in the specimen will appear darker than the surrounding background. Where retardation of undiffracted light occurs, regions of greater optical path in the specimen appear bright against a darker background.

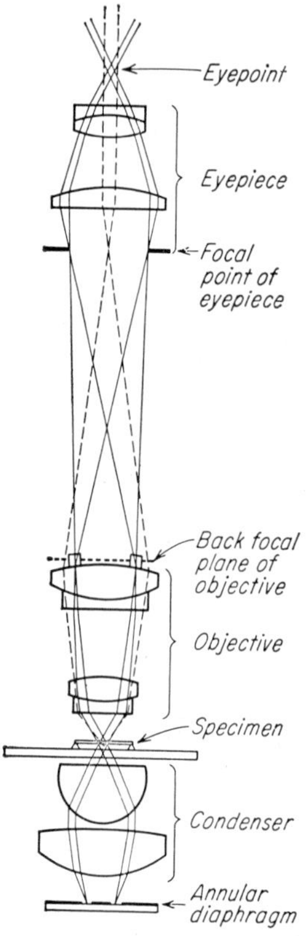

In Figure 2-23 photographs taken at magnifications of 900:1, 1700:1, and 2000:1 show fine particles of clay minerals in phase contrast. The range in diameter of the kaolinite particles a and b is 2 to 6.3μ. The range in diameter of the halloysite particles c and d is 2 to 6.3μ; while halloysite particles e and f are about 2μ in length. Both "bright" and "dark" contrast are illustrated.

Photomicrographs. Photographs of thin sections are frequently desired for purposes of record. These may be obtained quickly with simple equipment unless prints of exceptional quality are required. In the latter case a special study of equipment available on the market is desirable.

A small camera designed for 35-mm film may be fastened to a tube above the microscope (Figure 2-24). A viewing lens is attached to the side of the tube. An exposure meter is placed between the viewing lens and the camera. The entire assembly is arranged to fit the tube of the microscope above the ocular. The excellence of the photomicrographs secured will depend upon the quality of the illumination, focus, exposure, and the area selected for photography.

Good quality microscope lamps with suitable filters will provide a satisfactory illumination. Focus may be adjusted with the aid of the viewing lens. The exposure may be determined with the photometer. Study of photomicrographs in various textbooks and professional journals will serve as a guide in selecting areas suitable for photography.

Exposure meters used with the microscope are microphotometers and will need to be calibrated for the particular equipment available. A se-

Solid lines represent direct rays
Dotted lines represent diffracted rays

Fig. 2-22. Phase contrast arrangement with an annular diaphragm in the front focal plane of the substage condenser and an annular phase shifting element in the back focal plane of the objective. (*American Optical Co.*)

ries of trial exposures will first be necessary. The exposure reading for each exposure, as well as the time, should be recorded. When a satisfactory exposure has been secured, the time and exposure reading should be noted. For example, suppose the time is 10 seconds and the meter reads "5" when a good photograph is secured. For another exposure the meter

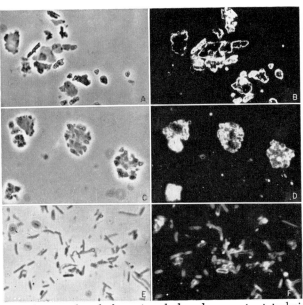

Fig. 2-23. Microphotographs of clay minerals by phase contrast technique. Mounts (c) and (d) were immersed in a mixture of butylcarbitol and clove oil ($n = 1.500$); (e) and (f) in glycerine ($n = 1.463$). (*Courtesy Dr. H. Piller, Carl Zeiss, Gottingen, West Germany.*)

(a) Kaolinite, Schnaittenbach.—(900:1). Phase contrast, light field, ordinary polarized light.
(b) Kaolinite, Schnaittenbach.—(900:1). Phase contrast, dark field.
(c) Halloysite, Lawrence Co., Ind.—(1700:1). Phase contrast, light field, ordinary polarized light.
(d) Halloysite, Lawrence Co., Ind.—(1700:1). Phase contrast, dark field.
(e) Halloysite, Lawrence Co., Ind.—(2000:1). Phase contrast, light field, ordinary polarized light.
(f) Halloysite, Lawrence Co., Ind.—(2000:1). Phase contrast, dark field.

reads "2.5." Then the required time for the second exposure would be 5 seconds.

Where larger photomicrographs are desired cameras equipped for cut films or plates may be used in place of the small camera mentioned above. In general, photomicrographs of thin sections are taken with $3.2\times$ or $10\times$ objectives since the depth of the section interferes with the focus at high magnification. At the same time the textures ordinarily observed often appear to better advantage at lower magnifications.

Adjustment of the Polarizing Microscope. Four separate steps may be outlined to arrange the polarizing microscope for the examination of thin sections:

1. Centering the stage with the field
2. Crossing the nicols
3. Testing the crosshairs
4. Determining the vibration plane of the lower nicol

1. *Centering the Stage with the Field.* The stage is centered when the axis of rotation coincides with the tube axis of the microscope, the tube axis standing perpendicular to the center of the field of view. Screws on the side of either the objective collar or the stage (Figure 2-25) are used to align the tube axis and the stage. A simple procedure is followed. While looking through the instrument at the field of view, pick out an easily recognizable point, and then rotate the stage. The point should describe a concentric circle of rotation about the intersection of the crosshairs. If it does not, rotate the stage until the point is farthest from the intersection of the cross-hairs, bring it in halfway by means of the centering screws, and then bring it to the center of the stage by actually moving the slide itself. Rotate the stage, and repeat the operation if the centering has not been completed the first time.

FIG. 2-24. Photomicrographic camera, exposure meter, and viewing lens. (*Courtesy of Paul Rosenthal, 505 Fifth Ave., New York 17, N.Y.*)

2. *Crossing the Nicols.* The planes of vibration of the two prisms should be set at right angles to each other. The plane of vibration of the analyzer is usually fixed by the manufacturer either from left to right or up and down as one observes the microscopic field. The lower nicol is adjusted at right angles by rotating it in the substage collar until the field becomes dark, with both nicols in the path of light. The nicols should remain in the position giving maximum darkness. A small pin usually fits into a notch at this position.

3. *Testing the Crosshairs.* The crosshairs in the ocular may be either

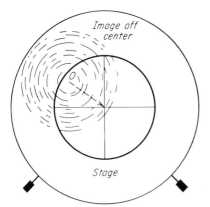
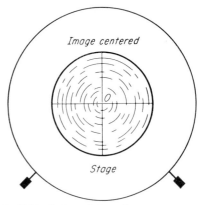

FIG. 2-25. Diagram illustrating centering the field of view of the microscope.

the spiderweb type or lines engraved on a glass plate. In either case it is important that the hair lines be parallel to the planes of vibration of the two nicols. Ordinarily these are set by the optical firm supplying the microscope, and the ocular is so arranged that it will not fit the tube of the microscope in other than the correct position. The adjustment should be checked occasionally, how-ever, and in case the alignment is inaccurate, the crosshairs should be reset by an experienced technician.

A slide containing small elongated rectangular crystals of natrolite (Fig-ure 2-26) is useful to test the setting of the crosshairs with the planes of the nicols.[6] The natrolite becomes dark between crossed nicols when the edges of the crystals are parallel to the vibration directions. A slide containing a small natrolite crystal may be placed upon the stage be-tween crossed nicols and turned until it becomes dark. If the crosshairs

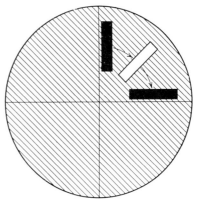

FIG. 2-26. Testing the adjustments of the crosshairs with natrolite frag-ments.

are in adjustment, the web lines should be parallel or at right angles to the straight lines of the crystal. This is true in each of the four positions of extinction. In 45° intermediate positions the natrolite will show max-imum illumination.

4. *Determining the Vibration Plane of the Lower Nicol.* After the other adjustments have been made, the vibration direction of the lower nicol

---

[6] If natrolite is not available, any crystalline material with straight-line edges and parallel extinction may be substituted.

can be determined with either fibrous tourmaline fragments or a rock
section containing biotite showing cleavage.

Tourmaline (Figure 2-27a) has maximum absorption when it is
oriented with the c-axis (usually the long direction of a crystal or fragment) in a direction at right angles to the plane of vibration of the
polarizing prism. Biotite (Figure 2-27b), on the other hand, is darkest
when the cleavage is parallel to the vibration direction. Note the positions
of greatest and least darkness, observing with the upper nicol thrown

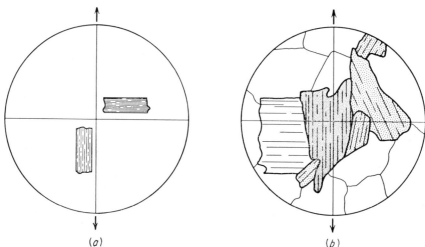

(a)   (b)

Fig. 2-27. Determining the vibration plane of the lower nicol: (a) elongated
tourmaline fragments; (b) biotite in thin section.

out from the tube. These indicate either the vibration direction or the
normal to the vibration direction, depending upon whether the slide is
biotite or tourmaline.

REFERENCES

Allen, R. M.: "The Microscope," D. Van Nostrand Company, Inc., Princeton,
    N.J., 1940.
Amici, G. B.: Ann. chim. et phys., 3d ser., vol. 12, p. 114, 1844.
Beck, Conrad: "The Microscope," R. & J. Beck, Ltd., London, 1938.
Belling, John: "The Use of the Microscope," McGraw-Hill Book Company, Inc.,
    New York, 1930.
Bennett, Alva H., Harold Osterberg, Helen Jupnik, and Oscar W. Richards:
    "Phase Microscopy," John Wiley and Sons, Inc., New York, 1951.
Berek, Max: "Anleitung zu optischen Untersuchungen mit dem Polarisations-
    mikroskop," Verlag Schweitzerbart, Stuttgart, 1953.
Bertrand, E.: Z. Kryst., vol. 1, p. 69, 1877.
Bertrand, E.: Bull. soc. franç. minéral., vol. 1, pp. 27, 97, 1878.
Bertrand, L., and M. Roubault: "L'emploi du Microscope Polarisant," Paris,
    1936.

Burri, C.: "Das Polarisationsmikroskop," Basel, 1950.

Chamot, E. M., and C. W. Mason: "Handbook of Chemical Microscopy," vol. 1, John Wiley & Sons, Inc., New York, 1930.

Ehringhaus, A.: "Das Mikroskop," Leipzig, 1943.

Gage, S. H.: "The Microscope," Comstock Publishing Associates, Inc., Ithaca, N.Y., 1925.

Hallimond, A. F.: "Manual of the Polarizing Microscope," Cooke, Troughton & Simms, Ltd., York, England, 1953.

Hartshorne, N. H., and A. Stuart: "Crystals and the Polarizing Microscope," Edward Arnold & Co., London, 1950.

Johannsen, A.: "Petrographic Methods," 2d ed., McGraw-Hill Book Company, Inc., New York, 1918.

Marshall, C. R., and H. D. Griffith: "Introduction to the Theory and Use of the Microscope," Routledge and Kegan Paul, Ltd., London, 1928.

Michel, K.: "Die Grundlagen der Theorie des Mikroskops," Stuttgart, 1950.

Niggli, P.: "Lehrbuch der Mineralogie und Kristallchemie," 3d. ed., vol. 2, Verlag Gebrüder Bomtraeger, Berlin, 1942.

Piller, H.: Die Phasenkontrastmikroskopie als Hilfsmittel zur Bestimmung feinkörniger, speziell dünner, transparenter Minerale, Heidelberger Beitr. Mineral. u. Petrog., vol. 3, pp. 307–334, 1952.

Raaz, Fr., and H. Tertsch: "Geometrische Kristallographie und Kristalloptik und deren Arbeitsmethoden," Vienna, 1939.

Spitta, E. J.: "Microscopy," E. P. Dutton & Co., Inc., New York, 1920.

Wahlstrom, Ernest E.: "Optical Crystallography," John Wiley & Sons, Inc., New York, 1943.

Zernike, F.: Phase Contrast, a New Method for Microscopic Observation of Transparent Objects, Physica, no. 9, p. 686, 1949.

CHAPTER 3

A Summary of the Properties of Light

Theories of Light. Since light crosses interstellar space, penetrates transparent solids or liquids, and also travels through a vacuum, a medium has usually been postulated by which it could be conveyed. The medium is the ether, which has been assumed to permeate all matter and to pervade all space. Modern studies have shown, however, that in order to account for certain things the ether must be endowed with the most extraordinary physical properties, and according to some concepts it is unnecessary. The source of the light and its effect on the eye are apparent, but some explanation must be advanced to account for its transmission.

Several prominent theories have been advanced. According to one, a beam of light consists of a stream of minute particles, or "corpuscles," given off at high velocity by the sun or any luminous body. The corpuscles travel through space in straight lines and eventually reach the eye. This is generally referred to as the corpuscular theory, a theory that received much attention because it was supported by the famous physicist Sir Isaac Newton.

Another theory was first advanced by the Dutch scientist Christian Huygens in the latter part of the seventeenth century. According to Huygens, the ether is supposed to vibrate, and light is transmitted through it by the vibration of particle after particle in waves. The phenomena of light such as reflection, refraction, diffraction, and interference may be readily explained in accordance with this theory. The theory of Huygens, however, failed to explain the apparent rectilinear motion of light and was not accepted by Newton.

A modification of the wave theory was proposed by the Scottish physicist James Clerk Maxwell (1873), who considered light as made up of waves but said that the waves were electromagnetic. According to Maxwell, a wave consists of rapidly alternating electric and magnetic fields normal to each other and normal to the direction of propagation of light. Hertz (1888) succeeded in producing waves having properties similar to light waves by electricity. As a result of the work of Maxwell, Hertz, and other experimenters, the electromagnetic theory of wave motion was for a time generally accepted.

Toward the end of the last century evidence began to appear that did not accord with the electromagnetic theory. It was found that the space around certain metals would become electrically conductive when the metal was exposed to light. Then the electron was discovered in 1897, and it was assumed that the photoelectric effect was due to the emission of electrons as the metal became exposed to light. This was based on the fact that expulsion means energy, and it was presumed that the energy in the case of the photoelectric effect would come from light. However, the energy given by light is so small that it could not account for the emission of electrons. This led to the assumption that the light was concentrated in points and not uniformly distributed. At about this time Planck developed the assumption that radiating oscillators in a black body radiate energy discontinuously in units called *quanta*. Einstein in 1905 suggested that the absorption of light in the photoelectric process might also be in quantum units. Later experiment demonstrated that the quanta of Einstein were of the same size as those postulated by Planck.

As a result of these developments the explanation of light seems to rest upon two apparently contradictory theories, the wave theory being more appropriate for phenomena such as reflection, refraction, interference, diffraction, and polarization, whereas the quantum theory is more applicable to the recent discoveries in the field of X rays, radiation, and photoelectricity. Speaking of the two theories, Einstein has stated as follows:

We have good proof that both waves and particles exist. Our present effort is to understand how this is, to find a theory that will unify the nature of light. The composition of a two-point view has not yet been found. It is a quest of science in which our present methods are imperfect.

Nomenclature of the Wave Theory. The nomenclature of the wave theory used in this text is summarized in the following paragraphs.

Displacement. In wave motion the form of the wave may be described if particles in the medium are assumed to be displaced in sequence. The form of displacement represents a curve combining movement around a circle with motion along a straight line.

Vibration direction = electric vector = electrical displacement. The vibration direction lies in the wavefront and is perpendicular to the ray in isotropic media. In anisotropic crystals it is not perpendicular except in limited directions.

Wavelength. The distance between two successive crests or troughs, or any corresponding distance along the wave (denoted by the Greek letter lambda, λ). λ is usually measured in millionths of a millimeter or millimicrons ($m\mu$).

Wavefront. The surface determined at a given instant by all the parts of a system of waves traveling along the same direction and in the same phase. In space, in air, or in any other optically isotropic media when light moves along parallel lines the wavefront is perpendicular to the direction of transmission. In anisotropic media the wavefront is perpendicular only in certain directions.

Wave normal. The direction perpendicular to the wavefront. In isotropic substances the wave normal and the ray direction are the same.

Frequency. The number of vibrations in a given unit of time. Ordinarily several trillion per second in the case of light waves.

Phase. The relative position of corresponding points on different waves moving along the same line. Two points on waves are in the same phase when they are in the same relative position in regard to the crest or trough of the wave and are both moving either toward or away from the line of transmission. Two points are in opposite phase when they are in the same relative position but when they are moving in opposite directions with reference to the line of transmission. Other phase differences may occur.

The phasal difference represents the portion of a wavelength by which one wave train fails to match the other.

Amplitude. The maximum displacement of a wave from the line of transmission.

Period. The time interval necessary for a wave to undergo a complete oscillation.

Crest. The point of the wave with the maximum upward displacement.

Trough. The point of the wave with the greatest downward displacement.

Beam. A group of light waves following along the same path. A familiar example is the white beam of a motion-picture projector clearly visible in the dusty atmosphere of the theater. Beams can be made narrower and narrower.

Ray. The straight-line path followed by light in moving from one point to another in a given medium. The ray is perpendicular to the electrical field and is the direction of propagation of the energy.

Refractive Index. The refractive index is equal to the ratio of the wave-normal velocity in a vacuum to the wave-normal velocity (not the ray velocity) in the medium, whether isotropic or anisotropic.

Monochromatic Light. Light of a single wavelength. In practical tests light is frequently used covering a small range of wavelengths but appearing as one color to the eye.

Light Vector. The action of light may be described as depending upon the periodic alternation of a light vector that lies parallel to the plane of the wavefront and in isotropic media is perpendicular to the direction of propagation. In anisotropic media the vector is still parallel to the plane of the wavefront but, aside from certain limited positions, is not perpendicular to the direction of propagation.

In the case of monochromatic light, the light vector follows the laws of simple harmonic motion, the vibration period T depending upon the color of the monochromatic light. The wavelength λ—*i.e.*, the distance between two successive like points on a wave train—is equal to the velocity of propagation v multiplied by the vibration period:

$$\lambda = vT$$

In any transparent mass λ is fixed, and v varies with T. The intensity of light is the average of the intensities in the various light-vector quadrants and varies with the amplitude.

The light wave is electromagnetic with two vector movements in the system. In isotropic media these are transverse and perpendicular to each other, one limited by the magnetic field of force, the other by the electric field of force. These are connected with two other vectors distinguished in isotropic media by their magnitude and in anisotropic media also through variation in direction. These two vectors may be called the *electric vector* and the *magnetic vector*. The first of these measures the electrical displacement; the second, the magnetic displacement or induction. Maxwell worked out equations applicable to the movement of these vectors (although the movement had been originally worked out before vector analysis was introduced). Experimental evidence has shown that the vibration direction of light corresponds to the electrical displacement (electric vector) in isotropic bodies. In anisotropic bodies it has been shown to correspond to either the electrical displacement (electric vector) or the electrical field. In the electromagnetic theory light is assumed to correspond to the electrical displacement (electric vector), an assumption made plausible by the conception of light as an electrolysis.

Speed of Light. Light waves travel along the direction of transmission at a speed of approximately 186,284 miles per second. The same law of frequency used in the case of sound applies to light and is expressed by the equation

$$f = \frac{v}{\lambda}$$

or

$$v = f\lambda$$

In this equation the frequency f is obtained by dividing the velocity v by the wavelength λ. In the case of violet light ($\lambda = 0.000037$ cm) the velocity ($v = 186{,}284$ miles per second) divided by the wavelength gives a frequency of 800,000,000,000,000 (eight hundred trillion) vibrations per second.

Wave Motion. An idea of the behavior of light waves may be gained by a study of waves generated by simple harmonic motion and uniform rectilinear motion.

Simple harmonic motion is uniform motion in a circular path as it would appear projected on the diameter of a circle. If a particle as illustrated in Figure 3-1 is assumed to move clockwise around the circumference of a circle, occupying various positions in turn, the projections on

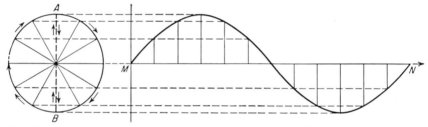

Fig. 3-1. The harmonic curve produced by movement around a circle combined with motion along a straight line.

the vertical diameter AB will be at the intersections with the horizontal dotted lines shown in the figure. If observed from the side along the plane of the circle, the particle will appear to oscillate back and forth with varying velocity. If, in addition to the harmonic motion, the particle moves along a straight line MN at a uniform rate (rectilinear motion), it will no longer move in a circular path but will follow a curve of the type illustrated in the projection. The projection on the vertical diameter of the circle, however, will still be the same. The curve is a harmonic curve, which has the form of a sine curve.

Differences in phase produce a number of resultant forms when two or more waves follow the same line (Figure 3-2). Two sets of waves may be equal and opposite, thus nullifying each other (Figure 3-2a). Other sets may be equal in amplitude and wavelength but differ in phase. The latter sort will produce a resultant R of intermediate crest and increased amplitude (Figure 3-2b).

When two waves are equal in phase, wavelength, and period but differ in amplitude, a resultant R is produced of the same phase and wavelength with increased amplitude (Figure 3-2c).

The Color of Light. The brightness of a ray is determined by the amplitude of the wave vibration. Light, on entering various bodies, undergoes a change in velocity. A corresponding change must occur, therefore, in either the wavelength or the frequency. Since the vibration period remains the same for a given color, the change occurs in the wavelength. The wavelength will differ even for the same color in different bodies;

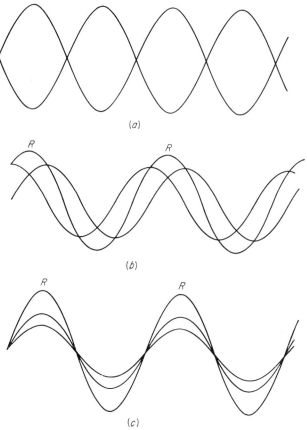

(a)

(b)

(c)

FIG. 3-2. Combinations of waves produced by several phase differences. (a) The phase difference is ½ λ, and the two waves are equal and opposite in phase. (b) The resultant wave (R) produced by two equal waves of slight path difference. (c) The resultant wave (R) produced by two waves of equal length and identical phase, but differing in amplitude.

thus the number of vibrations per second or the frequency of the waves reaching the eye determines the color.

Waves of visible light vary in length, the longest being red and the shortest violet. The portion of the spectrum directly visible to the eye varies between relatively narrow limits. The extreme wavelength of red light is 0.0000759 cm, and the relative wavelength of extreme visible violet is 0.0000393 cm. In terms of millimicrons (the units commonly employed in dealing with light), the figures are:

$$\text{Red light} \quad = 759 \text{ m}\mu$$
$$\text{Violet light} = 393 \text{ m}\mu$$

White light, or ordinary light, is a combination of all the different wavelengths visible to the eye in one simultaneous effect. When only one wavelength is observed, light is singly colored, or monochromatic. White light may be considered composed of seven different colors. These grade into each other, forming a continuous spectrum. The colors of the spectrum are frequently represented by arbitrarily chosen wavelengths representing mean values of the various colors, as follows:

$$\text{Red} \quad = 700 \text{ m}\mu$$
$$\text{Orange} = 620 \text{ m}\mu$$
$$\text{Yellow} = 560 \text{ m}\mu$$
$$\text{Green} \quad = 515 \text{ m}\mu$$
$$\text{Blue} \quad = 470 \text{ m}\mu$$
$$\text{Indigo} = 440 \text{ m}\mu$$
$$\text{Violet} = 410 \text{ m}\mu$$

The electromagnetic spectrum (Figure 3-3) extends far beyond the range of visible light. The mechanisms by which the different radiations

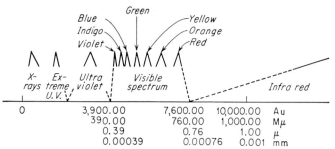

FIG. 3-3. The approximate range of visible spectrum.

are produced, however, must be much different because of the great difference in frequency.

REFERENCES

Coker, E. G., and L. N. G. Filon: "A Treatise on Photo-elasticity," Cambridge University Press, London, 1931.

Crew, H.: "The Wave Theory of Light," American Book Company, New York, 1900.

Edser, E.: "Light for Students," Macmillan & Co., Ltd., London, 1930.

Hardy, A. C., and F. H. Perrin: "The Principles of Optics," McGraw-Hill Book Company, Inc., New York, 1932.

Heyl, P. R.: The History and Present Status of the Physicist's Concept of Light, *J. Opt. Soc. Am.*, vol. 18, pp. 183–192, 1929.

"Huygens' Treatise on Light," trans. by Silvanus P. Thompson, Macmillan & Co., Ltd., London, 1912.

Newton, Sir Isaac, "Opticks," repr., McGraw-Hill Book Company, Inc., New York, 1931.

Pockels, F.: "Lehrbuch der Kristalloptik," B. G. Teubner, Leipzig, 1906.

Saunders, F. A.: "Survey of Physics," Henry Holt and Company, Inc., New York, 1930.

Webster, D. L., E. R. Drew, and H. W. Farwell: "General Physics for Colleges," Appleton-Century-Crofts, Inc., New York, 1926.

Whittaker, E. T.: "History of the Theories of Aether and Electricity," Longmans, Green & Co., Ltd., London, 1910.

CHAPTER 4

Refraction

Snell's Law. The Index of Refraction. When light passes obliquely from one medium to another in which it travels with a different velocity, it undergoes an abrupt change in direction. This abrupt change in direction is known as *refraction*. The relationships of the incident and refracted

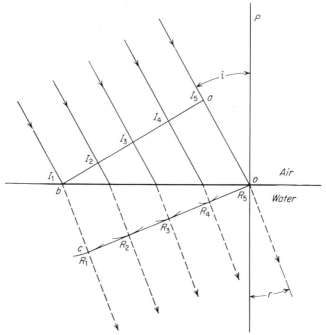

FIG. 4-1. Light being refracted on passing from a rare into a denser medium.

light may be illustrated by the adaptation of the construction of Huygens shown in Figure 4-1.

Let us suppose, for example, that a rare medium—air—is in contact with a denser medium—water. An incident beam *I* strikes the surface of the water obliquely, making an angle *i* with a perpendicular *P*. When the trace of the plane normal to the incident beam I strikes the surface at I_1, the point I_5 is still a considerable distance above the bounding plane. The positions I_2, I_3, and I_4, together with corresponding intermediate points, are also above the surface.

Let the beam advance until the ray at I_5 has reached R_5. During this advance the ray at I_1 has penetrated the denser medium and has continued with diminished velocity until it has arrived at the circumference of a circle with a radius I_1R_1, which represents the distance traveled in the denser medium. Similarly, I_2 has penetrated to the circumference R_2, I_3 to R_3, and I_4 to R_4. A tangent common to these circles represents the new wavefront, and the new beam is perpendicular to the new wavefront. The spherical waves sent out from b and other points on the bounding plane destroy each other except along bc and corresponding directions.

In the above construction, the distances I_5R_5 and I_1R_1 may be considered proportional to the relative velocities of light in the two media.

It is apparent from the relationship of the lines of the diagram that

$$\sin i = \frac{ao}{bo}$$

or

$$bo = \frac{ao}{\sin i}$$

also

$$\sin r = \frac{bc}{bo}$$

or

$$bo = \frac{bc}{\sin r}$$

Since bo is common, the equations may be combined, and

$$\frac{ao}{\sin i} = \frac{bc}{\sin r}$$

or

$$\frac{ao}{bc} = \frac{\sin i}{\sin r}$$

The index of refraction is determined by the distance light will travel in a given time interval through a transparent substance as compared with air. In Figure 4-1 light travels the distance ao in air, while it travels the distance bc in water. It follows, therefore, that the index of refraction

$$n = \frac{ao}{bc}$$

or

$$n = \frac{\sin i}{\sin r}$$

It appears from the foregoing equation that for any angle of incidence *the ratio of the sine of the angle of incidence to the sine of the angle of refraction is a constant.* It is also true that the respective velocities of light in the two media bear the same ratio. The relationship between the sines of the two angles and the velocities is known as *Snell's law.* It was discovered by Snell in 1621 but was not made known until after his death.

Let n be the index of refraction of a transparent material referred to air.[1] Then $V =$ the velocity in air, and $v =$ the velocity in the transparent material; also

$$n = \frac{V}{v}$$

If n_1 and n_2 are the indices of refraction of two different materials, then

$$\frac{n_1}{n_2} = \frac{v_2}{v_1}$$

Thus the indices of refraction of two transparent substances are inversely proportional to the velocities of light in the two media.

The angles i and r may be measured experimentally for many substances, thus determining n. The index of refraction depends both upon the substance and upon the kind of light. The indices of isotropic substances or general values are designated by the letter n. The extreme values for hexagonal or tetragonal minerals are designated by n_ε and n_ω. Orthorhombic, monoclinic, and triclinic crystals have their extreme values designated by n_γ (greatest), n_α (least), and n_β, the value in a direction at right angles to the two others.[2] The following table gives examples of values for the indices of refraction of several well-known minerals that occur throughout the normal range:

Minerals	(Na_D)	Indices of refraction
Fluorite................	....	$n = 1.4338$
Quartz*................	....	$n_\epsilon = 1.5533; n_\omega = 1.5442$
Calcite*...............	....	$n_\omega = 1.6585; n_\epsilon = 1.4863$
Apatite*..............	....	$n_\omega = 1.6461; n_\epsilon = 1.6417$
Aragonite*...........	....	$n_\alpha = 1.5301; n_\beta = 1.6816; n_\gamma = 1.6859$
Garnet (grossularite)........	(Yellow)	$n = 1.7714$
Sphalerite..............	(Yellow)	$n = 2.3692$

* Quartz, calcite, and apatite are anisotropic with a range of values for refractive indices between n_ϵ and n_ω, the two extremes. Refractive indices of aragonite vary between n_γ and n_α.

[1] The refractive index of dry air at 760-mm pressure referred to a vacuum is only slightly different from unity (1.000274 at 15°C); therefore, indices of refraction of material substances referred to air are approximately equal to their indices referred to a vacuum (the latter are called the *absolute refractive indices*).

[2] In American technical journals dealing with optical descriptions of minerals, many authors omit the letter n and use the Greek letters α, β, γ, ϵ, and ω alone in recording indices of refraction outside the isometric system.

Ordinarily, transparent minerals with a high index of refraction (1.9 or more) have the brilliant appearance called *adamantine luster,* while minerals with a lower index of refraction have a *vitreous luster.*

Dispersion. The index of refraction for the violet end of the spectrum is greater than for the red end of the spectrum and on refraction red is deviated less than violet. The ordinary refraction of the two is indicated in Figure 4-2.

The difference between the index of refraction for red and the index for violet is often briefly referred to as the dispersion. A cut prism placed in the path of a beam of white light produces a beautiful display of spectrum colors. The difference between the angle d_r and the angle d_v registers the dispersive power of the prism (see Figure 4-10).

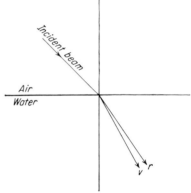

Minerals differ widely in their dispersive power. One having the least dispersion is fluorite; a mineral with one of the highest values is diamond. The "fire" or brilliant play of colors of the cut diamond is due to the high dispersion from the prismlike faceted gem stone. Fluorite, on the other hand, if cut and faceted, appears correspondingly dull. Because of its low dispersion, optically clear fluorite

Fig. 4-2. Variation in the angles of refraction for light of different colors.

is in demand for microscope lenses of high magnification to be corrected for chromatic variation. Comparative figures for the dispersion of fluorite and the diamond are given:

Fluorite		Diamond	
Illumination	Index of refraction, n	Illumination	Index of refraction, n
Red $K(A')$, $\lambda = 768.2$.......	1.43095	Red (B line).............	2.40735
Violet $H(G')$, $\lambda = 434.1$......	1.43963	Violet (H line)...........	2.46476
Dispersion...............	0.00868	Dispersion...............	0.05741

All minerals have some dispersive power, but fluorite and diamond represent approximately the two extremes.

On account of the dispersion of minerals, accurate determinations of indices of refraction are made with monochromatic light. In routine study, however, the highest accuracy is seldom necessary, and white light is generally employed. As a matter of fact, white light as usually employed in determining mineral indices gives an average value for practical purposes somewhat comparable to yellow. The dispersive effect with white light is also extremely useful for several common tests.

Critical Angle. In the formula $n = \sin i/\sin r$ the angle of incidence may vary between 0° and 90°. When $i = 0°$, the incident beam strikes the bounding surface at right angles. Sin i in this case $= 0$, and r must also equal 0. Thus an incident beam going from a rarer medium into a denser one is not refracted to either side but merely suffers a loss of velocity.

If $i = 90°$, sin $i = 1$, and the equation becomes $n = 1/\sin r$. In this case, since n is a constant for a particular substance, the angle of refraction also becomes fixed. When $i = 90°$, the angle of refraction is known as the *critical angle*. The critical angle is important in the practical determination of indices of refraction.

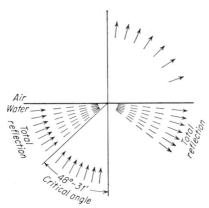

FIG. 4-3. The relation between refraction of light passing from a denser medium into a rarer medium and reflection beyond the critical angle.

Total Reflection. Figure 4-3 shows light going from water into air (or from a denser medium into a rarer medium). A ray striking the surface of the water vertically from below continues out into air along the same path. If the path deviates from the vertical, the beam is refracted—*i.e.*, bent away—from the perpendicular at the surface. When an angle of 48°31′ with the vertical is reached (the critical angle), the beam grazes the surface. For any angle greater than the critical angle, however, light is reflected downward. This phenomenon is known as *total reflection.*

If the angle with the perpendicular is increased until light travels along the surface between the air and water or strikes the surface at a grazing incidence, the beam is turned downward at the critical angle on the opposite side of the perpendicular to the bounding surface.

The same principle applies to all dense substances in contact with air. In practical determinations with a refractometer a glass hemisphere of high refractive index serves as the dense medium; light is directed against the hemisphere by a mirror, and the critical angle is determined with a measuring telescope.

Indices of Refraction of Anisotropic Minerals. Minerals belong to two optical classes: (1) isotropic and (2) anisotropic.

Minerals such as opal, glass, and other substances lacking regular internal structure and other minerals such as diamond, garnet, spinel, fluorite, etc., crystallizing in the isometric system are isotropic. Minerals crystallizing in the other crystal systems are anisotropic.

Light traveling through anisotropic minerals is doubly refracted. Thus a beam of monochromatic light passing obliquely from air into an anisotropic medium not only is bent to one side but also is broken into two beams. At the same time each of the two beams is polarized—*i.e.*, limited to a single plane of vibration, as will be explained in the chapter on polarized light. In addition, each beam is differently refracted for different colors of light.

Double refraction of two rays occurring in anisotropic minerals is illustrated in Figure 4-4. The incident beam is broken into two sets of rays, white light producing two dispersed spectra with opposite directions of vibration. Monochromatic red light will yield two angles of refraction, and monochromatic violet light will also yield two different angles. In each case of monochromatic light and also in the case of white light the directions of vibration are opposed but may not be

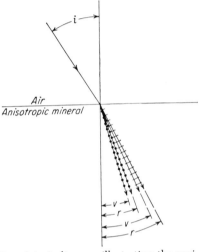

Fig. 4-4. A diagram illustrating the variation of the angle of refraction for red and violet in an anisotropic mineral.

exactly at right angles in the mineral. On emerging into air on the opposite side of a mineral plate, however, the vibration is at right angles.

Measurement of Indices of Refraction by Refractometers. Several types of refractometer have been devised for determining the indices of refraction of liquids or of solids. A glass hemisphere is utilized in different ways.

Figure 4-5 illustrates the determination of the index of refraction by the method of total reflection. Light is directed against the surface of a glass hemisphere from below at an angle of refraction greater than the critical angle. The light rays are reflected downward from the upper surface of the hemisphere and emerge on the opposite side. The material to be determined, either a mineral plate with a polished lower surface or a liquid, is placed on the hemisphere. If the material is a mineral plate, a thin film of oil of high refractive index is placed between the hemi-

sphere and the mineral. The light from the mineral is reflected through
the hemisphere in part and produces an image in the observing telescope
focused at o, as illustrated in the figure. The upper half of the field will
be dark, while the lower half is illuminated (or vice versa if the image
is inverted). If monochromatic light is used and the mineral is isotropic,
the boundary between the light and dark areas will be sharp, marking
the critical angle accurately (Figure 4-5a). On the other hand, in the case
of white light the colors of the spectrum lie *between* the light and dark

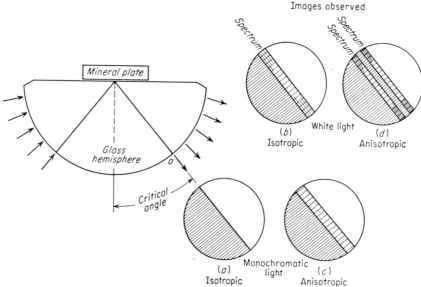

Fig. 4-5. Illumination from below in determining the critical angle by total reflection.

areas (Figure 4-5b). If the mineral is anisotropic and the observation
occurs with monochromatic light, two boundary lines will be seen spaced
a short distance apart (Figure 4-5c). If an anisotropic mineral is observed with white light, the two boundaries will be marked by spectra
(Figure 4-5d). When the anisotropism is not strong, the two spectra
frequently overlap. The light waves of each image from the anisotropic
mineral are polarized at right angles to the other.

Instruments operating on this principle are arranged with graduated
scales and verniers for measuring the critical angle. When the critical
angle is known, the index of refraction is computed from Snell's law,
$\sin i$ being equal to 1. The wavelength is controlled at the source by using
monochromatic light.

The method of grazing incidence can be applied with the same glass
hemisphere used for the method of total reflection. Light enters the min-

eral from the side and is refracted downward through the hemisphere as shown in Figure 4-6. In this case the upper half of the field of view is dark, and the lower half is illuminated. Otherwise the same principles prevail that apply to the other method. The contrast between the two fields is more pronounced when the mineral is illuminated by grazing incidence.

Whether employing total reflection or grazing incidence, the index of refraction of the glass hemisphere must be accurately known. This is usually ascertained by determining the index of refraction by total reflection in reference to air with the mineral plate removed, before de-

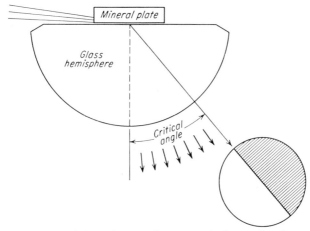

FIG. 4-6. Determination of the index of refraction with the incident beam grazing the surface of the hemisphere.

termining the index of refraction of the mineral. The index of the liquid used for mounting the mineral plate can also be determined by total reflection if a few drops are smeared on the upper surface of the hemisphere. The refractive index equation for the determination of the mineral may be stated:

$$n \text{ (mineral)} = n \text{ (glass)} \times \sin r$$

where n (mineral) = index of refraction of the mineral
  n (glass) = index of refraction of the hemisphere
  r = critical angle for the mineral as read with the refractometer

The glass used in constructing hemispheres has a high index of refraction, usually about 1.80. The mineral should have a polished surface to be placed toward the hemisphere, and a liquid with a high index of refraction is pulled by capillary attraction between the mineral and the hemisphere. Methylene iodide ($n = 1.74$) is usually preferred for this purpose.

Figure 4-7 is an illustration of one of the standard Abbe (Zeiss) refractometers commonly used in determining the indices of refraction of liquids (also of minerals and crystals). The refractive index is read off a graduated sector, and the instrument may be quickly set for reading directly. A scale is arranged in the image of the eyepiece that gives the values of indices of refraction for all angles within the range of the instrument, which extends from $n_D = 1.3$ to $n_D = 1.7$.

A refractometer of this type consists essentially of a double prism that receives the liquid to be tested, a telescope for viewing the line of the critical angle, and a scale sector for reading the angle. The double prism is made up of an illuminating prism F (Figure 4-8) with a ground-glass surface and a refracting prism P that operates on the principle of grazing incidence. The refracting prism takes the place of the glass hemisphere in other refractometers. A compensating device is inserted in the telescope to approximate monochromatic light (D line of sodium). The refractometer is usually adjusted for use by testing the instrument with a glass plate of known index.

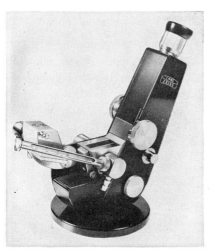

FIG. 4-7. The Abbe refractometer. (*Carl Zeiss, Inc.*)

Index of Refraction by the Prism Method. In Figure 4-9 a beam of monochromatic light strikes the prism ABC. At AB the beam R is bent toward the perpendicular OP.
At BC the beam R' emerges and is bent away from the perpendicular $O'P'$. R' continues in a straight line from this point, making an angle of deviation d with the original direction.

When the angle d is the minimum that can be observed when the prism is turned with respect to the beam (the angle of minimum deviation) and the angle p of the prism is also known, the index of refraction of the glass of the prism may be computed. The formula by which the index is computed is

$$n = \frac{\sin \frac{1}{2}(d + p)}{\sin \frac{1}{2}p}$$

p = angle of the prism
d = angle of minimum deviation of the beam
n = index of refraction of the prism

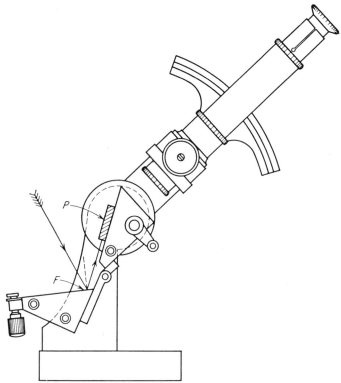

Fig. 4-8. Sectional view of the refractometer. (*Carl Zeiss, Inc.*)

When the beam of light striking the prism is not monochromatic but consists of the various wavelengths that combine to produce ordinary light, a spectrum is produced as shown in Figure 4-10.

The prism formula is particularly useful for determining the indices of refraction of glass prisms, transparent crystals, and hollow prisms filled with oil. A prism is adjusted vertically on a one-circle goniometer and the prism angle measured by obtaining reflections first from one side and then from the other and reading the angle on the graduated circle. With the same set-up a beam of light is passed

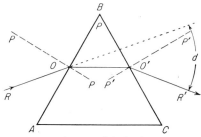

Fig. 4-9. A beam of light bent to one side by passing through a glass prism.

through the prism and the angle of minimum deviation is measured. The index of refraction is then computed directly from the formula given above, utilizing the angle of the prism and the angle of minimum deviation.

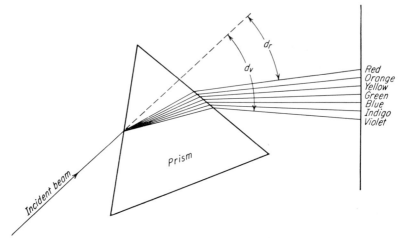

Fig. 4-10. Diagram illustrating the variation in the angle of minimum deviation of a prism with the wavelength of light.

Hollow prisms made of specially ground thin glass or plates with parallel surfaces or selected glass slides cut and cemented together are useful for determining the indices of refraction of liquids. Figure 4-11 illustrates a hollow prism made of glass plates of equal thickness and having parallel surfaces. Bakelite may be used to cement the glass plates to a solid prism. In ordinary determinative work, one prism cut at 45° is usually sufficient. Two prisms, one cut at 30° for high determinations and one at 60° for lower values, may be employed. Occasionally microscopic slides will possess the parallelism of surfaces required for the prism walls. Such

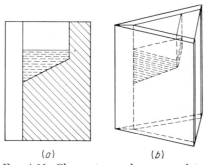

(a)   (b)

Fig. 4-11. Glass prism to be mounted in a goniometer for determining the indices of refraction of liquids. (Hollow space for liquid in upper portion of wedge between the plates.)

slides should be tested by observing the reflection of a hanging window cord drawn taut by a suspended weight or some other suitable straight line from both surfaces of the slide. The slide should be held close to the eye to observe this and turned until the reflections from both the upper and the lower surface can be seen at the same time. If the straight lines are parallel and uniformly distant in each image, the slide is satisfactory. It should also be tested in two perpendicular positions. When a good slide is found, it should be cut into two pieces, one for each side of the prism. The two parts are beveled and cemented[3] to a solid glass wedge. If the walls of the hollow prism are made of glass with parallel sides, correction for the glass is not necessary. It is best, however, to assume an exaggerated bevel and mount the two sides in opposed positions. Any existing lack of parallelism will be largely corrected in this way. Index of refraction determinations using this method are useful for determining the indices of refraction of liquids beyond the range of commercial refractometers. The method is also suitable when a refractometer is not available and as a check when it is available.[4]

If the same prism is always used, a chart may be prepared giving the index of refraction corresponding to each angle of minimum deviation for a given wavelength. If the chart covers the range of indices of refraction from 1.400 to 1.850, it will include all ordinarily determined values. Indices of refraction may be determined with the light of a sodium flame obtained by holding an asbestos sheet previously saturated in salt in a fan-flame burner. Light from a mercury-vapor arc or white light transmitted through a standard color filter is also occasionally employed. A helium-gas tube gives an ideal sodium line.[5]

A convenient method of securing a sodium flame has been suggested by F. Lowell Dunn, M.D., of Omaha, Nebr. He uses a *coarse* alundum filtration crucible filled with salt and suspends it over a Méker burner. A molten hemisphere of NaCl forms in the bottom of the crucible, which gives a sodium flame of extremely high intensity. The burner should be placed under a hood and at a safe distance from the microscope.

Special light bulbs giving a strong sodium light have been developed by the General Electric Company (Figure 4-12). These require about 20 minutes to acquire the proper color value but after developing the correct intensity furnish an excellent source of illumination.

The refractive indices of the various types of glass used in optical equipment are determined to the eighth decimal place with sodium light, mercury-vapor light, and several other light sources. Such precision is not employed in examining minerals with the microscope, nor is it possible without a special goniometer.

The Determination of the Index of Refraction with the Microscope. The index of refraction of a mineral is seldom determined completely in examination of thin sections. The slices are mounted in Canada balsam, and the usual test consists in ascertaining whether a given mineral has

[3] Bakelite resinoid, baked at 70°C for 10 hr and followed by baking at 125° for 10 hr, will make a solid prism. Bakelite varnish containing china oil is affected by index liquids and should be avoided.
[4] Hollow prisms of several types have been developed by Dr. E. S. Larsen of Harvard University, Dr. C. S. Ross of the U.S. Geological Survey, and Dr. H. E. Merwin of the Geophysical Laboratory.
[5] Employed in the laboratories of the U.S. Geological Survey.

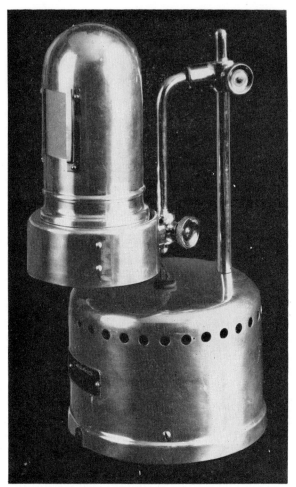

Fig. 4-12. Sodium laboratory arc furnishing a strong source of sodium light. (*Nela Specialty Division, Lamp Division of General Electric Co.*)

an index of refraction greater or less than balsam. The indices of adjacent minerals are also compared with each other.

The indices of refraction of adjacent transparent substances can be compared in several ways. The two most useful methods are the method of central illumination and that of oblique illumination.

A method of direct determination with the microscope exists, but unfortunately it is not sufficiently accurate with thin sections.

The Method of Central Illumination. The test is best made with a magnification of 80 or greater, with the iris diaphragm partly closed. It is quite sensitive to small differences in refractive indices at such magnifications. If monochromatic light is employed, it is possible to distinguish between the indices of refraction of two minerals even when they differ by as little as one in the third place of decimals.

The test may be applied to thin sections of transparent minerals in comparing their relative indices of refraction with adjacent minerals or balsam. The phenomenon used in making the test depends upon the total reflection of light incident at more than the critical angle when passing from a mineral of greater to a mineral of lesser index in a thin section. The test is employed for comparing the indices of refraction of the various minerals of thin sections with balsam, for comparing the minerals with each other when observed in contact, and for comparing fragments of minerals with various immersion media in which they may be mounted. Light enters the section from below and is transmitted through both media. At the bounding edge both reflection and refraction take place, and a portion of the entering beam is bent either to one side or to the other, depending upon the relative indices of refraction of the adjacent media. If the two indices happen to be the same, no refraction takes place. In case the index of refraction of one is greater than that of the other, light will strike an inclined boundary between the two in some place at an angle greater than the critical angle. A portion of the beam will be deflected toward the mineral with the greater index. If the boundary between the media is not inclined, grazing incidence may occur, bringing about the same effect. The deflection results in a light blur, visible through the microscope just inside the boundary of the mineral grain of greater index. The blur is more apparent if the iris diaphragm is partly closed and if the tube of the microscope is slightly raised. It forms an irregular white line; and as the tube is raised still farther, an illusion is produced, the line appearing to move toward the center of the mineral. If the tube is lowered, the effect is reversed. In reference to the mineralogist F. Becke the blur is often called the *Becke line.*

Since the index of balsam is known (approximately 1,537), minerals may be quickly divided into two groups, one with indices greater than balsam, the other with indices less than balsam. It is convenient to remember in making the test that when the tube is *raised*, the line moves toward the medium having the *higher* refractive index. Conversely, when the tube is *depressed*, the line moves toward the medium having the *lower* index (Figure 4-13).

Explanation of the White-line Effect. Hotchkiss has given an explanation of the refraction and reflection involved in the method of central illumination. The construction shown in Figure 4-14 is modified from his explanatory diagram.

Two minerals, A and B, are assumed to be in contact in a thin section with a vertical bounding plane, YZ. A is the mineral with a lesser index

$(n = 1.50)$, and B has a greater index, 1.70. A cone of light rays enters the two minerals from the balsam below, divided evenly on both sides of the bounding plane. The cone of light may be represented by the rays 1, 2, 3, and 4 with angles of inclination as indicated in the diagram.

The critical angle in mineral B with respect to the bounding plane is about 62°. The rays of light within B (3 and 4) which strike the surface

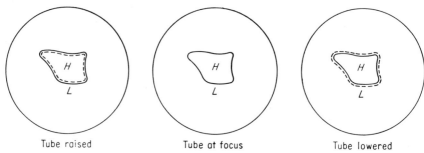

| Tube raised | Tube at focus | Tube lowered |

FIG. 4-13. Central illumination, $n >$ balsam.

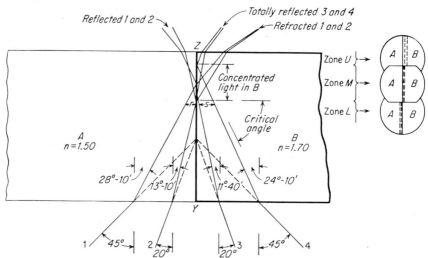

FIG. 4-14. A theoretical explanation of the movement of the light line in central illumination. (*Modified from Hotchkiss.*)

YZ at an angle greater than the critical angle are totally reflected. The rays of light within A (1 and 2) are split at the bounding surface, part being refracted into B and part being reflected back into A. The comparative intensity of the reflected and refracted rays depends upon the character of the bounding plane. If the contact surface is highly polished, more light is reflected and less refracted. If the surface is rough, as is usually the case, more light is refracted into B.

A band of light appears within the mineral of higher index at level *M*. Within this vertical distance nearly all the light of the cone is concentrated in *B*. If the plane of focus of the microscope is brought within this zone, a band of light is visible within the mineral with a higher index. If the plane of focus is elevated by raising the microscope tube to level *U*, the band becomes broader and furnishes the illusion of moving toward the center of *B* and away from the bounding plane. If the plane of focus is lowered to level *L*, on the other hand, a greater concentration of light is present in *r* than in *s*, and the light band will appear to be within the mineral with a lower refractive index. The circles adjacent to the braces and indicating the vertical extension of the zones are intended to illustrate the positions of the white line corresponding to different elevations of the plane of focus.

Oblique Illumination. The method of inclined or oblique illumination is more convenient for making the same relative comparisons of refractive indices outlined above, but at a magnification of about 50 or lower. A larger area of the thin section is included within this field, and the method allows the observer quickly to compare a large number of mineral grains; also, it provides an easier interpolation of values between two mounting media.

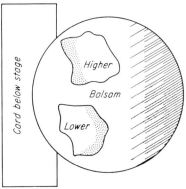

Fig. 4-15. Illustrating oblique illumination with the condenser removed. Higher = mineral grain, *n* > balsam. Lower = mineral grain, *n* < balsam.

The effect is best observed without a condenser lens. Oblique illumination may be secured by inserting a card below the stage cutting off half of the light. This darkens one-half of the field, at the same time allowing the opposite half to be illuminated largely by oblique rays (Figure 4-15). A similar effect may be secured by inserting a narrow card in the accessory slot above an objective of moderate power (with the condenser in the system). This effect may be either the same or reversed, depending upon the focal length of the condenser.

Individual crystals of minerals will be unevenly illuminated by the method of oblique illumination. One side of the mineral will be dark, and the opposite side will be light. When the card is inserted below the objective, the shadow will appear either on the side of a mineral toward the dark half of the field or on the side away from it. When the shadow appears on the side away from the dark half, the index of refraction of the mineral in question is greater than that of the adjacent medium; if on the side next to the dark half, the index of the mineral is less. In case the index of refraction of the mineral is about equal to the index of the mounting material and white light is employed, one side will be blue while the other is red. When the card is inserted in the accessory opening, the shadow in the mineral is on the side of the field next to the dark area if the index of the mineral is greater than balsam.[6]

The index of a known mineral should be tried first in making this test in order to be sure of the set-up in the microscope.

Double Diaphragm Method. Saylor's investigation of the sensitivity of various methods of matching indices of refraction with the microscope has led to the proposal of the double-diaphragm method, a modification of the method of inclined illumination. This is more particularly applicable to the immersion method, as described in Chapter 9. The set-up, with a mineral fragment mounted in an immersion liquid of higher index, is shown in Figure 4-16. The solid lines show the light rays entering the mineral, and the dash lines indicate emerging rays.

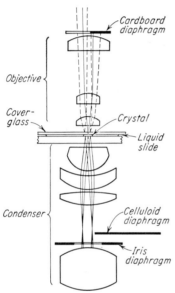

FIG. 4-16. Double diaphragm method of oblique illumination. (*C. P. Saylor.*)

Relief. Certain minerals stand out strongly in the field of the microscope, others are moderately visible, and frequently the mineral is hardly visible at all. This appearance or visibility of outline and surface is described as *relief*.

The relief of a mineral mounted in balsam depends upon the difference between the index of refraction of the mineral and balsam. Minerals with low indices of refraction (cryolite, $n = 1.364$) and high indices of refraction (spinel, $n = 1.75$) have strong relief. On the other hand, such a mineral as apophyllite has approximately the same index of refraction as balsam and consequently is hardly visible in thin section.

Anisotropic minerals with a wide divergence between the two extremes of refractive indices exhibit a variation in relief as the stage of the microscope is rotated. Calcite furnishes one of the best illustrations of this feature. The ray vibrating parallel to the short diagonal of the cleavage rhombohedron has nearly the same index as balsam. When this

---

[6] Another simple way to secure the effect of oblique illumination suggested by Dr. J. D. H. Donnay consists in shading the field by partially inserting the frame containing the analyzing nicol.

direction is parallel to the lower nicol, a calcite cleavage fragment on the stage of the microscope shows low relief. When the cleavage fragment is turned at right angles until the long diagonal is parallel to the lower nicol, light travels through the mineral with the velocity of the higher index, and the same grain stands out with high relief. A number of common minerals vary in relief with direction.

The relief of a mineral may be estimated as *low, moderate, high,* or *extremely high.* In the tables to follow, such a descriptive term is given for each mineral.

REFERENCES

Becke, F.: *Sitzber. Akad. Wiss. Wien,* C11, Abt. 1, pp. 358–378, 1893.

Graham, G. W.: *Mineral. Mag.,* vol. 15, pp. 341–347, 1910.

Hotchkiss, W. O.: *Am. Geol.,* vol. 36, pp. 305–308, 1905.

Saylor, C. P.: Accuracy of Microscopical Methods for Determining Refractive Index by Immersion, *Nat. Bur. Standards, Research Paper* 829, vol. 15, pp. 277–294, 1935.

Wright, F. E.: The Methods of Petrographic-microscopic Research, *Carnegie Inst. Pub.* 158, 1911.

CHAPTER 5

Plane Polarized Light in Minerals

Polarized Light. In the foregoing it has been assumed for descriptive purposes that light may be considered as wave motion. This condition holds for ordinary white light or for monochromatic light of any sort. It is also assumed that the vibrations take place in all directions around the line of transmission. Many times, however, the tendency to vibrate in all directions around the line of transmission is modified, and the waves become restricted for the most part to a single plane of vibration. When vibration is thus restricted, light is said to be *polarized*.

Polarization of light may be demonstrated in several ways: (1) by reflection from a polished surface; (2) by repeated refraction at an angle through several plates of thin glass; (3) by absorption by certain crystals such as tourmaline or herapathite (polaroid); (4) by cleavages or prisms of optical calcite.

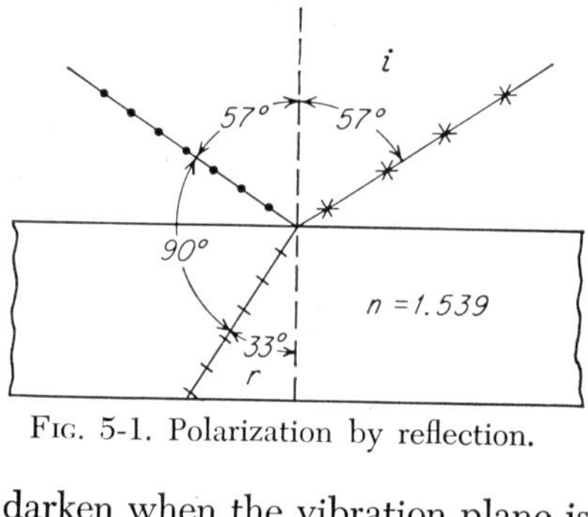

Fig. 5-1. Polarization by reflection.

Polarization by Reflection. Light reflected obliquely from a polished surface, such as a table top or a mirror, is partially polarized. If the reflection is examined through a polarizing sheet, the field of view will darken when the vibration plane is turned at right angles to the plane of reflection of the polished surface.

According to Brewster, the polarization with a glass plate is at a maximum when the directions of reflection and refraction are 90° apart (Figure 5-1). At such an angle r becomes the complement of i, and the formula $n = \sin i / \sin r$ may be written $\sin i / \cos i = \tan i = n$. Thus, at the angle of maximum polarization the tangent of the angle of incidence equals the index of refraction of the reflecting substance. The angular relationships for a plate $n = 1.539$ are shown in Figure 5-1.

A sectional view of an old-fashioned polariscope is shown in Figure 5-2. Reflection from glass plates yields polarized light which passes through a nicol prism. The instrument was used before the advent of the modern polarizing microscope for the study of mineral plates.

Polarization by Absorption. Tourmaline yields polarization by absorption. Light that strikes the crystal vibrating in a variety of planes is strongly absorbed except along one plane. The rays of light that emerge limited to this plane of vibration are thus plane-polarized. The crystallographic axis c (often the long direction of the crystal) lies parallel to the plane of vibration.

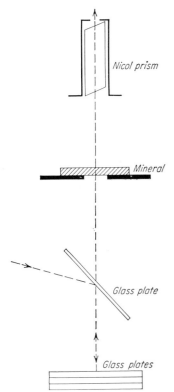

Observation through another plate of tourmaline cut in a similar fashion and superimposed at right angles effectively reveals the polarization. Light transmitted through the two is eliminated where plates overlap and the overlapping portion is dark (Figure 5-3).

Thin crystals of a strongly absorptive compound, iodocinchonidine-sulfate, were described in 1852 by William Bird Herapath, M.D. (Figure 5-4). Because of their strong absorption in one direction corre-

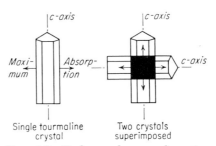

FIG. 5-2. Polarization by reflection in a polariscope.

FIG. 5-3. Darkness due to absorption produced by two superimposed tourmaline crystals.

sponding to the behavior of tourmaline, the crystals were referred to as "artificial tourmalines." The material was subsequently called *herapathite* in honor of the discoverer. Methods now exist for producing thin transparent sheets containing small crystals of herapathite in parallel orientation embedded in a plastic binder. Two overlapping sheets of this material are illustrated in Figure 5-5. It is possible to prepare such polarizing sheets covering more than a square foot in area.

Several of the microscopes described in this text are equipped with polarizing plates. Instruments manufactured in the United States utilize plates marketed under the trade name "Polaroid." The plates not only provide excellent optical effects, but permit improvements in microscope design through a saving in space. Polaroid sheets are useful for optical

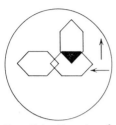

demonstration and for supplementary uses, particularly where a wide field of polarized light is required.

Double Refraction (Birefringence). Light in passing through a large number of transparent minerals is doubly refracted into two beams vibrating along planes that are approximately at right angles to each other.[1] Transparent minerals, with the exception of those crystallizing in the isometric (cubic) system, and amorphous minerals are doubly refracting (anisotropic).

FIG. 5-4. Crystals of herapathite showing an area of extinction where individuals with directions of greatest absorption at right angles are superimposed. (*After Herapath*, 1853.)

A good illustration of double refraction and accompanying polarization by a mineral occurs in transparent calcite, or Iceland spar. Objects viewed through a rhombic block of Iceland spar appear double; if such a cleavage is placed over a dot within a circle marked on a piece of paper, the dot will appear to the eye as two dots and the circle as two circles (Figure 5-6). The light

FIG. 5-5. Two disks of herapathite (Polaroid) mounted on glass plates photographed with the planes of polarization at right angles. (*Polarizing Instrument Co.*)

giving rise to one image will be composed of waves vibrating parallel to the long diagonal of a rhombic surface; that giving rise to the other will be composed of waves vibrating parallel to the short diagonal (Figure

[1] F. E. Wright has demonstrated that the precise determination of the angle between the two beams is a matter of careful physical measurement. In discussing double refraction, the amount of variation from 90° will not be taken into account, and the two rays will be considered in simple terms as about at right angles.

5-7). The two light rays have been differently refracted, and the indices of refraction are different. The extreme indices of calcite are 1.516 and 1.658 with a difference of 0.142. In the position indicated the two indices are far apart.

A large quartz sphere such as the crystal ball more than a foot in diameter in the United States National Museum in Washington exhibits easily visible double refraction. Here the indices are 1.544 and 1.553 with a difference of 0.009. To exhibit the same separation of images shown by calcite, quartz must have a thickness some 15 times as great. The calcite of Figure 5-6 is about 4 inches across. Even a quartz sphere of museum size does not show as much separation of images.

No double refraction is noted when crystals such as calcite or quartz are observed in the direction of the principal crystal axis (*c*-axis) which is also the optic axis. The same applies for all hexagonal or tetragonal crystals.

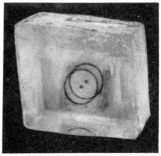

Fig. 5-6. Double refraction illustrated by a cleavage rhomb of transparent calcite or Iceland spar.

The direction of the optic axis is one of isotropy. In any other direction the mineral is anisotropic. In the latter cases light is polarized into two rays vibrating at right angles to each other. One vibrates at right angles to the optic axis (the *ordinary ray*), the other in a plane parallel to the optic axis (the *extraordinary ray*). In

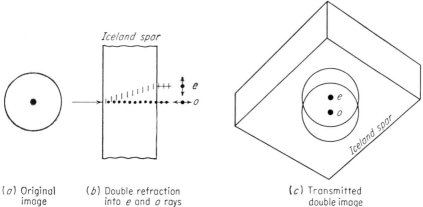

(*a*) Original image   (*b*) Double refraction into *e* and *o* rays   (*c*) Transmitted double image

Fig. 5-7. Separation of extraordinary (*e*) and ordinary (*o*) ray images in Iceland spar.

calcite the ordinary ray vibrates parallel to the long diagonal of a rhombic face of the cleavage rhombohedron as shown in Figure 5-8. The extraordinary ray vibrates in a plane passing through the optic axis and parallel to the short diagonal.

Optical Indicatrix. The indicatrix serves to illustrate the optical features of a crystal. It consists essentially of a surface generated around a point with the indices of refraction serving as radii.

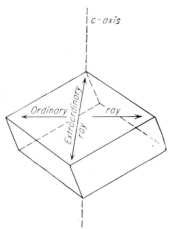

FIG. 5-8. The extraordinary and ordinary rays in a calcite cleavage.

The indicatrix for tetragonal and hexagonal crystals (Figures 5-9a,b) is a spheroid of rotation. The index for the extraordinary ray shows a range in values, while the index for the ordinary ray remains constant. The index ϵ coincides with the axis of principal symmetry in the crystal (c-axis). When ϵ is greater than ω the spheroid is prolate and the crystal is optically positive (quartz). When ϵ is less than ω the spheroid is oblate and the crystal is optically negative (calcite).

The indicatrix for orthorhombic, monoclinic, and triclinic crystals is a triaxial ellipsoid (Figure 6-16) and is related to the symmetry of crystals in these three systems. It forms a useful device for explaining the optical properties of biaxial crystals.

The principal section of a uniaxial indicatrix (Figure 5-10) may be used to examine the directional features of a wave normal and the corresponding ray where both are inclined to the axes. The section is prolate

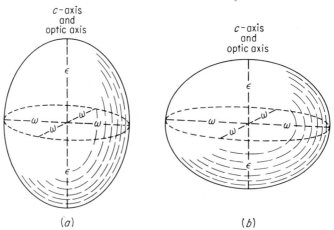

FIG. 5-9. Uniaxial indicatrix. (*a*) Positive. (*b*) Negative.

with the major axis LL' equal to 2ϵ corresponding to the c-axis of the crystal. The minor axis SS' is equal to 2ω and lies in a plane normal to the c-axis of the crystal.

The direction of an intermediate wave normal is indicated by the line *OD*. Along this line one set of waves vibrates in the plane of the section, while the other set vibrates in a plane perpendicular to the plane of the section.

The index of refraction of the set perpendicular to the plane of the section is ω and the minor semiaxis of the indicatrix corresponds to this value. The index of refraction of the set in the plane of the section corresponds to the semiaxis *OV* (or *OW*). Both sets of waves vibrate perpendicular to the wave normal *OD*.

Along the principal axes of the indicatrix the direction of the wave normal coincides with the direction of the corresponding ray. Elsewhere the ray and wave normal differ in direction.

In Figure 5-10 the line *OT* indicates the direction of the ray corresponding to the wave normal *OD*. The position *T* is the point of tangency on the ellipse of the line *DT* perpendicular to *OD*.

The wave velocities may be obtained from the properties of the ellipse. The area of the parallelogram (dashed lines in Figure 5-10) equals the area of the rectangle (solid lines in Figure 5-10).

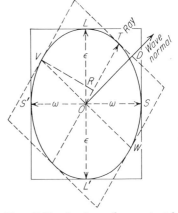

Fig. 5-10. Section of a uniaxial positive indicatrix.

The conjugate radii are *OT* and *OV*. The area of the parallelogram is given by $2VR \cdot 2OT$ where *VR* is normal to *OT*.

The velocity of the component of the ray *OT* which vibrates normal to the principal section is $1/\omega$. The velocity of the component which vibrates in the principal section is $1/VR$.

In the direction of the optic axis (*LL'*), the wave normal and ray directions coincide, there is a constant index ω, and the velocity $1/\omega$ is also constant.

In the direction perpendicular to the optic axis, light consists of two sets of waves, one vibrating parallel to the optic axis, the other vibrating at right angles. The rays travel parallel to the wave normal. One ray component is the extraordinary ray. This vibrates parallel to the optic axis, has an index ϵ and has a velocity proportional to $1/\epsilon$. The ordinary ray vibrates normal to the optic axis, has an index ω, and has a velocity proportional to $1/\omega$.

Nicol Prism. The nicol prisms in the polarizing microscope utilize the principle of double refraction to produce polarized light. Optically clear calcite is used, and a prism is made of two parts cemented together with Canada balsam. The two halves form a prism of the type illustrated in Figure 5-11. Light entering the base of the prism is broken into extraordinary and ordinary rays. The extraordinary ray has an index of refraction $n = 1.516$ at the angle of incidence for the prism; the ordinary ray has an index of refraction $n = 1.658$. The index of the extraordinary ray is close to the index of refraction of balsam, $n = 1.537$. The index of the ordinary ray, however, is considerably greater. Both rays strike the cementing plane of balsam obliquely. The obliquity of the ordinary ray exceeds the critical angle between the ordinary ray and balsam. As a result, it is not refracted through the balsam but is reflected to the side of the prism. Since the extraordinary ray does not exceed the critical angle between the extraordinary ray and balsam, it passes on through the prism with little deviation.

The extraordinary ray is polarized with one plane of vibration; consequently, the light emerging from the prism and made up entirely of the extraordinary ray is plane-polarized.

Modifications permit an enlarged field (Thompson) and a more compact prism (Ahrens). In the Ahrens prism (Figure 5-12) the optic axis of calcite lies at right angles to the path of light through the microscope.

Interference between Crossed Nicols. When two nicol prisms are superimposed with their planes of vibration at right angles to each other, the nicols are said to be crossed. The polarizing microscope is normally used with the prisms in this position. Once adjusted, the plane of each nicol

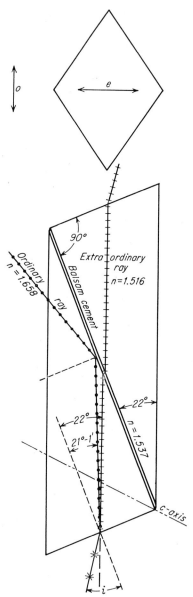

Fɪɢ. 5-11. The polarization and deviation of light in a nicol prism.

remains fixed, but the upper nicol slides in or out of the tube of the micro-scope. Crossed nicols produce darkness when the stage is unoccupied or when it holds optically isotropic materials such as glass or opal or crystals of the isometric system of crystallization. Minerals crystallizing in crystal systems other than the isometric are anisotropic and in most positions produce a range of interference colors between crossed nicols.

In Figure 5-13 polarized light is shown passing through a mineral plate after leaving the lower nicol. Light strikes the lower surface of the min-eral plate vibrating in one plane. On entering the plate, it is broken into

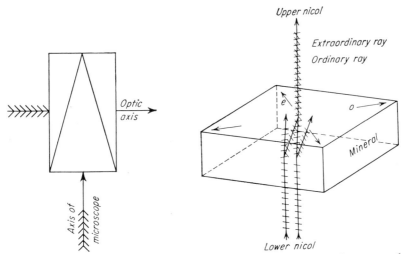

FIG. 5-12. A block of calcite with square cross section cut to form a polarizing prism. (*After C. D. Ahrens.*)

FIG. 5-13. The vibration directions of the extraordinary and ordinary rays in an anisotropic mineral illuminated with polarized light.

two sets of rays. Both sets are polarized, but at right angles, and light travels at different velocities within the mineral along each plane. As a result, when the two sets of rays emerge on the upper side of the plate, one set has traveled farther than the other. Both travel along a straight line to the analyzer and continue to vibrate at right angles.

Irregular grains of anisotropic minerals on the stage of the microscope resolve light from the polarizer into the separate extraordinary and ordi-nary rays for each mineral (Figure 5-14). A wide range in directions may result but in each crystal the extraordinary and ordinary rays are at right angles.

In the analyzer, whether polaroid or a nicol prism, the two rays are resolved to a single plane as indicated in Figure 5-15. Thus the two rays emerge from the analyzer vibrating in the same plane. However, the initial phase separation due to the mineral is retained. As a result, when the ordinary and extraordinary rays emerge from the analyzer they are in a position to interfere, and interference colors are observed. An outline of the mechanism is shown in Figure 5-16. In this relationship the separation of the e and o rays, as determined by the thickness, position, and indices of the mineral, yield phase differences as waves emerge from the analyzer. Here resolution of effective components of each takes place into the plane of the analyzer, as illustrated diagrammatically in Figure 5-15. As a result of this resolution, two rays emerge from the analyzer.

The interference color produced depends upon the nature of the light and the amount of retardation of one set of waves with respect

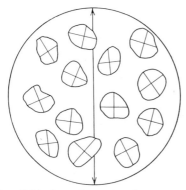

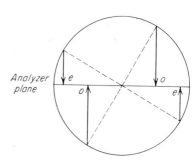

Fig. 5-14. Irregular mineral grains on microscope stage above polarizer. Light is polarized by each grain into ordinary and extraordinary rays at right angles.

Fig. 5-15. Resolution of extraordinary and ordinary rays of the mineral into the plane of polarization of the analyzer.

to that of the other. The retardation can be determined with a fair degree of precision from the interference color and is expressed by the Greek letter Δ. The value of Δ is expressed in millimicrons (millionths of a millimeter $= m\mu$), the same units used to measure the wavelength of light.

The retardation may be changed through a wide range by (1) varying the thickness t of the mineral, (2) changing the orientation in such a way as to change the indices of refraction n_1 and n_2 of the two rays emerging from the mineral. This relationship may be expressed by the equation

$$\Delta = t(n_2 - n_1)$$

In the equation, t represents the thickness of the mineral expressed in millimeters, n_2 is the greater index of refraction, and n_1 is the lesser index of refraction for a particular orientation.

Phase Difference. The two rays emerging from the mineral have a phase difference P. This difference is equal to the retardation divided by the wavelength:

$$P = \frac{\Delta}{\lambda}$$

Since it has just been shown that

$$\Delta = t(n_2 - n_1)$$

it follows that $P = \dfrac{t(n_2 - n_1)}{\lambda}$

When the retardation is some whole multiple of a wavelength $(n\lambda)$, the waves emerging from the upper nicol become equal and opposite in phase. The resultant is then equal to zero, and the field produced is dark (Figure 5-17).

Midway between, maximum intensity occurs. Here the retardation is $[(2n + 1)/2]\lambda$, and the components of the waves in the plane of the upper nicol are equal and on the same side of the line of transmission. The resultant wave is equal to the sum of the two components (Figure 5-18).

Interference Colors. If the mineral plate lies with the planes of vibration parallel and perpendicular to the planes of the polarizing devices, no light passes through the analyzer, and the mineral is in a position of extinction. On the other hand, if the plate is rotated to either side, the field of the analyzer is no longer dark but becomes illuminated with interference colors. The interference colors vary with the thickness of the mineral section, the nature of the mineral, the way in which the mineral section is cut, and the light employed. The explanation of the relationship of these various factors involves many of the principles of optical mineralogy. It is desirable for the sake of simplicity to consider the variables one at a time.

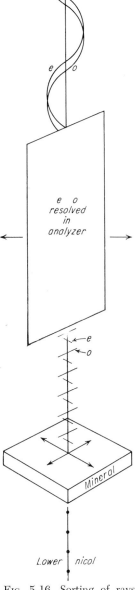

Fig. 5-16. Sorting of rays by the analyzer when the nicols are crossed.

If the thickness of a mineral plate between crossed nicols is changed, though the orientation remains the same, a change in interference color ensues. One of the best ways to illustrate this phenomenon is by means of the quartz wedge that accompanies the polarizing microscope.

Figure 5-19 is a diagram illustrating a portion of a quartz wedge cut along the c-axis and varying in thickness from 0.0 to 0.10 mm. The wedge is placed between crossed nicols in a position at 45° to the planes of the nicols. In this position it becomes brilliantly illuminated with interference colors. The colors gradually merge into each other and change

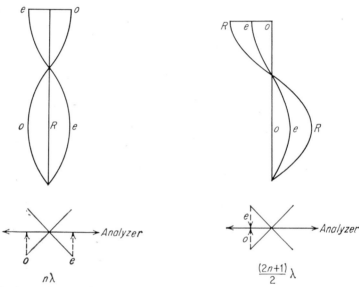

FIG. 5-17. Resolution of waves in analyzer for retardation of whole wavelength or multiples.

FIG. 5-18. Resolution of waves in analyzer for retardation of one-half wavelength or multiples.

with increase or decrease in thickness along the wedge. Any one thickness yields a uniform band of one color across the wedge. The quartz wedge should be placed on the stage of the microscope and moved back and forth in order to observe the full range of color due to varying thickness.

Each portion of the wedge is subject to the equation

$$\Delta = t(n_2 - n_1)$$

Since the optic axis of the wedge remains parallel to the stage, $(n_2 - n_1)$ is fixed and equals 0.009, the accepted value for quartz. Consequently, the retardation Δ varies with the thickness t.

When t is zero, the retardation in any light is also zero, and the field of view is dark. In white light, when t increases, a definite sequence of colors ensues. Starting with gray and continuing through bluish gray, white, yellow, orange, in the order named, the colors are striking to the

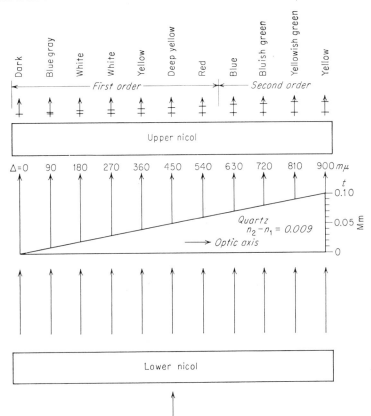

Fɪɢ. 5-19. Interference colors due to a portion of a quartz wedge between crossed nicols with white light.

eye. In the thicker portion of the wedge, however, less contrast appears; and in wedges several times as thick the colors at the thick end are faint iridescent tints.

If the source of illumination is monochromatic the effect produced is illustrated in Figure 5-20. In this case, when the thickness reaches such a point that the retardation becomes equal to one wavelength, the two monochromatic waves are equal and opposite in phase and nullify each other, causing darkness. As a result, dark bands will occur at all points where the retardation is a whole multiple of λ. Conversely, at odd multiples of $\frac{1}{2}\lambda$, maximum intensity will occur. Here the two waves are equal and in the same phase.

The interference colors due to white light may be considered as a composite of the various wavelengths of the spectrum. The relationship of the interference colors to the monochromatic components is illustrated in Figure 5-21. The range in interference colors through four orders is

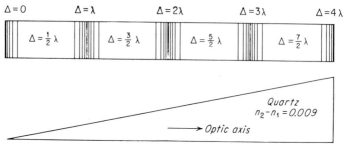

FIG. 5-20. Alternate dark and light bands produced by monochromatic light with a quartz wedge between crossed nicols.

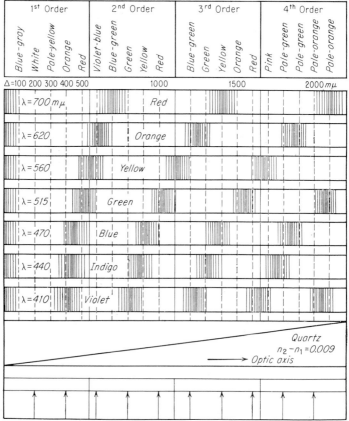

FIG. 5-21. The relationship between interference colors due to monochromatic light and colors due to white light.

shown at the top of the figure. The corresponding cumulative monochromatic wavelengths are shown below.

The various monochromatic beams, on passing through a wedge, produce dark bands at different thicknesses. Likewise, maximum intensity
occurs at corresponding intermediate intervals. The difference between the
wavelengths at the opposite ends of the spectrum is such, however, that
the first dark band for violet occurs almost in the first position of maximum intensity for red. For violet the band is approximately 410 mμ,
and the wavelength for red is about 700 mμ. At $\Delta = 410$ mμ the interference color is close to orange. The orange is a composite in which the
colors at the red end of the spectrum predominate and colors at the
violet end are minimized. The per cent of maximum intensity for red
at $\Delta = 410$ mμ is about 83. The maximum intensity for red occurs at
$\frac{1}{2}\lambda$ or 350 mμ. The per cent of this maximum at 410 mμ would be

$$\frac{2(\lambda r - \lambda v)}{\lambda r} \times 100 = \frac{2(700 - 410)}{700} \times 100 = 83 \text{ per cent}$$

If the wavelengths are known, it is possible to compute the per cent of
any given monochromatic light present in an interference color of a
given retardation.

Application of the Color Chart to the Study of Minerals. The *interference color chart* is constantly employed in the study of minerals by
means of polarized light. The maximum double refraction, or the greatest
difference between n_2 and n_1, is approximately constant for a given
mineral. If this constant is substituted in the equation $\Delta = t(n_2 - n_1)$, a
straight-line curve is the result. In the case of quartz, where

$$(n_2 - n_1) = 0.009$$

the relation between thickness and retardation is shown in Figure 5-22.
Where $n_2 - n_1$ is maximum a normal sequence of colors prevails for
most anisotropic minerals. A few, such as idocrase, with abnormal dispersion fail to follow the normal sequence and must be considered independently. However, the relationship of the chart is adequate to yield
the color of quartz of a given thickness or the thickness of quartz having
a given interference color.

Similar lines based on the maximum $n_2 - n_1$, or birefringence, may be
drawn for other minerals. The color chart (facing page 168) gives the
lines of maximum double refraction for the common minerals.

In the color chart interference colors with Δ less than 550 mμ belong
to the *first order*. Violet ($\Delta = 550$) forms the boundary of the first
order and is known as *sensitive violet*, since a small change either way

produces a decided color difference. From violet $\Delta = 550$ to violet $\Delta = 1128$ the colors belong to the second order. From violet $\Delta = 1128$ to violet $\Delta = 1652$ they belong to the third order. Above the fourth order colors are not easily separated. The colors at the end of the first order and the beginning of the second are the most striking and brilliant. At the end of the fourth order they merge into each other, forming tints of green and pink tending toward grayish white. Care should be taken to distinguish these colors from the blue gray, white, and yellowish white of the lower first order.

Uncertainty concerning the order of a given color may be eliminated by using a mica plate. The mica plate is cut with such thickness that it increases or decreases retardation of a section by about $\frac{1}{4}\lambda$ (sodium light). Such an increase or decrease in the lower first or second orders produces a set of colors markedly different. In higher orders little visible change occurs. For example, in the case of first-order yellow $\Delta = 400$ mμ, an increase in Δ of 175 mμ will result in violet $\Delta = 575$ mμ, and a decrease of the same amount will produce white $\Delta = 225$ mμ. The same increase or decrease in retardation above the fourth order would produce little change perceptible to the eye.

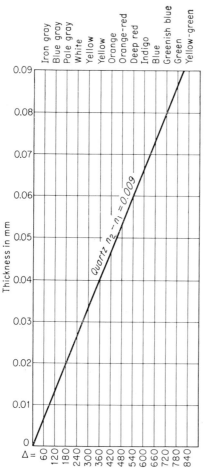

FIG. 5-22. Variation of double refraction with thickness in quartz.

Determination of Retardation with a Berek Compensator. M. Berek (1913) described a rotary calcite compensator of simple mechanical construction which may be used to measure retardation (Figure 2-19). A calcite plate 0.1 mm thick, cut normal to the optic axis, rests on a rotating axis in a metal holder. The frame may be inserted in the accessory slot of the microscope. The rotation of the compensator plate is registered on a graduated drum attached to the axis of rotation. The drum is graduated with a vernier reading to tenths and may be calibrated to read degrees.

The plate in the compensator is held in a small ring that may be easily removed, and a plate of different thickness may be substituted. The range of the plate ordinarily employed covers retardations from zero to the fourth order.

The axis of rotation of the compensator is arranged diagonally to the polarization planes of the two nicols. If the planes of the nicols are north and east, the tube slot holding the compensator will be northwest. The compensator is marked with two arrows: H_1, parallel to the

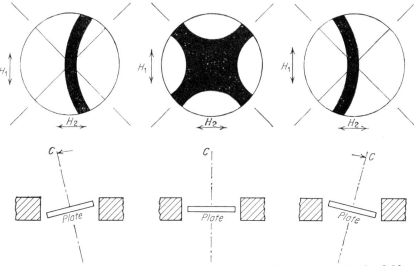

FIG. 5-23. The vibration directions and movement of the color rings in the field of the ocular when using the Berek compensator.

axis of rotation or along the accessory slot, is the slow-ray vibration direction; H_2, at right angles to the axis of rotation, indicates the trace of the projection of the plane containing the inclined c-axis of calcite and marks the fast-ray vibration direction.

The compensator is first set with the plate horizontal within the frame and inserted. Between crossed nicols a large dark cross will appear in the field. When this cross coincides with the crosshairs of the microscope, the compensator is in the zero position (see Figure 5-23). If the compensator drum is then turned either to the left or to the right, the various orders of interference colors appear in the field in a sequence corresponding to the order of the quartz wedge.

The compensator may be used to determine the retardation of a mineral grain between crossed nicols as follows: The grain in question is moved to the center of the field and placed in the 45° position with the slow-ray vibration direction of the mineral parallel to H_2 of the compensator. The compensator is then inserted and rotated first to the right and then to the left, stopping in each case when the interference color of the mineral has been completely reduced to extinction. The measured difference between the opposite readings is divided by two and the value inserted in a simple formula supplied by the makers of the instrument. Solution of the formula gives the correct retardation for the mineral grain.

A view of the Berek compensator is shown in Figure 2-19. Figure 5-23 indicates the views obtained in the microscope field with the compensator plates horizontal and rotated either to the right or to the left.

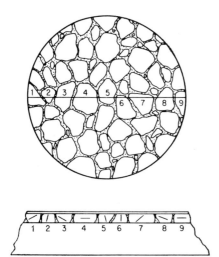

FIG. 5-24. Determination of thickness of section in quartzite.

The vertical sections in the lower part of Figure 5-23 indicate the inclination of the c-axis, and the upper diagrams represent corresponding microscope fields. With monochromatic light, light and dark bands are produced on either side of a central cross. With white light, the bands on either side of the dark cross indicating the zero position are colored.

When the compensator is inserted above a doubly refracting crystal in a thin section, the dark cross disappears. As the plate is rotated, however, the interference colors are changed until complete compensation occurs as mentioned above.

Determination of Thickness of Section. Let us suppose that Figure 5-24 represents a thin section containing numerous small quartz grains in random orientations. Grains 1 to 9 along the horizontal crosshair in the field of the microscope are oriented with optic axes in the positions shown in the sectional view. Most are inclined; occasionally a few are vertical and a few are horizontal. Horizontal axes are in the correct position to provide a maximum value of $(n_2 - n_1)$. All are of uniform thickness; hence grains with horizontal axes will show the highest order of interference or maximum retardation. In a thin section the grains with the highest order interference color as observed by means of the color chart will be grains in a position to exhibit the maximum $(n_2 - n_1)$. In the case at hand, grain 4 is in the correct position. If grain 4 should be straw yellow, the thickness of the section as determined by the color chart would be 0.03 mm. Other interference colors appear, but only those with axes in an approximately horizontal position will be as high in the first order as straw yellow.

In any thin section, if sufficient grains of a known mineral are present in random orientation and the highest order of interference color can be determined, it is possible to ascertain the thickness of section by reference to the color chart. It is also possible to reverse the process if the thickness is known and determine the double refraction of an unknown mineral. Likewise, in a slide containing two or more minerals, one of which is known, it is possible to determine the thickness of the section from the known mineral and determine the double refraction of the unknown minerals from the determined thickness and the observed interference colors.

Direction of the Vibration of Slow or Fast Rays. It is frequently important to ascertain the planes of vibration of the two rays vibrating at right angles in an anisotropic mineral grain. The two rays have different indices of refraction, the one with the greater index being the slow ray and the one with the lesser index, the fast ray. The determination of the fast- and slow-ray directions is accomplished between crossed nicols, the location of the two rays being established by observing the position of extinction. When the mineral becomes dark, the vibration directions of the two rays are parallel to the planes of vibration of the nicol prisms. Since the planes of vibration of the nicols are parallel to the crosshairs in the ocular, the vibration planes in the mineral will also be parallel to the crosshairs when in the extinction position.

A mica plate or gypsum plate is used to tell which of the two rays is fast and which is slow. When the positions of the vibration directions of the rays are ascertained, the mineral is turned from extinction to the position of maximum interference. Next, either the gypsum or the mica plate is inserted in the tube of the microscope with the slow-ray vibration direction parallel to one of the vibration directions of the mineral. If the order of color increases, the parallel direction is the slow-ray vibration direction of the mineral. If it decreases, the direction represents the fast ray. One direction being known, the other is the opposite. The mica plate is usually used for minerals with weak double refraction, and the gypsum plate is employed in the case of stronger double refraction. When the mineral has very strong double refraction, a quartz wedge may be used. Since the quartz wedge varies in retardation from zero to the fourth order, a variety of colors will be produced, the color at a particular part of the wedge depending upon the thickness. When the slow ray coincides with the slow-ray direction in the mineral, a corresponding reinforcement in retardation will occur. Thus the color of the mineral will suddenly change to a color of higher order, dependent upon the portion of the wedge superimposed. When the slow-ray direction in the wedge is opposed to the slow-ray direction in the mineral, subtraction occurs.

Extinction. A doubly refracting crystal, mineral plate, or grain, when dark between crossed nicols, is in the position of extinction. Frequently, minerals have prominent cleavage lines or crystal boundaries that enable one to refer the angle at which extinction occurs to a crystallographic feature. In the absence of a reference feature, the extinction angle becomes indeterminate. Parallel, symmetrical, and inclined extinction are illustrated in Figure 5-25.

Parallel Extinction. Frequently minerals have a single plane of cleavage. The traces of the cleavage planes appear in thin sections as irregularly spaced lines. If the mineral becomes dark between crossed

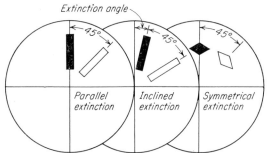

FIG. 5-25. Relative positions of greatest and least illumination in parallel, inclined, and symmetrical extinction as observed between crossed nicols.

nicols, with the cleavage parallel to the vibration directions of the two nicols, the extinction is said to be parallel.

A number of minerals crystallize in such a way that sections are elongated, square, or rectangular. Square or rectangular cleavage patterns may also be observed. If these minerals become dark between crossed nicols, with the cleavage directions parallel to the vibration planes of the nicols, they are said to have parallel extinction.

Inclined or Oblique Extinction. Many minerals extinguish between crossed nicols when cleavages or crystal boundaries lie at oblique angles to the planes of vibration of the two nicols. These are said to have inclined extinction.

In this case it is necessary to know the position of either the fast-ray vibration direction or the slow-ray vibration direction in the mineral grain. The extinction angle is usually determined in terms of the slower of the two rays, or the one having the greater index of refraction. The nature of the two rays is determined with one of the accessory plates of the microscope.

Several different angles of extinction are usually observed for the same mineral in a given section, as illustrated in Figure 5-26. The maximum reading on the slow-ray vibration direction with the plane of vibration of the analyzer is a convenient value to determine. In the case of observation with the microscope, the stage is rotated until the mineral lies in a position of extinction. The upper nicol is then pushed to one side, and the angle between the vertical crosshair (parallel to one of the nicols) and the cleavage line or crystal boundary is determined by readings on the graduated stage of the microscope. The nicols are then crossed again and the crystal turned to the extinction position, the angle

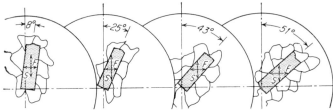

FIG. 5-26. Diagram illustrating various positions of an elongated mineral with a maximum extinction angle of 51° on the slow ray as it might appear in thin section.

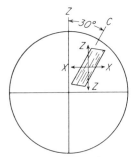

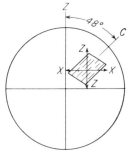

FIG. 5-27. Hornblende of Fig. 8-32 in the position of maximum extinction between crossed nicols. C ∧ Z = −30°.

FIG. 5-28. Hedenbergite of Fig. 8-33 between crossed nicols in the position of maximum extinction. C ∧ Z = −48°.

being measured. Next, the direction of vibration of the slow ray is verified by using an accessory plate. A series of readings should be repeated with different crystals until it seems certain that the largest angle for a particular mineral has been found. When the angle is determined, it is necessary to refer to a description of the optical directions in the crystal in order to ascertain the proper reference plane for the extinction angle.

The mineral descriptions in Part 2 of this text include the angles of extinction. The angle between Z and the c-axis of a crystal is frequently recorded. Since Z is a slow-ray direction and prominent cleavages or crystal boundaries are often referred to the c-axis, it is usually possible to interpret the extinction from the orientation diagram. Figures 5-27 and 5-28 furnish illustrations of such interpretations.

Symmetrical Extinction. A number of minerals form cleavage patterns or crystals with rhombic cross sections. In many instances these become dark between crossed nicols when the planes of vibration of the nicols are parallel to the diagonals of the rhombic patterns. Extinction of this type is described as symmetrical. Several minerals forming crystals with square outlines may also yield symmetrical extinction.

Elongation. Occasionally crystal grains develop with an elongated habit and straight edges. These may have a lathlike shape under the microscope, may resemble small needles, may occur in long crystals, or may show several other shapes of similar development.

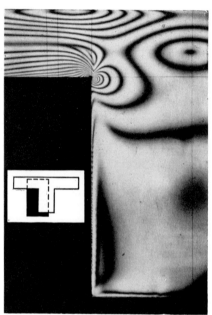

When such crystals are anisotropic, it is possible to determine the fast- and slow-ray vibration directions with one of the marked accessory plates. In case the vibration direction of the slow ray of the crystal is parallel to the long direction, the mineral is said to have *positive elongation*. When the vibration direction of the slow ray lies across the crystal in the short direction, the mineral has *negative elongation*. These two terms may be stated briefly as *length-slow* and *length-fast*, length-slow indicating that the vibration direction of the slow ray is parallel to the length of the crystal, and length-fast indicating the parallelism of the vibration direction of the fast ray.

Fig. 5-29. Photograph between crossed nicols of equal interference areas in strained bakelite cut in the form of a structural T and placed under pressure. (*Courtesy of Photo Elastic Laboratory, Department of Civil Engineering, Columbia University; photograph by Raymond D. Mindlin.*)

Anomalous Interference. Occasionally minerals normally assumed to be isotropic become anisotropic and give interference effects between crossed nicols. The abnormal production of interference colors often of a low order is called *anomalous*. Figure 8-26 represents a thin section of garnet that exhibits symmetrically arranged bands of interference colors photographed between crossed nicols. X-ray studies show that the same garnet is still isometric in crystallization, so the colors are truly anomalous.

Interference colors and structural patterns may be produced by strain in the crystals. According to Crookes, the great Cullinan diamond, measuring almost 4 inches across, exhibited pronounced anisotropy due to strain.

Idocrase in thin section often shows an unusual sequence of interference colors, Berlin blue predominating. Although this mineral is tetragonal and normally doubly refracting, the interference colors do not follow the color chart and are anomalous. Clinozoisite, zoisite, brucite, and some varieties of chlorite furnish other examples of anisotropic minerals that yield anomalous interference colors.

Equal interference areas are frequently produced in isotropic bakelite through strain. In Figure 5-29 a portion of a small bakelite frame cut in the form of a T is shown between crossed nicols. The T would have a shape illustrated by the insert, the portion photographed being outlined by the dotted lines. The photograph was obtained by utilizing monochromatic green (5461 A) in the mercury spectrum.

REFERENCES

Ahrens, C. D.: New Polarizing Prism, *J. Roy. Microscop. Soc.*, vol. 9, pp. 397–398, 1886.

Berek, M.: Zur Messung der Doppelbrechung hauptsächlich mit Hilfe des Polarisationsmikroskops, *Centr. Mineral., Geol.*, pp. 427–435, 1913.

Bouasse, H.: Optique cristalline doublé réfraction polarisation rectiligne et elliptique, Paris, 1925.

Drude, Paul: "Theory of Optics," trans. by Mann and Millikan, Longmans, Green & Co., Inc., New York, 1925.

Groth, P.: "The Optical Properties of Crystals," trans. by B. H. Jackson, John Wiley & Sons, Inc., New York, 1910.

Hartshorne, N. H., and A. Stuart: "Crystals and the Polarizing Microscope," Edward Arnold & Co., London, 1934.

Johannsen, A.: "Manual of Petrographic Methods," McGraw-Hill Book Company, Inc., New York, 1918. A summary of the various types of polarizing prisms will be found on pp. 158–175.

MacCullagh, James: Crystalline Reflexion and Refraction, *Trans. Roy. Irish Acad.*, vol. 18, pp. 31–74, 1837.

Miers, H. A.: "Mineralogy," 2d ed., rev. by H. L. Bowman, Macmillan & Co., Ltd., London, 1929.

Schuster, A., and J. W. Nicholson: "Theory of Optics," Edward Arnold & Co., London, 1924.

Thompson, S. P.: On a New Polarizing Prism, *Rep. Br. Assoc. Advance. Sci.*, vol. 51, pp. 563–564, 1881.

Tutton, A. E. H.: "Crystallography and Practical Crystal Measurement," 2d ed., vol. 2, Macmillan & Co., Ltd., London, 1922.

Weinschenk, E.: "Petrographic Methods," trans. by R. W. Clark, McGraw-Hill Book Company, Inc., New York, 1912.

Winchell, A. N.: "Elements of Optical Mineralogy, Part I: Principles and Methods, 5th ed., John Wiley & Sons., Inc., New York, 1937.

Wright, F. E.: The Transmission of Light through Transparent Inactive Crystal Plates, etc., *Am. J. Sci.*, 4th ser., vol. 31, pp. 157–211, 1911.

The student is referred to comments by Tunell and Morey regarding certain fundamental optical properties (*Am. Mineralogist*, vol. 17, pp. 365–380, 1932).

CHAPTER 6

Convergent Polarized Light

General Statement. A conoscopic lens combination is used in the microscope to obtain interference figures (see Chapter 2). Such figures are particularly useful for determining the optical directions in crystals. Their interpretation involves the principles outlined in the preceding chapter on polarized light, combined with the use of convergent light.

A large transparent crystal plate may be used to observe an interference figure without a microscope. A sheet of mica between crossed polaroid sheets, illuminated by a window and held close to the eye, reveals an excellent biaxial figure. The eye provides conoscopic vision. Large quartz plates reveal a uniaxial figure in similar fashion.

In obtaining interference figures of small crystals the microscope is necessary. The elements in the optical train should be exactly aligned and properly centered. It is best to use a moderately high magnification, preferably a 4-mm objective, although an 8-mm objective is sometimes satisfactory and may be more easily manipulated. An auxiliary condenser is inserted across the axis of the microscope below the stage. The front lens of the condenser throws a concentrated convergent beam against the mineral plate (Figure 6-1). Some microscopes are also provided with a diaphragm between the polarizer and the lower component of the condenser. The diaphragm limits the field of view and helps to improve the outer portion of the interference figure. A Bertrand lens is inserted in the tube of the microscope above the analyzer. This lens brings the image of the interference figure into focus in the ocular. Good figures of small size can be obtained by removing the ocular and not using the Bertrand lens. A black disk with a small hole in the center

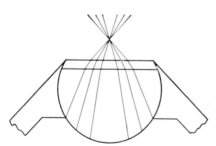

Fig. 6-1. Convergent light produced by the front lens of the condenser.

may be used to replace the ocular when an interference figure is obtained without the Bertrand lens.

Anisotropic minerals yield two types of interference figures: uniaxial and biaxial. Minerals crystallizing in the hexagonal and tetragonal systems are uniaxial; those crystallizing in the orthorhombic, monoclinic, and triclinic systems are biaxial. Occasionally biaxial crystals have such a small axial angle as to appear uniaxial, and conversely on certain occasions normally uniaxial crystals may become biaxial because of strain. Such variations should be considered and may indicate structural features of interest. In general, however, crystals follow the normal pattern.

Formation of Interference Figures. Convergent polarized light passing through an anisotropic crystal plate yields a range in retardation between crossed nicols. The effect is similar in a number of respects to the retardation obtained with the quartz wedge, as described in the discussion of parallel polarized light. The use of a quartz plate instead of a wedge, and convergent light instead of parallel light, produces interference colors dependent upon the convergence of the beam. Variation in the angle of illumination of the oblique rays results in a range of values of n_2 and n_1 for a doubly refracting mineral. Varying values of n_2 and n_1, in turn, cause varying retardation.

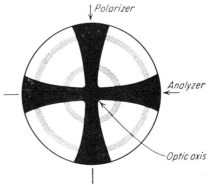

Fig. 6-2. A uniaxial interference figure looking down on an optic axis.

A quartz plate yields a striking interference effect with the optic axis of the plate at right angles to the microscope stage. A black cross is superimposed on concentric circles of interference colors. Here the thickness remains constant, and the retardation ranges from zero at the center to a maximum in the outermost color circle. The angle of incidence on the quartz plate due to the convergent beam employed also ranges from zero at the center of the field to a maximum on either edge. As a result, the difference $(n_2 - n_1)$ also changes from zero, at the center where the incident beam is parallel to the optic axis, to a maximum value at the edge of the field. Darkness occurs at the center and where the vibration directions of the plate are parallel to the vibration directions of the nicols. The cross marks positions of extinction. Vibration directions will be arranged tangentially and radially throughout 360° of rotation. As a result, vibration directions of the extraordinary and ordinary rays from the plate will be parallel to the vibration planes of the nicols in certain directions. The two directions are directions of

extinction and in general uniaxial minerals form dark cross arms at 90°
(Figure 6-2). In biaxial minerals the positions of extinction follow a more
complex pattern, and the interference figure is no longer a simple cross
but changes as shown in Figure 6-3. The different orders of color are
concentric with low orders at the center. Where the mineral remains in
the same position the number of color bands observed in a particular
field is dependent upon the thickness of the plate and the double refraction.

Monochromatic light produces alternate dark and light bands in interference figures. The dark bands correspond to retardations of $n\lambda$, and
the intermediate maximum colored bands correspond to a retardation of
$(2n + 1)\lambda/2$. The relationship is similar to the result when mono-

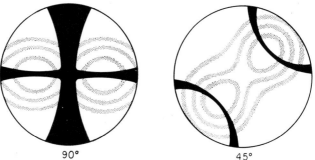

90°   45°
Fig. 6-3. A biaxial interference figure in 90° and 45° positions.

chromatic light is passed through a quartz wedge. The colors in interference figures produced by white light are a combination of the different monochromatic wavelengths in an analogous manner to the interference color chart where white light may be considered as a
summation of the various monochromatic wavelengths.

Uniaxial Interference Figures. In hexagonal and tetragonal minerals
the optic axis coincides with the c-axis of the crystal. Likewise, the center
of the cross in the interference figure marks the optic-axis position. If
the optic axis of the mineral coincides with that of the microscope, the
uniaxial figure will be centered with the two arms crossing at the intersection of the crosshairs in the microscope.

However, if the optic axis is inclined to the axis of the microscope,
the point of intersection of the cross arms will fall away from the intersection of the crosshairs. It frequently falls outside the field of the microscope. If the center of the axial cross does not coincide with the center
of the field, the point of intersection of the arms will move around the
crosshair intersection when the stage is rotated, describing a circle and
returning to its original position after rotating 360°. The intersection of

the cross arms marks the point of emergence of the optic axis, and its deviation from the center of the field is a measure of the angle between the optic axis and the axis of the microscope.

Although uniaxial figures are frequently eccentric in position, the cross arms remain parallel to the planes of vibration of the nicols. Because of

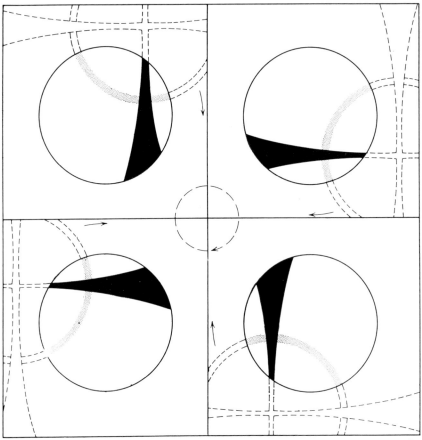

FIG. 6-4. Uniaxial interference figure in eccentric positions. Dotted lines indicate the movement of the figure around the field of the microscope as the stage is rotated.

this fact the arms sweep the field first from one side, then from another as the stage is rotated. It is important to note whether the arms remain parallel to the crosshairs, since arms in certain biaxial figures also cross the field. The latter are curved or crescent shaped, however, and swing across the field rather than sweep parallel to the nicols. Several eccentric positions of a uniaxial figure are shown in Figure 6-4.

The number of color bands in uniaxial interference figures varies with the thickness of the section and the double refraction of the mineral. Thick sections may give a number of orders of colors, whereas a thin section of the same mineral may not yield bands of color above the first order. If two plates are made of different minerals, both of identical orientation and having the same thickness, the mineral with the greater double refraction will develop the greater number of color bands. The relation between uniaxial figures due to mineral plates of the same thickness but differing in double refraction is shown in Figure 6-5.

Vibration Directions in Uniaxial Crystals. In uniaxial crystals one significant ray vibrates parallel to a plane that includes the c-axis of the crystal; another vibrates parallel to a plane at right angles. The two are

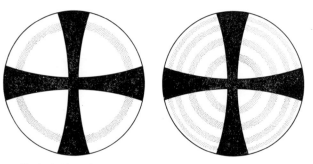

Weak double refraction   Strong double refraction

FIG. 6-5. The comparative effect of strong and weak double refraction on the color bands of a uniaxial interference figure.

refracted differently and consequently travel different distances in passing through the mineral plate.

When the rays vibrate parallel to the nicols, resolution is zero, and darkness occurs—hence the axial cross in the interference figure. At the 45° position the greatest intensity occurs, and the interference colors are most brilliant.

When two sets of rays are formed by the passage of light through a uniaxial crystal, one set travels with uniform velocity in all directions and is known as the *ordinary ray;* the other varies in velocity with direction and is called the *extraordinary ray.* If light were to radiate out from the center of a solid mass of such an anisotropic medium, at a given instant the wavefront of the ordinary ray would be spherical, whereas the wavefront of the extraordinary ray would be ellipsoidal. Any section of the wavefront produced by the ordinary ray would therefore be a circle. One section of the wavefront due to the extraordinary ray would be a circle; but others would be ellipses. Figure 6-6 illustrates sections which include the optic axis. If the velocity of the extraordinary ray is greater, the ellipse lies outside the circle, and the mineral is optically negative. If the velocity of the ordinary ray is greater, the ellipse lies within the circle, and the mineral is optically positive. Uniaxial positive and negative minerals are listed in Table 10-8.

The velocities represented in the diagram Figure 6-6 are the reciprocals of the indices of refraction. The ray velocities have equal values in the direction of the c-axis, where the circle and ellipse coincide, and are most unequal in a direction at right angles to the c-axis. The greatest and least indices of refraction are observed at right angles to the c-axis.

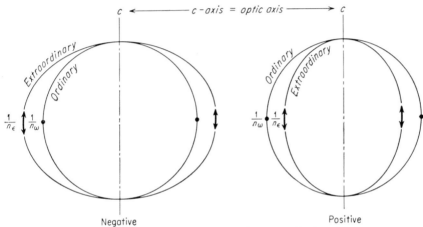

FIG. 6-6. Sections of ray surfaces for uniaxial minerals.

In these directions (only) the indices of refraction are the reciprocals of the ray velocities.

The indices of refraction of the two rays at right angles to the c-axis are represented by n_ε and n_ω. n_ε is the index of the extraordinary ray, n_ω the index of the ordinary ray. In positive minerals n_ε is greater; in negative minerals n_ε is less.

In Figure 6-7 convergent light is shown striking the surface of a mineral plate such as quartz, cut normal to the c-axis. The convergent beam is refracted and broken into two rays. The extraordinary ray e is radial in arrangement, is more refracted, and has the lesser velocity. The ordinary ray o is tangential in arrangement, is less refracted, and has the greater velocity. Although the diagram is simplified by using two lines to represent the e and o rays, actually there are many multiples of each of the two rays. The radial and tangential arrangement, however, obtains throughout.

Positive and Negative Sign of Uniaxial Crystals. The optic signs of uniaxial minerals may be determined from interference figures with the aid of accessory plates. As shown in Figure 6-7 the extraordinary ray vibrates in the *principal plane* parallel to the c-axis; the ordinary ray vibrates at right angles. If the ray vibrating in the principal plane is the slow ray, the mineral is said to be positive; if fast, it is negative. In Figure 6-7 the mineral is positive since the slow ray e vibrates parallel to the c-axis.

An accessory plate may be used to show the position of the slow ray with reference to the c-axis. If a mica plate, gypsum plate, or quartz wedge is inserted in the accessory slot cut in the tube of the microscope, the color bands of the interference figure will change position. The color bands behave differently in alternate quadrants. In one set the

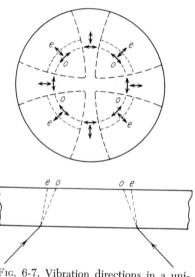

color circles will increase in diameter due to increased retardation; in the alternate set decrease will occur due to decreased retardation. When the slow ray of the accessory plate is parallel to the slow ray in the interference figure an increase in retardation occurs and vice versa. If the retardation is increased parallel to the slow ray of the interference figure, the mineral is positive. If decreased, the mineral is negative. The displacement of the color bands is illustrated in Figure 6-8. In quadrants 1 and 3 the color bands move toward the center; in quadrants 2 and 4 they move away from the center. Quadrants 1 and 3 represent increase in retardation, whereas quadrants 2 and 4 represent decrease in retardation. In the illustration the slow ray of the mica plate is parallel to quadrants 1 and 3.

FIG. 6-7. Vibration directions in a uniaxial positive interference figure. $o =$ fast ray (least refracted); $e =$ slow ray (most refracted). Velocity of $o = \dfrac{1}{n_\omega}$; velocity of $e = \dfrac{1}{n_\epsilon}$.

In Figure 6-9 fast and slow directions for a mica plate are indicated in four positions around the circular field. The extraordinary and ordinary rays lie in 45° planes. The interference cross becomes white, the interference for a ¼λ mica plate.

The slow-ray direction is marked on each accessory. If a mica plate is inserted with the slow ray in the (1-3) position, the retardation along the extraordinary ray in the (1-3) quadrants will in effect be reinforced. At the same time, an effect of subtraction will occur in the (2-4) quadrants. The color bands of the interference figure will be displaced by this superposition. Where reinforcement occurs, the bands will move toward the center of the circle. Where subtraction occurs, the bands will move in the opposite direction.

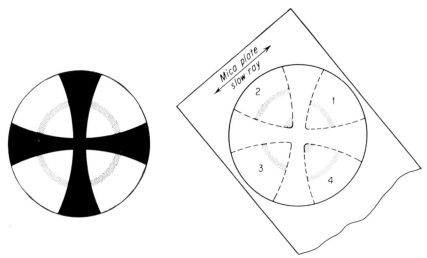

FIG. 6-8. Determination of the optic sign for a uniaxial positive mineral.

In optically positive minerals subtraction occurs at right angles to the direction of the slow ray in the accessory. In negative minerals the subtraction is in the quadrants lying along the slow-ray direction.

When a mica plate is inserted, decrease in retardation often produces two black dots in alternate quadrants at the center of an interference

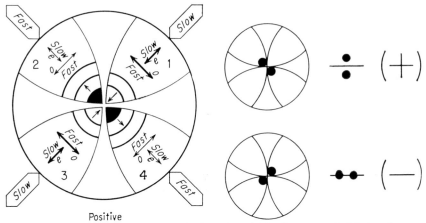

Positive

FIG. 6-9. The vibration directions in both accessory plate and mineral for a uniaxial positive figure.

FIG. 6-10. Key to uniaxial interference figures.

figure. The direction of the two dots forms a plus with the vibration direction of the slow ray of the mica plate in positive uniaxial minerals and a minus when the minerals are negative. This relationship is empirical and indicative but it serves to keep in mind the fast- and slow-ray vibration directions in uniaxial crystals (Figure 6-10).

If minerals have strong double refraction the gypsum plate may be more useful for determining the optical character of a uniaxial mineral than is the mica plate. With the gypsum plate two bright blue areas often form in opposite quadrants of the interference figures. These stand out particularly in figures given by minerals of moderate or intermediate double refraction. When the optical character is positive, as in the case of quartz, the two blue areas occur in opposite quadrants parallel to the slow-ray vibration direction of the gypsum plate (see Figure 6-11a). When the optical character is negative, as in the case of calcite, the two blue areas occur in opposite quadrants at right angles to the slow-ray vibration direction of the gypsum plate (see Figure 6-11b). The blue areas at times

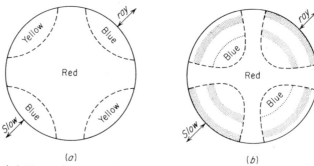

(a)   (b)

Fig. 6-11. (a) Uniaxial positive. Quartz cut perpendicular to the optic axis as viewed in the interference figure with a gypsum plate. (b) Uniaxial negative. Calcite cut perpendicular to the optic axis as viewed in an interference figure with a gypsum plate.

form dots (second-order blue), but these should not be confused with the mica dots (first-order black with a bluish fringe).

Biaxial Interference Figures. Under normal conditions minerals crystallizing in the orthorhombic, monoclinic, and triclinic crystal systems give biaxial interference figures. Rarely, because of crystallization under strain, hexagonal or tetragonal minerals, normally uniaxial, are anomalous and produce biaxial figures.

Biaxial interference figures are produced by the same optical arrangement of the microscope employed for uniaxial figures. Unlike uniaxial figures, curves of biaxial figures assume different relative forms as the stage is rotated. Double refraction, orientation, and thickness of section govern the character of biaxial interference figures.

As the stage is rotated a biaxial figure assumes a range of complex patterns. Figure 6-3 illustrates a symmetrical biaxial interference figure in two positions at 90° and 45°. The 45° position is the most useful for ordinary optical determinations and is often employed in the study of biaxial minerals. The figure in this position is described as an *acute bisectrix* figure at 45°.

The 45° Acute Bisectrix Figure. Figure 6-12 indicates the nomenclature of the parts of an acute bisectrix figure at 45°. The different features may be described as follows:

Isogyres. The two broad black curves, or brushes, which mark the areas of extinction, are known as isogyres. Strong dispersion produces red and blue fringes on the margins of the isogyres. By noting the distribution of the colored fringes in the interference figure one may determine the character of the dispersion. In minerals with strong dispersion the curves

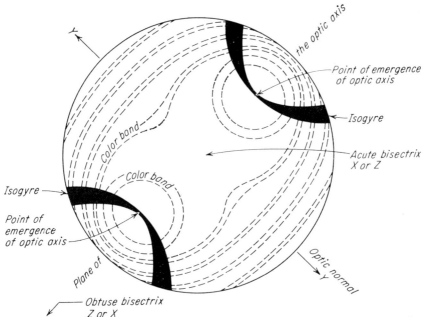

Fig. 6-12. The parts of a biaxial interference figure perpendicular to the acute bisectrix in the 45° position.

are not so black or so sharp as in the case of minerals with weak dispersion.

Points of Emergence of the Optic Axes. The vertices of the two crescentlike curves mark the points of emergence of the optic axes. The amount of separation of these points differs with different minerals but is a constant for an individual mineral. The line between the two points of emergence subtends the optic axial angle.

Johannsen has suggested the word *melatope* for the point of emergence.

Plane of the Optic Axes. The plane of the optic axes, or axial plane, includes the two points of emergence of the optic axes, the acute bisectrix direction, and the obtuse bisectrix direction.

Color Bands. Interference color bands representing positions of equal retardation are distributed in symmetrical curves around the points of emergence of the optic axes and are called *isochromatic curves.*

X, Y, and *Z.* The three axes *X, Y,* and *Z* are distributed in the interference figure as shown in the diagram. *Y* is normal to the plane of the optic axes. If the acute bisectrix is *X,* the obtuse bisectrix is *Z,* and vice versa.

Optic Normal. The direction at right angles to the plane of the optic axes is referred to as the optic normal. It is the axis *Y.*

Eccentric Biaxial Figures. Since biaxial minerals as observed in thin section may be cut at any angle, a variety of modifications of the biaxial interference figures result. A single isogyre may swing across the field in one figure, another may yield an optic axis, another may show the

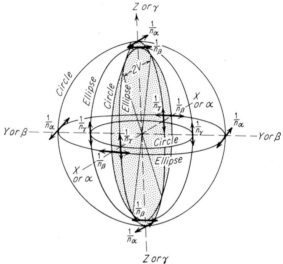

Fig. 6-13. Biaxial ray surface.

acute bisectrix, etc. The most useful figures for optical determinations of mineral properties are either acute bisectrix or optic-axis figures. In optic-axis figures (see Figure 6-24) the convex side of the isogyre in the 45° position indicates the direction of the acute bisectrix.

Optic-axis figures and most acute bisectrix figures are given by mineral sections showing comparatively low-order colors between crossed nicols in parallel light. Examination of a number of crystals of miscellaneous orientation between crossed nicols will often quickly reveal those most likely to give interference figures of useful orientation in convergent light.

Optical Directions in Biaxial Minerals. In all biaxial minerals the various optical features may be conveniently oriented by reference to three axes, *X, Y,* and *Z,* arranged at right angles to each other (Figure 6-13). *X, Y,* and *Z* indicate the ease of vibration of light in the mineral. Light traveling normal to *X* vibrates parallel to the axis and has the maximum velocity for the mineral $1/n_\alpha$. Light traveling normal to Z vibrates parallel to the axis and has the minimum velocity for the mineral $1/n_\gamma$. The axis Y lies at right angles to the plane of X and Z. Light traveling normal to Y vibrates parallel to the axis and has an intermediate velocity $1/n_\beta$.

In a given mineral, light vibrating parallel to X will form the fast ray. Light vibrating parallel to Z is the slow ray, and light vibrating parallel to Y will be intermediate in velocity. Thus, when the direction of observation lies along the X axis, XZ will indicate the slow ray and XY the intermediate ray; similarly, when the direction of observation is the Z axis, ZX will be the fast ray and ZY the intermediate ray. When the direction of observation is the Y axis, YX will be the fast ray and YZ the slow ray.

The fast- and slow-ray directions corresponding to the various directions of observation along the axes may be indicated as shown in the table below.

Direction of observation	Two rays observed	Velocities	
X	Faster ray	$1/n_\beta$ = intermediate ray	
	Slower ray	$1/n_\gamma$ = slowest ray	
Y	Faster ray	$1/n_\alpha$ = fastest ray	
	Slower ray	$1/n_\gamma$ = slowest ray	
Z	Faster ray	$1/n_\alpha$ = fastest ray	
	Slower ray	$1/n_\beta$ = intermediate ray	

When the direction of observation lies along the X axis, light vibrating parallel to the plane XZ will have the greatest index of refraction, and light vibrating parallel to the plane XY will have an intermediate index of refraction. When the direction of observation lies along the Z axis, light vibrating parallel to the plane ZX will have the least index of refraction, and light vibrating parallel to ZY will have an intermediate index of refraction. When the direction of observation lies along the Y axis, light vibrating parallel to the plane YX will have the least index of refraction, and parallel to YZ will have the greatest index of refraction.

Within certain limits, the axes X, Y, and Z have positions in minerals that are dependent upon the system of crystallization. In orthorhombic minerals, X, Y, and Z are fixed with respect to the crystallographic axes a, b, and c. In the monoclinic system one of the three axes (often Y) coincides with the crystallographic axis b. In the triclinic system there are no limitations of position according to the crystallographic axes.

The optical directions in biaxial minerals may be represented in several ways. One of the most generally used devices is the ray surface illustrated in Figure 6-13. Another is the index ellipsoid of Figure 6-16. The ray surface is developed on X, Y, and Z arranged at right angles to each other. The index ellipsoid (optical indicatrix) may be developed on the same axes, but by convention α, β, and γ are usually used instead of X, Y, and Z. The accompanying table furnishes a comparison of the two systems of representation.

COMPARISON OF THE BIAXIAL RAY SURFACE AND THE INDEX ELLIPSOID

Comparative features	Distance from center to surface	
	Biaxial ray surface	Index ellipsoid
Axial directions		
Least velocity..........	Z	γ
Greatest velocity........	X	α
At right angles.........	Y	β
Major semiaxis...........	$1/n_\alpha$ and $1/n_\beta$	n_γ
Intermediate semiaxis.....	$1/n_\alpha$ and $1/n_\gamma$	n_β
Minor semiaxis...........	$1/n_\gamma$ and $1/n_\beta$	n_α
Optic axes...............	Secondary optic axes or biradials	Primary optic axes or binormals
Surface.................	Double	Single

The correlation of the ease-of-vibration directions, whether designated by X, Y, and Z or α, β, and γ, with biaxial interference figures of different sign is shown in Figure 6-14.

Let us assume a single crystalline mass of a biaxial crystal of sufficient size to allow examination of light variation in the system. If light were to radiate out from the center of a solid mass of such an anisotropic medium, at a given instant the wave front produced would be a double-sheeted surface with sections as illustrated in Figure 6-13. The optic axes lie in the plane of X and Z and the acute angle $2V$ between the optic axes varies between 0 and 90°.

If the axis Z is the bisectrix of the acute angle between the optic axes, the mineral is said to be optically positive. If the axis X is the acute bisectrix, the mineral is said to be optically negative.

Two wavefronts appear in each section along the axes—one a circle, the other an ellipse. The size of each circle is determined by the velocity of the light ray vibrating parallel to the axis around which it is generated. Around X the radius of the circle is $1/n_\alpha$; around Y the radius is $1/n_\beta$; and around Z it is $1/n_\gamma$. Since n_α is the least index of refraction and $1/n_\alpha$ indicates the greatest velocity for the system, the circle around X

is the greatest. Since $1/n_\beta$ is intermediate in velocity, the circle around Y will have intermediate size. Since $1/n_\gamma$ represents the least velocity, the circle around Z will be smaller than the circles around the two other axes. Three combinations of ellipses and circles are represented. In the section perpendicular to Y and in the plane XZ, the circle with radius $1/n_\beta$ intersects an ellipse with major and minor semi-axes $1/n_\alpha$ and $1/n_\gamma$, respectively. In the section perpendicular to Z and in the plane XY, the smallest circle, radius $1/n_\gamma$, lies within the ellipse with major and minor semiaxes $1/n_\alpha$ and $1/n_\beta$, respectively. In the section perpendicular to X in the plane XZ the largest circle, radius $1/n_\alpha$, lies outside the ellipse with major and minor semiaxes $1/n_\beta$ and $1/n_\gamma$, respectively.

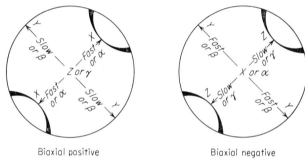

Bioxial positive   Bioxial negative

Fig. 6-14. Ease-of-vibration directions X, Y, and Z, or α, β, and γ, with reference to biaxial positive and negative interference figures. Corresponding fast- and slow-ray directions are also indicated.

Light vibrating parallel to Z will radiate outward from the center in the plane XY. The wavefront will be circular, and the velocity will be $1/n_\gamma$. Similarly, light vibrating parallel to X will travel outward in the plane YZ with a circular wavefront, and the velocity will be $1/n_\alpha$. Likewise, light vibrating parallel to Y will travel in the plane XZ with a circular wavefront and a velocity $1/n_\beta$. In each of these instances n_α, n_β, and n_γ represent, respectively, the least, intermediate, and greatest indices of refraction of the mineral.

The planes XY, YZ, and XZ are especially significant. Sections along each of these planes are illustrated in Figure 6-15, a, b, and c.

In the plane XZ the ellipse and circle will cross at four points. At these four points no difference in wave velocity exists. These points of intersection mark the position of the *secondary optic axes*, or *biradials*. In most crystals these secondary optic axes lie very near the *primary optic axes* but are not identical with them.

Index Ellipsoid (Optical Indicatrix). It is convenient to represent the optical relations of orthorhombic, monoclinic, and triclinic crystals by means of the *index ellipsoid* or optical indicatrix (Figure 6-16). Geometri-

cally the figure is a triaxial ellipsoid. The origin lies at the center of
the ellipsoid, the coordinate axes are the axes of the ellipsoid, and the
coordinate planes are the principal planes.

The semiaxes of the ellipsoid are assigned the values of the indices
of refraction n_α, n_β, and n_γ. The *principal sections* are any combination

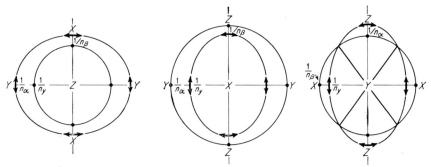

FIG. 6-15. Sections of biaxial ray surface. (*a*) Section perpendicular to Z. (*b*) Section perpendicular to X. (*c*) Section perpendicular to Y.

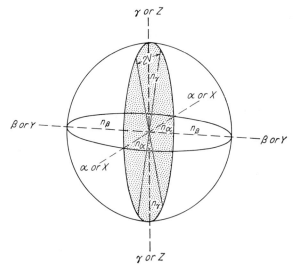

FIG. 6-16. Index ellipsoid for biaxial crystals.

in which a plane contains two axes. These sections are ellipses and have
as major and minor semiaxes any pair of the values n_α, n_β, and n_γ.

With the exception of the two circular sections, all of the plane sections that are cut through the center of the ellipsoid are ellipses (Figure
6-17). The two circular sections include the semiaxes with length n_β;
thus the length of the radius of each circular section equals n_β. The directions perpendicular to the two circular sections are called the *optic*

axes, or *binormals.* These are sometimes called the *primary optic axes* and differ slightly from the secondary optic axes (biradials) of the biaxial wave surface.

The optical properties of light rays may be determined in any given direction in a triaxial ellipsoid as shown in Figure 6-18. The semiaxes are n_γ, n_β, and n_α, respectively, and S'S represents the direction of propagation of light along a given line. If the direction of S'S is known, the

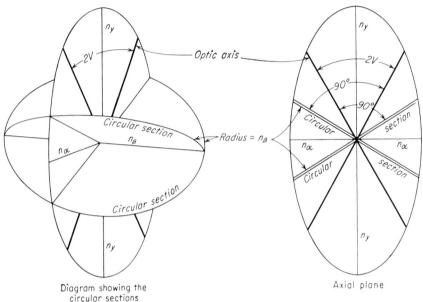

Fig. 6-17. The relationship between the two circular sections, the optic axes, and ellipsoidal axes (n_α, n_β, and n_γ) in the index ellipsoid.

following three pairs of optical properties become known by construction:

1. The vibration directions of the two rays traveling along S'S.
2. The two corresponding indices of refraction, n_2 and n_1.
3. The directions of the two wave normals.

If the direction of the diameter S'S is known, the position of the planes tangent to S'S at the two ends of the diameter also becomes known. It is then possible to pass a parallel diametral plane through the ellipsoid intersecting the center and equidistant between the two tangent planes. The diametral plane through the center will cut an elliptical section in all but two possible positions of S'S. These two exceptional positions are the optic axes, and here the sections cut are circular. The elliptical section furnishes measurements from which the optical properties can be determined. The diametral plane will have major and minor axes. These axes mark the vibration directions of the two rays traveling along $S'S$. The major and minor radii represent the refractive indices of the waves associated with the two rays, equaling n_2 and n_1. The wave normal corresponding to the ray propagated along $S'S$ and vibrating along the major axis lies in a plane through $S'S$ and the major axis and is normal to the axis. Similarly, the wave normal corresponding to the ray propagated along $S'S$ and vibrating along the minor axis lies in a plane through $S'S$ and the minor axis and is normal to the axis.

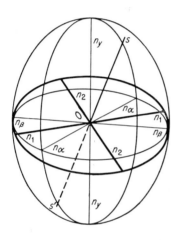

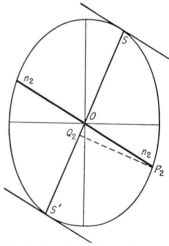

Fig. 6-18. A ray OS in an index ellipsoid with a conjugate plane through O and parallel to tangent planes at S and S'.

Fig. 6-19. Section through an ellipsoid showing the ray OS together with traces of tangent and diametral planes.

The section which includes SOS' and $n_2 - n_2$ is shown in Figure 6-19. A similar section at right angles would include SOS' and $n_1 - n_1$ as may be visualized from Figure 6-18.

A perpendicular from the intersection of $n_2 - n_2$ with the circumference of the ellipse would be the line $P_2 - O_2$. The reciprocal $1/P_2O_2$ represents the velocity of the ray propagated along the line SOS' and vibrating along the axis $n_2 - n_2$. In a similar manner a reciprocal $1/P_1O_1$ would represent the velocity of the ray propagated along the line SOS' and vibrating along the axis P_1O_1 (Figure 6-18)[1].

The Axial Angles 2E and 2V. The observed axial angle is greater than the true axial angle within the mineral. This is due to the refraction of

[1] The foregoing discussion is largely based upon a paper, The Ray Surface, the Optical Indicatrix, and Their Interrelation, by Dr. George Tunell (*Wash. Acad. Sci.*, vol. 23, p. 235, 1933).

the oblique rays, as illustrated in Figure 6-20. The angle $2E$ is the angle in air, while $2V$ is the internal angle.

Mallard's equation ($D = K \sin E$) may be used to determine the approximate axial angle with the microscope. In the equation, K is a constant for a particular microscope, D is one-half the distance between the points of emergence, and E is one-half the axial angle in air.

The computation of the axial angle in a mineral from the observed axial angle in air depends upon the formula

$$\sin E = n_\beta \sin V$$

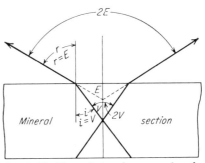

Fig. 6-20. The relation between the observed angle $2E$ and the angle $2V$ in biaxial minerals.

When $n \sin V$ is equal to 1, the angle $2E$ becomes $180°$, and the axial angle in air cannot be measured. The value of an observed angle may be reduced to measurable dimensions by immersing the objective in oil of known refractive index.

Large axial angles need to be measured with a rotation device. Such devices for rotating crystals in a vertical circle may be adapted to the stage of the microscope; otherwise special apparatus must be employed.

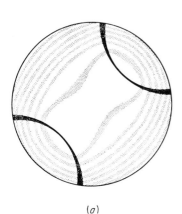

(a)   (b)

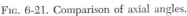

Fig. 6-21. Comparison of axial angles.

(a) Aragonite   (b) Barite
    $2V = 19°$ $2V = 37°30'$
    $n_\gamma - n_\alpha = 0.155$ $n_\gamma - n_\alpha = 0.012$

Variation in Axial Angle. Figure 6-21 illustrates two biaxial interference figures in the $45°$ position. The figure on the left represents aragonite and that on the right represents barite. The sections have each been cut normal to the acute bisectrix and are approximately equal in thickness. Two variables remain to produce differences in the diagram: variation in the axial angle 2V and variation in the double refraction $n_2 - n_1$.

The figure on the left represents the approximate position of the two isogyres in relation to the field of the microscope for $2V = 19°$ (aragonite). The figure on the right represents barite drawn to the same scale with $2V = 37°30'$.

The dotted lines indicate the distribution of the color bands. Aragonite has a double refraction of 0.155, and barite is 0.012. Aragonite has more bands for the same thickness of section.

It is worthwhile to record in a notebook the relative positions of the isogyres for angles in the neighborhood of 5°, 10°, 15°, 20°, 25°, 30°, 35°, and 40°. Such a record will assist in determining the approximate axial angle of an unknown mineral. Charts E, F, and G in Table 10-10 give values for common minerals.

It should be remembered that if the thickness remains the same, the number of color bands of interference figures will increase or decrease with increase or decrease in double refraction.

Determination of the Optic Sign of a Biaxial Mineral. The optic sign is conveniently determined with the mineral in the 45° position with a quartz wedge. In some cases a mica plate or gypsum plate may be preferred.

When the direction X is the acute bisectrix, the mineral is negative. If Z is the acute bisectrix, the mineral is optically positive. As stated, X, Y, and Z are the axes of ease of vibration. Light traveling through a crystal normal to X has the maximum velocity for all directions in the crystal. Light traveling normal to Z has the least velocity.

A biaxial negative crystal in the acute bisectrix position at 45° may be used to illustrate the determination of the optic sign (see Figure 6-22). A biaxial figure of this type is first observed carefully in order to note the position of the color bands, both in the central area and within the two small areas inclosed by the concave portions of the isogyres. A quartz wedge is then inserted in the accessory slot with the slow ray parallel to the axial plane. Movement of the color bands takes place as the wedge is inserted.

The displacement of the color bands in a negative crystal is indicated by the arrows in Figure 6-22. As the wedge thickness increases the color bands in the central area move toward the two "eyes," or melatopes, of the interference figure. At the same time the bands on the opposite sides of the isogyres within the two small areas move away from the melatopes. As the wedge is withdrawn, the movement is reversed. If a positive crystal is substituted, the movement of the color bands is also reversed.

In the biaxial negative crystal illustrated, Z lies in the axial plane along the obtuse bisectrix, X is the acute bisectrix, and Y is the optic normal. Two rays travel along X with vibration directions at right angles to each other, being parallel, respectively, to Z and Y. The ray vibrating parallel to Z is the slow ray for the crystal velocity $(1/n_\gamma)$; that parallel to Y is intermediate in velocity, having the value $1/n_\beta$.

Two rays emerge in the central area of the interference figure at X, a slow ray, velocity $1/n_\gamma$, and an intermediate but faster ray, velocity $1/n_\beta$.

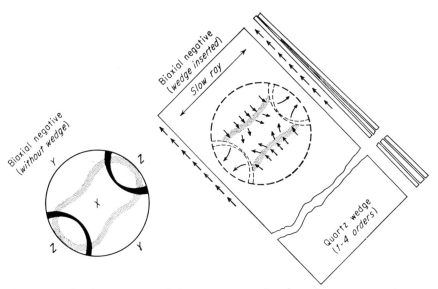

Fig. 6-22. The determination of the optic sign with a biaxial negative interference figure.

If the slow ray of the quartz wedge is parallel to the direction Z, increase in retardation occurs as the wedge thickness increases. If the quartz wedge is always inserted as indicated in Figure 6-22, an acute bisectrix biaxial negative interference figure in the 45° position will always show movement of the color bands toward the melatopes in the central area. Conversely, a biaxial positive figure treated in the same way will show movement in the opposite direction. Since the slow-ray vibration direction in the quartz wedge is marked, the slow-ray vibration direction in the interference figure is easily determined by comparison. Directions of movement for positive and negative biaxial figures in monochromatic light with the slow-ray vibration direction of an accessory plate super-imposed are shown in Figure 6-23.

The Optic-axis Figure. Interference figures produced by sections cut normal or nearly normal to one of the two optic axes of a biaxial mineral are useful for determination of optic sign. Such sections yield interference figures with a single isogyre in the field of view. The melatope, or point of emergence, may coincide with the axis of the microscope or may be slightly off center.

As the stage is rotated, the isogyre swings around the field, remaining centered or nearly centered, depending upon the eccentricity of the section. The color bands are arranged almost circularly around the melatope and vary in retardation with the double refraction of the mineral.

The curvature of the isogyre decreases with an increase in 2V. When the axial angle is large—i.e., near 90°—the isogyre is straight, and the acute bisectrix side of the interference figure becomes indistinguishable from the obtuse bisectrix side. When the angle is small, however, the

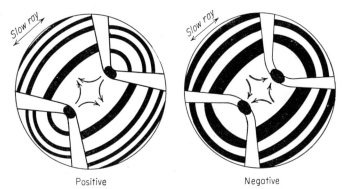

Positive   Negative

Fig. 6-23. Positive and negative biaxial crystals (indicating their appearance with a mica plate in monochromatic light).

isogyre is definitely curved in a crescentlike form. The convex side of the curve in the 45° position points toward the acute bisectrix, and the obtuse bisectrix is on the concave side.

Optic-axis figures showing even slight curvature are useful for determinations of the optic sign. The mica plate, gypsum plate, or quartz wedge may be employed, depending upon the double refraction of the mineral. The effect of the quartz wedge upon a biaxial positive optic-axis interference figure is shown in Figure 6-24. An optic-axis figure without the wedge inserted is shown on one side of the diagram, and the movement of the color bands caused by insertion of the wedge is shown on the opposite side.

Diagrams are shown in Figure 6-25, which should be of convenience in determining the signs of interference figures in the two most useful positions upon insertion of the quartz wedge. The same principles apply in utilizing mica and gypsum plates.

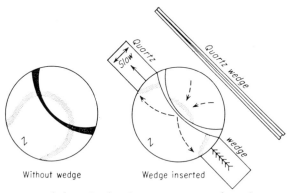

FIG. 6-24. Movement of the color bands in an optic-axis biaxial positive interference figure as an accessory plate is inserted.

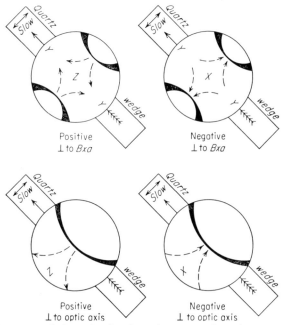

FIG. 6-25. Movement of the color bands to be expected as the quartz wedge is inserted in acute bisectrix and optic-axis interference figures of opposite sign.

Dispersion in Biaxial Interference Figures. The optic angle for light of one wavelength is frequently greater or less than for light of another wavelength. In the normal interference figure produced by white light this is usually detected by a peculiar arrangement of the color bands or by the development of blue and red fringes on the isogyres.

The dispersion recorded in most tables of optical mineralogy is that of the optic axes. The two extreme rays of the spectrum are used to designate the character of the dispersion. Thus, if the axial angle for red r is greater than that for violet v, the dispersion is expressed $r > v$. In case the reverse is true, the formula is $r < v$.

In many instances the dispersion can be determined by direct observation of the biaxial interference figure (Figure 6-26). If the isogyres of

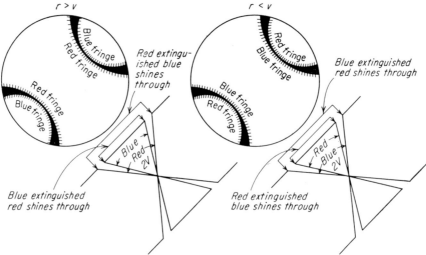

FIG. 6-26. Biaxial interference figures illustrating dispersion $r > v$ and $r < v$. The colored fringes as observed in the interference figure are reversed from the axial angles existing in the crystal due to extinction.

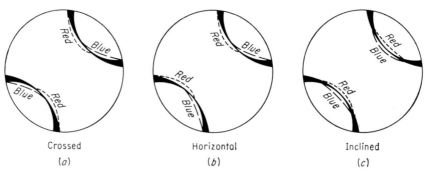

FIG. 6-27. Dispersion fringes for monoclinic crystals. (a) Crossed dispersion. (b) Horizontal dispersion. (c) Inclined dispersion.

the interference figure ($r > v$) have a distinct red fringe on the convex edges, the angle for red is greater than for violet. Both isogyres should be observed before reaching a conclusion. On the concave side of the isogyre, as illustrated in the figure, red light is extinguished, and consequently the concave fringe is blue in color. Blue is extinguished on the convex side, and the fringe is red.

The symmetry of the color distribution in the interference figure is a reflection of the symmetry of the crystal. It is well to remember that the symmetry elements of orthorhombic crystals include axes of twofold symmetry, planes of symmetry, and the center of symmetry. Here the common interference figure is symmetrical as shown in Figure 6-26. Less symmetrical dispersion is possible but not common for the interference figures of orthorhombic crystals.

Monoclinic crystals exhibit less symmetry. The fringes of the isogyres for monoclinic crystals exhibit *crossed, horizontal,* and *inclined* dispersion as shown in Figure 6-27.

Triclinic crystals have no plane of symmetry. Dispersion shows asymmetry which may in itself be distinctive.

The various types of dispersion arranged according to crystal system are as follows:

> Orthorhombic crystals:
> Dispersion of the optic axes.
> Crossed axial plane dispersion.
> Monoclinic crystals:
> Inclined dispersion (both bisectrices).
> Horizontal dispersion (acute bisectrix).
> Crossed dispersion (obtuse bisectrix).
> Triclinic crystals:
> Unsymmetrical dispersion.

These types are best distinguished by the use of light of various wavelengths. Red and blue color filters placed in front of the mirror of the microscope are convenient.

REFERENCES

Buchwald, E.: "Einführung in die Kristalloptik," Sammlung Göschen, Berlin, 1912.

Burri, C.: "Das Polarisations Mikroskop," E. Birkhäuser & Cie. A. G. Basel, 1950.

Evans, J. W.: "The Determination of Minerals under the Microscope," Thomas Murby & Co., London, 1928.

Fletcher, L.: "The Optical Indicatrix," Oxford University Press, London, 1892.

Groth, P.: "The Optical Properties of Crystals," trans. by B. H. Jackson, John Wiley & Sons, Inc., New York, 1910.

Johannsen, A.: "Manual of Petrographic Methods," McGraw-Hill Book Company, Inc., New York, 1918.

Tutton, A. E. H.: "Crystallography and Practical Crystal Measurement," vol. 2; "Physical and Chemical," 2d ed., Macmillan & Company, Ltd., London, 1922.

Wahlstrom, E. E.: "Optical Crystallography," John Wiley & Sons, Inc., New
    York, 1943.
Winchell, A. N.: "Elements of Optical Mineralogy, Part I: Principles and
    Methods," 5th ed., John Wiley & Sons, Inc., New York, 1937.
Wright, F. E.: The Index Ellipsoid, *Am. J. Sci.*, 4th ser., vol. 35, pp. 133–138,
    1913.
————: The Formation of Interference Figures: A Study of the Phenomena
    Exhibited by Transparent Inactive Crystal Plates in Convergent Polarized
    Light, *J. Opt. Soc. Am.*, vol. 7, pp. 779–817, 1923.

CHAPTER 7

The Universal Stage

Purpose. The universal stage (Figure 7-1) is designed to tilt the plane of a thin section at various angles to the plane of a microscope stage. It contains a series of graduated circles (Figure 7-2) which measure the angular positions of tilted sections. Such a device aids in the determination of optic orientation, 2V, optic sign, the directions of pleochroism,

FIG. 7-1. A four-axis universal stage showing the upper hemisphere and four graduated circles for angular measurement. (*E. Leitz, Inc.*)

dispersion, comparison of refractive indices, and the study of twinning. When temperature control is added (Emmons, 1943), the stage may be used with liquid mounts in the precise determination of refractive indices of mineral fragments. It is also employed in the analysis of crystal orientations in thin sections for the interpretation of structure or petrofabrics.

Stage Assembly. The universal stage is fastened with thumb screws to the microscope stage and the microscope slide rests on a circular glass plate in the center. Two glass hemispheres are provided to make the thin section visible at various angles of inclination. One is fastened beneath the glass plate and the other above the thin section. Special objectives are inserted in the microscope to obtain images from the curved surface of the upper hemisphere. Cedar oil or glycerin is used to make optical contact above and below the thin section, also between the lower hemisphere and the glass plate. The polarizing microscope employed must provide a large working distance between stage and objective and the

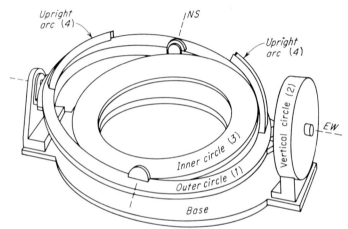

Fig. 7-2. Diagram of a four-axis universal stage. Four graduated circles are indicated. Axes *OV* and *IV* are perpendicular to circles (1) and (3), while axes *NS* and *EW* lie in the planes of the inner and outer circles.

area for horizontal rotation must be broad. Usually only research microscopes are adequate.

Graduated Circles. In the ordinary four-axis universal stage, measurements are made on four graduated circles, with the stage of the microscope providing a fifth circle. The axis of the microscope remains in the same vertical position at all times and may be designated as *Am*.

The four movable axes lie respectively normal to the four graduated circles (Figure 7-3) and may be designated as *OV* (vertical to outer circle), *IV* (vertical to inner circle), *EW* (normal to circular drum), and *NS* (normal to Wright arcs). When the stage is set with each circle at zero, *OV* and *IV* are vertical, *EW* is horizontal east-west, and *NS* is horizontal north-south.

The outer circle of the universal stage rotates around *OV* and lies in a horizontal plane in the zero position. An inner circle holds the slide and hemispheres. It lies in a horizontal plane in the zero position and rotates around *IV*.

The outer circle is not only free to rotate around the *OV* axis, but it

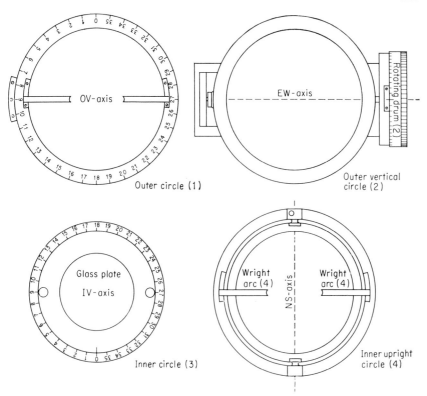

FIG. 7-3. The graduated circles of a four-axis universal stage.

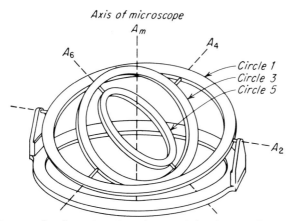

FIG. 7-4. Diagram of a five-axis universal stage (after Emmons). Axes A_1, A_3, and A_5 are perpendicular to the planes of the circles 1, 3, and 5. The planes of the circles are tilted around axes A_2, A_4, and A_6.

may be tilted from the horizontal in either direction about the *EW* axis. The angles of tilt are measured on the vertical drum at the side of the stage.

The inner circle measures angles around the *IV* axis. This circle may be tilted around the *NS* axis. Angles of tilt are measured on the two graduated Wright arcs which curve upward from the outer circle.

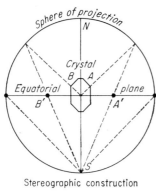

Stereographic construction

Plane of stereographic projection

Fig. 7-5. The projection of crystal faces *A* and *B* to *A'* and *B'* in the plane of stereographic projection. Faces parallel to the vertical axis are projected to the circumference.

The five-axis universal stage contains a third inner circle as illustrated in Figure 7-4. This circle holds the slide. Emmons (1943) recommends a five-axis stage and points out that the additional motion provided by an inner fifth circle is actually a simplification.

The Stereographic Plot. The angular relations of a universal stage may be conveniently plotted by means of a stereographic projection. Here the crystal is imagined to lie at the center of a sphere. The principal axis of the crystal coincides with the north-south polar axis of the sphere. The equatorial plane cuts the crystal and also the spherical system into upper and lower halves. In such a projection the points of intersection of radii with the spherical surface are projected on to the equatorial plane (Figure 7-5), thus reducing a large variety of angular measurements to a circular, two-dimensional plot.

Projection of a crystal face to the equatorial plane is accomplished in two operations. A radius normal to a crystal face is extended to the surface of the sphere. Then a chord is drawn to the opposite pole from the intersection of the normal with the spherical surface. The intersection of the chord with the equatorial plane is the point of spherical projection.

Where faces are parallel to the north-south polar axis, the radii lie within the equatorial circle, and face positions are plotted on the circumference. Where a face radius coincides with the principal axis and lies along the north-south pole, the face is projected as a point at the center of the equatorial plane.

In order to plot optical positions, optic axes may be treated as face radii normal to imaginary crystal faces. Thus they will appear as points on the stereographic projection. Arcs of circles representing angular positions are drawn on the projection forming a so-called stereographic net. Where the angular relationships are known from measurements with a universal stage, various positions may be plotted directly on the stereographic net essentially as latitude and longitude may be located on a map. It is convenient to plot positions on a transparent overlay placed on the net.

Positions are recorded in terms of ϕ (phi) and ρ (rho) angles (Figure 7-6). The angle ϕ is measured clockwise in the horizontal plane from the

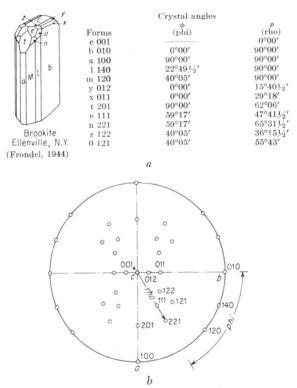

	Crystal angles	
Forms	ϕ (phi)	ρ (rho)
c 001		0°00′
b 010	0°00′	90°00′
a 100	90°00′	90°00′
l 140	22°49½′	90°00′
m 120	40°05′	90°00′
y 012	0°00′	15°40½′
x 011	0°00′	29°18′
t 201	90°00′	62°06′
e 111	59°17′	47°41½′
n 221	59°17′	65°31½′
z 122	40°05′	36°15½′
0 121	40°05′	55°43′

Brookite
Ellenville, N.Y.
(Frondel, 1944)

Fɪɢ. 7-6. A crystal drawing of brookite with a corresponding stereographic projection based on *phi* and *rho* angles.

east-west axes. The angle ρ is measured along a vertical plane from the north pole of the stereographic net.

Brookite furnishes one of the most remarkable examples of dispersion observed among minerals and may be used to illustrate a stereographic net. The optic plane lies along (100) for violet while the optic plane for red is (001). The optic directions as shown in Figure 7-7 may be compared with the geometric relations of the crystal (Figure 7-6) by means of the stereographic projection. The relative positions of the optical directions may be illustrated with the universal stage.

Adjustment. A modern, well-constructed universal stage ordinarily requires little adjustment. Nevertheless, attention should be directed to centering both horizontally and vertically. The first step is to center the microscope stage with the objective, using a dust particle on the glass plate of the universal stage as a reference point. Next, the microscope stage is locked and the outer circle of the universal stage is rotated, the center of rotation being brought into coincidence with the crosshairs. A small amount of horizontal leeway permits adjustment on the screws which fasten the universal stage to the microscope.

Vertical adjustment is largely fixed by the construction of the stage. Vertical deviation from the center of rotation may be detected by the

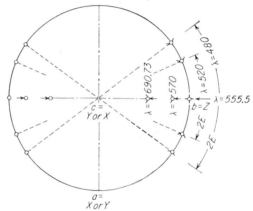

Fig. 7-7. The range in the optic plane and 2E for brookite with the wavelength of light as plotted on a stereographic projection. All variations are with reference to the crystallographic axes a, b, and c.

drift of particles along the crosshairs of the microscope field as a plane of the stage is tilted.

Illumination is one of the most critical factors. A strong, well-centered source of artificial illumination is essential. Some prefer an arc light. A substage diaphragm is desirable.

Cedar oil or glycerin is applied in three places for optical contact: between the lower hemisphere and the glass plate, between the thin section and the glass plate, and between the cover glass and the upper hemisphere.

Orientation with the Universal Stage. Extinction is the optical feature most frequently employed. Vibration directions shown by extinction in turn reveal the planes of optic symmetry. The planes of optic symmetry are adjusted to the crosshairs by oscillating the crystal to and from extinction.

A thin section may be fixed in position on the universal stage in such a way that the relative inclinations of the optic axes of several crystals may be shown on the same stereographic net. When the planes of the usual polarizing microscope are in alignment with the universal stage, the east-west crosshair will ordinarily mark the plane of the analyzer and the north-south crosshair the plane of the polarizer. The inclination of each optic axis as finally measured will furnish angular readings on the graduated circles which may be simplified to ϕ and ρ to plot on a stereographic net (Figure 7-8).

Location of the Uniaxial Optic Axis. The angular inclinations of optic axes in uniaxial crystals can be measured as truncated by the plane of

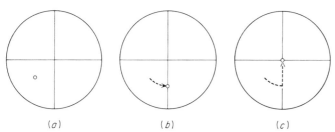

(a)   (b)   (c)

FIG. 7-8. Stereographic projections showing steps in the orientation of the optic axis of a uniaxial crystal. *a*. Optic axis inclined at random to the plane of a thin section. *b*. Rotated about the outer graduated circle to extinction. *c*. Tilted by the drum to coincide with the axis of the microscope. The crosshairs mark the planes of the nicols.

the thin section (Figure 7-9). The measurement of ϕ and ρ for a single optic axis is accomplished in two operations, each depending on extinction.

First, the axis is to be rotated until it lies along the east-west extinction plane of the microscope. The various circles of the universal stage and the microscope stage are set in initial position. The inner horizontal circle of the universal stage is rotated until the crystal under observation is in the extinction position. The optic axis will then lie within either the north-south vertical plane or the east-west vertical plane.

Second, the axis is to be tilted until it is vertical and in coincidence with the axis of the microscope. It will be assumed that the optic axis lies in the north-south plane. In this case it may be tilted to the vertical position by turning the drum on the side of the universal stage. The vertical position is recognized by a simple maneuver. As the drum is turned, the microscope stage is oscillated slightly to right and left until a point is noted at which extinction persists on either side notwithstanding the rotation. Such a point is the optic-axis position. If rotation of the drum causes the crystal to leave extinction, the optic axis lies within the east-west vertical plane. In this case the inner horizontal circle is rotated 90°. The optic axis will then lie along the north-south plane. The procedure outlined above is then followed to locate the optic-axis position. The position of the optic axis can then be located on a stereographic net. The angles ϕ (from the inner horizontal circle) and ρ (from the drum) may be plotted (Figure 7-9). By convention the poles in petrofabric work are ordinarily plotted in projection of the lower hemisphere. Occasionally the optic axis of a crystal lies too close to the plane of the thin section to permit tilting to a vertical position within the limits of rotation of the universal stage. In this case the angular position may be determined through the combined use of interference colors and extinction.

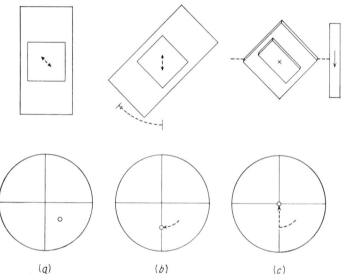

(a)   (b)   (c)

FIG. 7-9. Manipulation of a single optic axis to coincide with the microscope axis. (a) The uniaxial axis is shown in inclined position on the thin section (above) and on the stereographic projection (below). (b) The crystal is rotated to the extinction position about the vertical inner axis of the universal stage. (c) The axis is tilted to coincide with the crosshairs by turning the drum on the east-west axis.

The crystal is first rotated to a position of extinction by turning the inner horizontal circle. The optic axis will then lie in an inclined position either along the east-west or the north-south vertical planes. If the crystal remains in extinction as the drum is rotated, the axis lies along the north-south vertical plane. If it remains in extinction as the crystal is tilted by moving the circle along the Wright arcs, the axis lies in the east-west vertical plane.

When the plane is known the stage of the microscope is rotated $45°$ and the axis of the universal stage normal to the plane rotated until the crystal shows maximum interference. The angle between the plane of the section and the position of maximum interference then measures the inclination of the optic axis from the horizontal (or $90° - \rho$).

The sign of a uniaxial crystal is determined with the mica plate, gypsum plate, or the quartz wedge. When the direction of the optic axis in an individual crystal is known, the crystal may be tilted in the 45° position to observe interference colors along the axis. If the slow ray is normal to the axis the mineral is positive and, conversely, if the fast ray is normal to the axis the mineral is negative.

Optical Directions in Biaxial Crystals. The main objectives are to determine X, Y, and Z in terms of east, west, and vertical; to determine $2V$; and to determine the sign. These may be accomplished by observing maximum interference and extinction.

The circles are set at zero. The inner circle is then rotated to extinction. The vertical drum is next rotated. Extinction may possibly remain which indicates that the coincidence of X, Y, or Z with the east-west axis has already been accomplished. If extinction does not remain the drum is turned to the position of maximum illumination. The inner circle is then tilted along the Wright arcs to the right or left to minimum illumination. The drum is then returned to zero. Extinction should be complete, indicating a coincidence of X, Y, or Z with the east-west axis. If extinction is not complete estimates of maximum and minimum illumination should be repeated. When satisfactory extinction is obtained the ϕ and ρ angles can be indicated on a stereographic net. The next problem is to determine which of the three—X, Y, or Z—coincides with the east-west axis.

If Y coincides, the optic axes will lie along the vertical plane at right angles to the east-west axis. In this case, if the drum is turned, a position of minimum illumination will identify an optic axis. The axis position may be verified by rotating the microscope stage. The crystal will remain dark between crossed nicols during rotation. When verified, the position of the optic axis should be recorded on the stereographic net.

If either X or Z coincide with the EW axis, rotation of the drum with the microscope stage turned at 45° will cause an increase in interference. Then the drum is returned to zero and an accessory plate used to note whether the optical direction parallel to the EW axis is X or Z.

The final operation is the measurement of the second plane of optical symmetry. The microscope stage is returned to zero. The tilt on the Wright arcs is returned to zero. Then the inner circle is rotated 90° to the second extinction position. The manipulations indicated above are then repeated in order to determine which of the remaining two optical directions lies at 90° to the EW axis as already identified.

Illustrative Mounts. Special thin sections are convenient to illustrate the initial operation of a universal stage. A section cut at random from an irregularly oriented cluster of small, well-developed, hexagonal quartz crystals provides a useful example of a uniaxial positive mineral. The hexagonal outlines furnish geometrical guides to assist in visualizing the position of the optical indicatrix for individual crystals as the axes of the stage are rotated. The variation of the interference colors with orientation is well shown.

An individual optic axis steeply inclined to the plane of the section may be readily maneuvered into position in which it coincides with the axis of the microscope. The outer circle is rotated until the crystal becomes dark between crossed nicols. The principal optic planes then lie parallel to the planes of the nicols as shown by the crosshairs. As this move is made the microscope stage is oscillated at intervals. When the oscillation shows extinction on rotation from the plane of tilt as well as on the plane, the optic-axis position is indicated. The ϕ and ρ angles may then be measured.

A section cut from a plastic brickette of topaz crystals in disarray, but each with rhombic outlines, serves to illustrate biaxial orientation. The orientation for topaz may be simplified by tilting the universal stage until a crystal with rhombic outline is oriented with the crystallographic axes a, b, and c in coincidence with the extinction planes. With the crystal outlines as a preliminary guide, the procedure for crystals lacking facial boundaries is more readily understood.

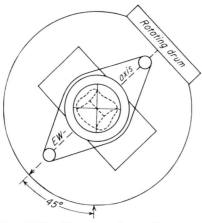

Fig. 7-10. Diagram of an illustrative biaxial exercise. A cleavage of muscovite is shown beneath the hemisphere of the universal stage. The acute bisectrix lies beneath the crosshairs and the axial plane is normal to the EW-axis. Either isogyre may be made to move to the crosshairs by rotating the drum.

Illustrative slides worthy of mention are brookite, showing dispersion of optic axes; piedmontite, which exhibits strong pleochroic color variation with direction; muscovite, with cleavage for the determination of 2V; vein quartz, with nearly parallel crystal axes to plot inclined axes; and coarsely twinned plagioclase, to indicate the orientation of twin individuals. Some slide manufacturers supply special sections of minerals suitable for exercises with the universal stage.

Illustrative Exercises. A simple illustration to introduce the use of the universal stage is to measure 2E for muscovite (Figure 7-10). A cleavage of muscovite about 1 cm square and about the thickness of a sheet of textbook paper is mounted on a glass slide using Canada balsam and a cover glass. The slide is then observed with convergent polarized light on the microscope stage (without the universal stage). The direction of the plane of the optic axes is marked with ink on the slide—or better, with a line drawn with a diamond point.

The universal stage is then set in position and centered. With circles and stage in initial position the muscovite slide is mounted between the hemispheres with the line indicating the axial plane parallel to the NS axis. A large sheet of a single muscovite crystal will yield an observable 90°-type biaxial interference figure in this position. The stage of the microscope is next set at 45° to the first position. The crosshairs will then indicate the acute bisectrix for the 45°-type interference figure. The axial plane is normal to the EW axis. If the drum on the outer vertical circle is turned, either isogyre may be made to appear beneath the crosshairs. The angle between may be measured directly. If n_β for muscovite and n for the glass hemisphere are known, 2V for muscovite may be computed from the angle measured.

A second illustrative exercise may be attempted as shown by the diagram in Figure 7-11. A thin section of a single crystal of aragonite of the type frequently present in sets of thin sections will serve. These are usually cut approximately normal to the acute bisectrix.

The thin section is mounted on the universal stage and maneuvered with the NS axis and the inner circle into the position of most complete extinction. At this position an interference figure is attempted. With the comparatively large crystals in

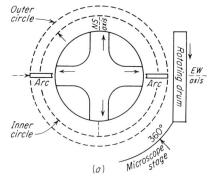

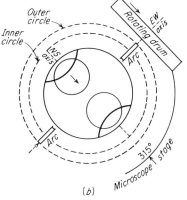

FIG. 7-11. Diagrams showing the adjustment of a large biaxial crystal on the universal stage. (a) The crystal is set to rotate in two vertical planes with apparent movement along the crosshairs. (b) The stage is in the 45° position and either isogyre may be moved to the intersection of the crosshairs by turning the drum which rotates on the EW-axis.

most sets a figure is obtainable. The figure in the 90° position (Figure 7-11a) is secured first. It should be centered with the inner circle and by tilting on the Wright arcs until it can be rotated either way along each arm of the cross without destroying the symmetry of the cross. In this position, rotating on the EW axis and on the NS axis will move the crosshairs along the extinction band in each case while the band itself remains parallel to either the vertical or the horizontal crosshair.

When the interference cross is centered as described above, the stage may be rotated 45° as shown in Figure 7-11b. With the interference figure in the 45° position, rotation along the *EW* axis provides measure-

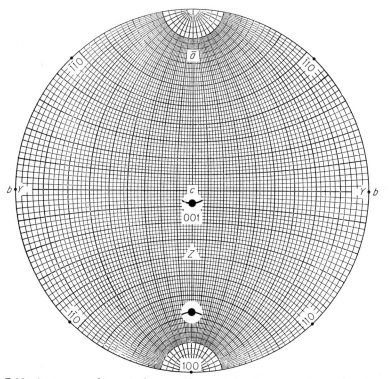

FIG. 7-12. A stereographic net showing the optical orientation of diopside (upper hemisphere). The crystallographic axes *a*, *b*, and *c*, the optic axes, the vibration axes *Y* and *Z*, the cleavage form {110}, and the crystal faces (100) and (001) are shown.

ment of the axial angle, subject to a small correction for the index of refraction of the glass hemisphere.

It is advisable to repeat this exercise using extinction to locate the positions of the optic axes without the benefit of the interference figures. The inner circle and the *NS* axis are used as before for the first adjustment. However, the bands of lowest extinction are sought in this case. When these are located and confirmed by rotating both north-south and east-west, the stage is again turned to 45°. The separation of two spots of low birefringence is measured by rotation along the *EW* axis. An area with slightly higher birefringence lies between. The X, Y, and Z directions may be ascertained through the use of accessory plates.

Stereographic Net. The angular relations of the optic axes, the axes X, Y, and Z, significant cleavages, and crystal faces when known may be shown on a stereographic net (Figure 7-12). The angular relations taken from the readings on the various circles of the universal stage are plotted. The stereographic projection provides a graphic solution for problems which involve angular relationships on a spherical surface.

It is frequently convenient in making a plot to determine the position of X, Y, or Z at an early stage and have one of the three coincide with the center of the stereographic net. A transparent overlay may then be used to plot other positions. If the net is mounted on heavy cardboard, a small thumb tack may be inserted through the back of the paper at the center to serve as a pivot of rotation for the overlay.

REFERENCES

Barrett, C. S.: The Stereographic Projection, *Trans. AIME, Met. Tech. Publ.* 819, 1937.

Berek, M.: "Mikroskopische Mineralbestimmung mit Hilfe der Universaldrehtischmethoden," Verlag Gebrüder Borntraeger, Berlin, 1924.

Emmons, R. C.: The Universal Stage, *Geol. Soc. Am., Mem.* 8, pp. 1–205, 1943.

Haff, J. C.: Fedorow (Universal Stage) Method of Indicatrix Orientation, *Quart. Colo. School Mines*, vol. 37, pp. 1–28, 1942.

Knopf, E. B., and E. Ingerson: Structural Petrology, *Geol. Soc. Am., Mem.* 6, 1938.

Reinhard, M.: "Universal Drehtischmethoden," B. Wepf & Co., Basel, 1931.

Turner, F. J.: Determination of Plagioclase with the Four-axis Universal Stage, *Am. Mineralogist*, vol. 32, pp. 389–410, 1947.

Wahlstrom, E. E.: "Petrographic Mineralogy," John Wiley & Sons, Inc., New York, 1955.

CHAPTER 8

General Features: Color, Mode of Aggregation, Cleavage, and Orientation

Color and Pleochroism. Many minerals are colorless, but color when present is a distinctive feature. Deeply colored minerals are more likely to be colored in thin sections than minerals with pale tints.

Minerals showing natural color are listed in Table 10-2. Among these, isotropic minerals yield no color change as the mineral is rotated in plane-polarized light. Anisotropic minerals exhibit a change in color in varying degrees as the stage is rotated. The change in color produced is known as *pleochroism*. Natural mineral color in thin sections is observed with the polarizer alone.

Hexagonal or tetragonal colored minerals are *dichroic*—i.e., the pleochroic coloring of minerals in these two systems as exhibited with the polarizer is twofold.

Orthorhombic, monoclinic, and triclinic minerals, when colored in thin section, exhibit three different colors and are *trichroic*.

The pleochroic colors are normally oriented with the axes X, Y, and Z of the crystal. In addition to the conventional colors of Table 10-2, white or neutral may represent a pleochroic change. Since X, Y, and Z are the vibration axes, color distribution is related to n_α, n_β, and n_γ and also the optic axes. The correlation of the relationships is best accomplished by reference to the interference figure in order to determine the directions of the axes. As soon as the acute bisectrix Z (if the mineral is positive) or X (if the mineral is negative) is known, the Bertrand lens and analyzer may be removed from the microscope tube and the corresponding natural color ascertained. The color produced by light vibrating in a plane at right angles to the axial plane is Y. The third color will be due to light vibrating parallel to the direction of the obtuse bisectrix. This will be X if the mineral is positive or Z if the mineral is negative.

In pleochroic uniaxial minerals, light vibrating parallel to the optic axis is one color, whereas light at right angles is another.

Biaxial minerals exhibit varying degrees of absorption of color. In common hornblende, for instance, light vibrating parallel to Z usually shows the most absorption, Y is less absorbed, and X is the least. This is recorded by means of the *absorption formula*

$$X < Y < Z$$

It is customary to record the absorption in terms of vibration parallel to the ease of vibration axes.

Form or Aggregation. A considerable number of the designs produced by groups of crystals observed in thin sections and cross sections of individual minerals are so unusual that the pattern exhibited aids in identification (Table 10-3).

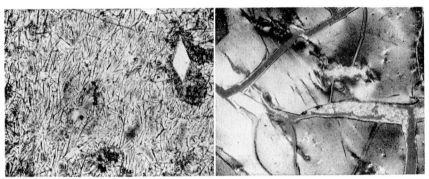

Fig. 8-1.   Fig. 8-2.

Fig. 8-1. (×33) Incipient crystals of rodlike aggregates in a groundmass of volcanic glass.
Fig. 8-2. (×33) Shatter cracks in halloysite (crossed nicols).

Many minerals assume a peculiar development with surprising consistency. Such a tendency in the case of individual crystals may be described as *habit*. *Aggregation* refers to the grouping of either a few or numerous small crystals. The pattern that a mineral group assumes may be described as its *mode of aggregation*. Both form and aggregation are much used features in mineral study.

Incipient Crystallization. Natural glass frequently forms from a viscous liquor that upon solidifying lacks crystallization and is isotropic. The material, however, contains constituents capable of producing a number of different minerals. Development of these minerals is hindered by the viscosity of the inclosing liquor during the period of crystallization, largely because of rapid cooling. Crystals may not develop, but instead needlelike aggregates, fernlike growths, and various odd designs form, representing the sudden arrest of crystallization. *Crystallites, margarites, trichites, microlites, globulites,* and *longulites* are names applied to various forms of incipient crystallization (Figure 8-1). Trichites are curved streaks of embryonic crystals in glass. Margarites are long streaks of globular forms resembling portions of strings of seed pearls in curved or straight lines. Longulites are small rodlike forms composed of groups of globulites. Crystallites are minute nuclei of crystallization suspended in glass. Microlites are small needlelike, almost crystalline forms.

Non-crystalline Isotropic Minerals. Minerals lacking directional qualities yielding double refraction are dark between crossed nicols. Such minerals are chiefly identified by means of their structure in thin section, combined with a determination of their indices of refraction.

Glass, opal, cliachite (bauxite), and collophane appear non-crystalline or microscopically amorphous.[1] In addition to incipient crystals, glass

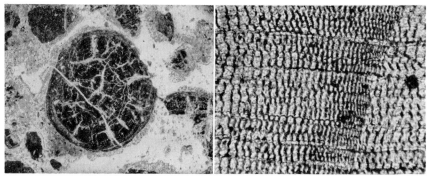

FIG. 8-3.   FIG. 8-4.

FIG. 8-3. (×33) Rounded sections of pisolitic bauxite made up of the mineral cliachite. Interstices (around holes in the section) contain gibbsite.
FIG. 8-4. (×33) Cellular structure of wood preserved in opal.

frequently exhibits flow lines, cracks, or concentric fractures. Opal is usually banded and may exhibit a play of colors. Shatter cracks are distinctive features in minerals of colloidal origin (Figure 8-2).

Cliachite, the amorphous mineral found in bauxite, occurs in pisolitic forms frequently cracked and fractured at random. Interstices between pisolites may be filled with gibbsite forming a fine-grained gray-and-white mosaic of small crystals (Figure 8-3).

The rounded, more or less spherical forms assumed by amorphous and metacolloidal minerals in open spaces are frequently described as *colloform.*

Materials of Organic Origin. In the study of thin sections, structures are occasionally encountered that are residual from organic life. Diatomaceous, radiolarian, or foraminiferal organisms have distinctive structures frequently preserved in minerals. Fossil diatoms and other micro-

---

[1] The term *microamorphous* is used because X-ray studies have shown these materials to have directional properties sensitive to short wavelengths.

scopic remains are usually opal and have the optical properties of that mineral. The original structures of the microorganisms, however, are on many occasions well preserved (Figure 8-7). Foraminifera are apt to yield calcite, usually finely crystalline in nature, and difficult to distinguish from aragonite unless the structure is sufficiently coarse to permit the rhombohedral cleavage to develop (Figure 8-8).

Fragments of former vegetable matter preserved as carbonaceous material—lignite, etc.—are usually black or brown in thin section. Cellular structures of wood as preserved in lignite are quite distinctive in thin section. Opal formed by the replacement of wood frequently exhibits cellular structure (Figure 8-4).

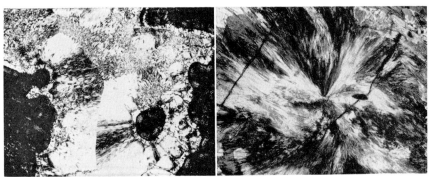

FIG. 8-5.   FIG. 8-6.

FIG. 8-5. (×33) Chalcedony between crossed nicols showing both radial aggregates and banded structure.

FIG. 8-6 (×33) A flamboyant radial aggregate of sillimanite between crossed nicols.

Collophane, the mineral constituent of fossil bone, frequently retains the structure of the bone that has been replaced.

Fine Aggregates. Minerals frequently form fine aggregates of distinctive pattern. Aggregate structure is emphasized between crossed nicols either by radial groups or by a fine-grained mosaiclike groundmass of small crystals (Figure 8-9).

In radial groups the small crystals converge like the spokes of a wheel. Radial uniformity of orientation produces with crossed nicols a dark cross parallel to the positions of extinction (Figure 8-5). This cross should not be confused with the axial cross of a uniaxial interference figure.

An illustration of a mineral aggregate is furnished at times by sillimanite (Figure 8-6). The needles of sillimanite, however, are not so regularly arranged as is the case of chalcedony.

Crosses due to radial arrangement of fine crystal groups in polarized light are frequently formed in microfossils replaced by calcite (Figure 8-10).

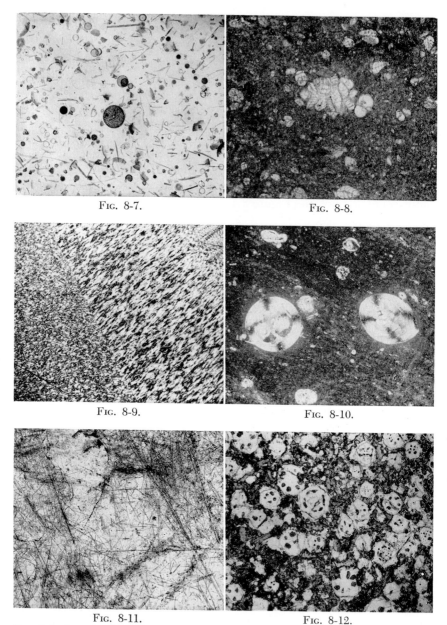

FIG. 8-7.

FIG. 8-8.

FIG. 8-9.

FIG. 8-10.

FIG. 8-11.

FIG. 8-12.

FIG. 8-7. (×33) The fine microorganic structures preserved in opal-forming fossil diatoms. Diatomaceous earth from Lompoc, California.

FIG. 8-8. (×33) Calcite in sections of fossil foraminifera scattered through carbonaceous shale.

FIG. 8-9. (×33) Mosaic structure in chalcedony. A "salt and pepper" aggregate of small crystals photographed between crossed nicols.

FIG. 8-10. (×33) A polarization cross in fossil foraminifera of calcite arranged in concentric bands of radial fiberlike crystals.

FIG. 8-11. (×33) Needlelike crystals of sillimanite in quartz.

FIG. 8-12. (×33) Euhedral crystals of leucite containing inclusions of glass.

Spherulitic crystallization in glassy flow rocks is strikingly illustrated between crossed nicols. Figure 16-43d represents a thin section containing spherulites photographed between crossed nicols. Spherulites of the feldspars or other minerals are often found suspended in volcanic glass of one form or another.

Parallel orientation of fibrous aggregates is illustrated by a thin section of chrysotile in serpentine (Figure 8-13). Veinlets of cross fibers arranged in parallel fashion perpendicular to the walls of the vein are common in serpentine. The fibers are moderately anisotropic, whereas the serpentine is almost dark between crossed nicols.

Inclusions. During crystallization small areas of foreign substances may be caught within what are otherwise clear crystals. In leucite, for example, small areas of volcanic glass are often distributed symmetrically as small isolated spheres suspended in the crystal (Figure 8-12).

Hypersthene (Figure 8-15) may contain areas of brown, flakelike inclusions frequently accompanied by a fine transverse system of lines usually described as *schiller structure.*

Small vermicular growths of quartz occur as inclusions in staurolite (Figure 8-29). Carbonaceous matter forms symmetrical inclusions in andalusite (Figure 8-24). Occasionally substances retained may be radioactive and during geologic time will continue to give off emanations until they finally lose their strength. Such inclusions, when trapped in colored minerals such as biotite, produce dark brown circular patches, frequently pleochroic. Figure 8-16 illustrates halos produced by radioactivity in biotite from western Connecticut.

Needlelike Crystals. A few minerals form fine, hairlike masses of crystals, usually penetrating some other mineral, such as mica or quartz. Sillimanite often occurs in minute needles penetrating quartz (Figure 8-11). Dumortierite occurs in a similar manner. Dumortierite is often pink and may impart to the hand specimen a color resembling rose quartz, although deeper in color. Rutile forms red or brown needles that may penetrate either quartz or mica. Tourmaline may also occur in similar fashion. The radiating crystals of tourmaline in quartz illustrated in Figure 8-14 are characteristic of luxullianite, a rock.

Although these occurrences are quite striking when observed, it should be remembered that the same minerals may occur in large crystals having an entirely different habit.

Bladed Crystals. Crystal groups may be composed of larger, coarser individuals causing lathlike sections under the microscope. Also, intermediate sizes of different form and development may occur. One illustration of a coarse-bladed type of development is furnished by kyanite, as illustrated in Figure 8-17.

Twin Crystals. The feldspars provide an outstanding illustration of

FIG. 8-13.   FIG. 8-14.

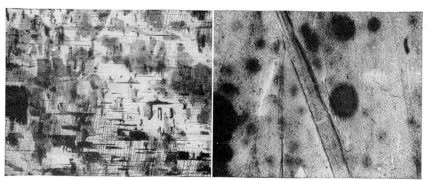

FIG. 8-15.   FIG. 8-16.

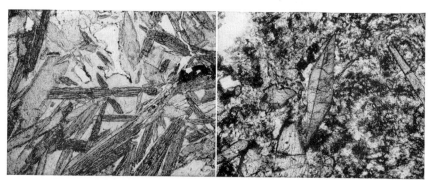

FIG. 8-17.   FIG. 8-18.

FIG. 8-13. (×33) Bands of asbestos fibers in serpentine (crossed nicols).
FIG. 8-14. (×33) Needlelike crystals of tourmaline arranged in radial groups.
FIG. 8-15. (×33) Schiller structure in hypersthene.
FIG. 8-16. (×33) Pleochroic halos in biotite.
FIG. 8-17. (×33) Bladed crystals of kyanite.
FIG. 8-18. (×33) Sphene twinned parallel to the length of the section.

lamellar twinning, particularly between crossed nicols. The twinning is for the most part polysynthetic, comprising multitudinous lathlike individuals (Figure 13-54). Orthoclase provides illustrations of coarser penetration and contact twinning. Microline provides an illustration of two types of lamellar twinning superimposed (Figure 13-41).

Numerous minerals provide illustrations of twinning. Calcite nearly always twins parallel to the long diagonal of the cleavage rhombohedron, and dolomite twins parallel to both the long and the short diagonal of the cleavage rhombohedron. Cassiterite, corundum, pyroxene, aragonite, amphibole, lazulite, and gibbsite are frequently found in twin crystals,

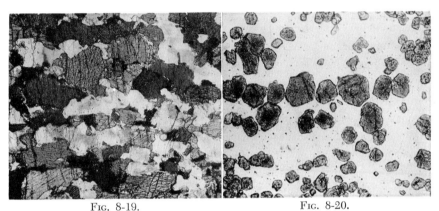

Fig. 8-19.   Fig. 8-20.
Fig. 8-19. (×33) Anhedral crystals of hornblende associated with quartz.
Fig. 8-20. (×33) Subhedral garnet in quartz.

the twinning being easily recognized by the different extinction of the various twin individuals between crossed nicols. The crystal of sphene in Figure 8-18 is twinned into individuals separated by a plane parallel to the length of the crystal.

Natural Crystal Form in Thin Section. There is a pronounced tendency among crystallized minerals of a given species to repeat habit of growth. Outlines viewed in thin section, due to natural crystal form, are significant.

Apatite, for example, frequently appears in small, lathlike, elongated crystals with hexagonal cross sections (Figure 8-22).

Corundum in mica schist may form skeleton crystals characterized by rounded elongate outlines (Figure 8-23).

Pyrite is often found in square areas, although triangular and other shapes also occur.

Well-developed crystals with geometrical boundaries are called *eu-*

hedral.[2] Crystals with rounded or irregular boundaries are *anhedral.*[3] Partially developed crystals may be called *subhedral.*

Anhedral, subhedral, and euhedral crystals are illustrated in Figures 8-19, 8-20, and 8-21, respectively. Subhedral garnet (Figure 8-20) should be compared with euhedral garnet (Figure 15-9).

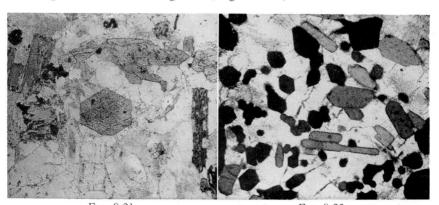

FIG. 8-21.   FIG. 8-22.

FIG. 8-21. (×33) Euhedral hornblende associated with biotite in thin section.
FIG. 8-22. (×33) Apatite crystals in thin section (crossed nicols).

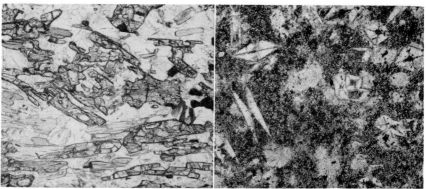

FIG. 8-23.   FIG. 8-24.

FIG. 8-23. (×33) Skeleton crystals of corundum in mica shist.
FIG. 8-24. (×33) Andalusite containing symmetrically arranged carbonaceous inclusions.

Isometric Crystals. Euhedral crystals may exhibit cross sections of such common isometric forms as the cube, octahedron, dodecahedron, and trapezohedron.

Leucite and analcime are illustrated in Figures 8-12 and 8-25. The outlines of both follow the trapezohedron.

[2] Also called *idiomorphic* or *automorphic.*
[3] Also called *allotriomorphic* or *xenomorphic.*

Occasionally isometric crystals are twinned, and in some cases weak anisotropism exists, although isometric minerals are normally isotropic. Pseudoisometric minerals such as leucite exhibit low first-order interference colors. Garnet from contact-metamorphic deposits in limestone may be strongly anisotropic (Figure 8-26).

Tetragonal Crystals. Small tetragonal crystals having euhedral development are not numerous. Cross sections are usually the normal sections to be expected from a tetragonal prism terminated with a bipyramid, as in zircon, or a combination of two prisms and two bipyramids, as in idocrase. The crystals are uniaxial, and sections cut normal to the *c*-axis give optic-axis interference figures. Twinning and cleavage accord with

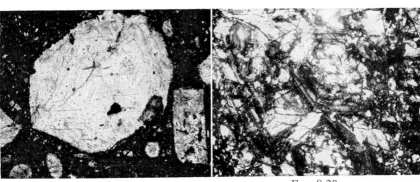

Fig. 8-25.   Fig. 8-26.

Fig. 8-25. (×33) A euhedral crystal of analcime.

Fig. 8-26. (×33) Isometric crystals of garnet showing anomalous anisotropism and banding between crossed nicols.

tetragonal symmetry. Crystals extinguish parallel to the crystallographic axes.

Hexagonal Crystals. A number of common minerals encountered in thin section are hexagonal in crystallization. Quartz, tourmaline, apatite, beryl, and nepheline are frequently encountered hexagonal crystals. The sections of those minerals may be hexagonal or triangular if normal to the *c*-axis, and rectangular or modified rectangular where cut along the *c*-axis. The crystals are frequently elongated parallel to the *c*-axis and exhibit parallel extinction with positive or negative elongation, depending upon the sign of the mineral. The hexagonal sections are either nearly or completely isotropic and yield uniaxial interference figures. Nepheline (Figure 8-27) frequently exhibits both hexagonal and rectangular sections. Apatite (Figure 8-22) furnishes both hexagonal and elongated, somewhat rounded, rectangular sections.

Rhombohedral crystals include the group of rhombohedral carbonates, and although these minerals are ordinarily found in matted masses of anhedral crystals, occasionally euhedral crystals occur. The euhedral crystals are rhombic in section and frequently exhibit cleavage lines parallel to the sides. The section of the rhombohedron normal to the c-axis may appear hexagonal.

Orthorhombic Crystals. A number of orthorhombic minerals encountered in thin sections exhibit euhedral crystals. Olivine, natrolite, barite, zoisite, andalusite, dumortierite, and topaz are among the most common. Euhedral olivine crystals (Figure 8-28) are frequently seen in thin sections of basic igneous rocks. The crystals are symmetrical with respect to the crystallographic axes and become extinct when the axes are parallel to the planes of vibration of the nicols. Lathlike crystals of natrolite with excellent parallel extinction mentioned in the discussion

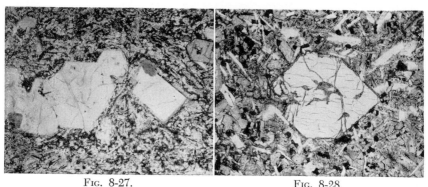

Fig. 8-27.   Fig. 8-28.

Fig. 8-27. (×33) Nepheline crystals showing both hexagonal and rectangular outlines.

Fig. 8-28. (×33) A euhedral crystal of olivine.

of the adjustments of the microscope are occasionally found in thin sections. Barite crystals may be square, rectangular, or elongated, with parallel or symmetrical extinction. Staurolite crystals (Figure 8-29) are often rectangular or rhombic. Andalusite forms symmetrical rhombic crystals (Figure 8-24).

Monoclinic Crystals. The pyroxenes, amphiboles, monoclinic feldspars, sphene, mica, epidote, and a number of other less common monoclinic minerals are frequently found in euhedral crystals in thin sections. The crystals exhibit inclined extinction when sections are cut either parallel to or near the plane of the a- and c-axis. Certain sections, however, may be so oriented as to furnish either symmetrical or parallel extinction. Each monoclinic crystal is an individual problem in optical orientation and should be considered by itself.

Figures 8-21 and 8-30 furnish comparative examples of euhedral amphibole and euhedral pyroxene. The views demonstrate both crystal boundaries and cleavage.

Triclinic Crystals. The plagioclase group, microcline, kyanite, and rhodonite, constitute the ordinary triclinic minerals found in thin section. The extinction is ordinarily inclined in all sections, and the extinction angles may be high.

Cleavage, Parting, and Fracture as an Aid in Distinguishing Minerals. Cleavage may be defined as the ever-present ability of a mineral to separate into smaller and smaller particles bounded by smooth surfaces parallel to the directions of faces of possible crystal forms. Cleavage is frequently of assistance in distinguishing minerals (Table 10-4). Unfortunately, many minerals show little or no cleavage. If cleavage is well developed, however, a mineral may be identified at times by this property

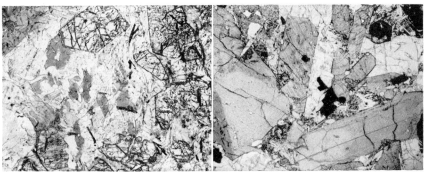

FIG. 8-29.   FIG. 8-30.

FIG. 8-29. (×33) Euhedral staurolite crystals in a ground mass of muscovite and other minerals.
FIG. 8-30. (×33) Euhedral crystals of pyroxene.

alone. In grinding thin sections cleavage planes often develop which appear in the finished section as lines or bands of varying width.

Some minerals separate only occasionally or break along planes of twinning. This may be called *parting*. It is not always present and may not continue to finer and finer particles. In an individual specimen, in so far as the effect produced is concerned, cleavage may be indistinguishable from parting.

Cleavage is a crystallographic feature and may be discussed in terms of direction. Cleavages in one, two, or three directions are frequent; fluorite and diamond cleave in four directions, while sphalerite cleaves in six directions.

In the appended tables for identifying common minerals encountered in thin sections, cleavage planes, fracture planes, or the tendency to break parallel to certain definite directions is indicated for each of the minerals included.

Cleavage in One Direction. A number of minerals have a single plane of cleavage, muscovite and topaz being examples (Figure 8-31). In thin section, crystals showing one direction of cleavage usually exhibit systems of parallel lines. Occasionally, a cleavage plane may be almost parallel to the section, in which instance practically no cleavage lines will appear.

In the case of fragments, minerals with one direction of cleavage usually lie flat upon the microscope slide and have irregular boundaries. The interference color is nearly always uniform for the area of the fragment except on the outer edge, where a number of color bands will be observed, forming color contours of minerals having strong double refraction. Frequently, similar orientation of interference figures occurs in such fragments since many lie in the same position.

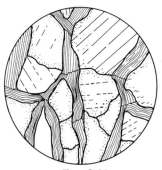 

Fig. 8-31.   Fig. 8-32.

Fig. 8-31. Anhedral topaz crystals with broadly spaced cleavage in one direction with penetrating muscovite having closely spaced cleavage in one direction.
Fig. 8-32. Anhedral hornblende with cleavage at 56° and 124° in a groundmass of feldspar.

Cleavage in Two Directions. Several common minerals develop prominent cleavage in two directions. The pyroxenes, amphiboles, and feldspars are outstanding illustrations.

Common hornblende of the amphibole group is distinguished from pyroxene by a difference in cleavage angle. The cleavage of hornblende (Figure 8-32) parallel to the rhombic prism {110} is in two directions at 56° and 124°. The cleavage of the rhombic prism in the case of pyroxene (Figure 8-33) is approximately 87° and 93°.

The two directions of cleavage may be at 90° in orthorhombic or tetragonal minerals. Figure 8-34 illustrates andalusite (orthorhombic), with two directions of cleavage at about 90° (89°12′).

Cleavage in Three Directions. The types produced due to cleavage in three directions vary considerably. One of the simplest types is that produced by cleavage parallel to the faces of the cube. In thin sections cleavage of this type produces square or triangular patterns. In fragments the boundaries tend to be square or rectangular. Cubic cleavage is restricted to the isometric system, where both sections and fragments are easily confirmed by the isotropic character of the material.

Rectangular cleavage resembles cubic cleavage in its appearance in both thin sections and fragments (Figure 8-35). Minerals having rectangular cleavage, however, may be easily distinguished owing to their anisotropism between crossed nicols.

FIG. 8-33.   FIG. 8-34.

FIG. 8-33. Euhedral pyroxene crystals showing two directions of cleavage in a groundmass of feldspar.

FIG. 8-34. Andalusite with cleavage in two directions at about 90°, cut by veinlets of fine muscovite with cleavage in one direction.

FIG. 8-35. Anhydrite (rectangular cleavage) and fluorite (octahedral cleavage) in the same thin section. The octahedral cleavage of fluorite produces a triangular pattern.

Rhombohedral cleavage is one of the most common types found within minerals, both in thin sections and in fragments. The common carbonate minerals have cleavage of this type. The pattern produced in thin section is crisscross in design, and the crystals usually show inclined cleavage planes penetrating the section. In addition, there is frequently a set of twin lines parallel to the long diagonal of the rhombohedron. Occasionally twinning may appear parallel to both the long and the short diagonal, as in the case of dolomite. In fragments, minerals with rhombohedral cleavage are usually flat lying, with a fairly well-developed rhombic section, and vary in relief with direction. The edges usually show wedgelike or inclined surface boundaries.

Cleavage in three directions is frequently produced by breaking parallel to various directions in crystals of the orthorhombic, monoclinic, and triclinic systems. In most instances, the part of the mineral under examination presents a special case. As a rule, however, cleavage of this type produces a crisscross of almost rectangular pattern in thin section, and in fragments the boundaries either are almost rectangular or may be flat lying, with wedgelike edges.

Cleavage in Four Directions. One common mineral, fluorite, has cleavage in four directions parallel to the faces of an octahedron (Figure 8-35). Cleavages of fluorite in thin section tend to develop triangular or rhombic patterns. In fragments the outlines of individual fragments are triangular or irregular with pointed edges. These are easily detected between crossed nicols on account of the isotropic character of the mineral. Occasionally spinel is found with an octahedral parting imperfectly developed but somewhat resembling octahedral cleavage. The diamond has octahedral cleavage but, needless to say, is not common in thin sections.

Cleavage in Six Directions. Sphalerite is one of the few minerals with cleavage parallel to the six different directions of a dodecahedron. The outlines of this figure may occasionally be detected in pieces of sphalerite within sections due to the intersections of inclined cleavage planes. In fragments sometimes almost perfect dodecahedrons may be observed.

Tendency to Break in Elongate Directions. Some minerals exhibit a decided fibrous structure, being made up of numerous small needles visible as parallel crystals beneath the microscope. These may vary in size from small elongated blades to minute capillary fibers. Coarser minerals of this sort change from fibrous to bladed shapes.

Orientation. The optical orientation of a mineral involves the correlation of the optical directions with crystallographic directions. In biaxial minerals the problem usually involves locating the position of the acute bisectrix, optic normal, and axial plane with respect to the axes a, b, and c of a crystal. The orientation of uniaxial minerals concerns the relation of the optical system to the c-axis.

In the following discussion it is assumed that the reader is familiar with the simple rules of description of crystals in the various systems and the conventions of orientation; otherwise a text on geometrical crystallography should be consulted.

Isometric System. Optical orientation in isometric crystals is eliminated since isometric crystals are isotropic, hence becoming non-directional as far as light is concerned.

Tetragonal and Hexagonal Systems. The optic axes of uniaxial minerals are parallel to the c-axes of tetragonal or hexagonal minerals. The direction may agree with either the fast or the slow ray of the mineral, depending upon the optic sign.

Orthorhombic System. The crystallographic axes *a*, *b*, and *c* of orthorhombic minerals correspond with the vibration axes *X*, *Y*, and *Z* but not necessarily in the order named. The crystallographic axis *a*, for instance, may be *X*, *Y*, or *Z*, and the same substitutions are possible for crystallographic axes *b* and *c*. If two vibration axes are fixed, however, the third becomes known. It is also evident that *X* and *Z* define the position of the axial plane; thus, if *a* = *Z* and *c* = *X*, the axial plane includes *a* and *c*. The axial angle 2*V* may vary in amount within the axial plane.

Orthorhombic crystals are indicated in several ways. The extinction is parallel to *a*, *b*, or *c*. Thus if *a*, *b*, and *c* can be ascertained from some

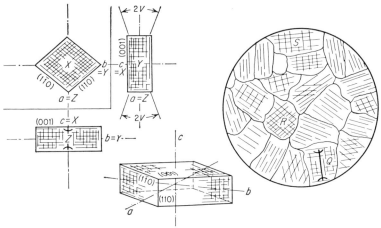

FIG. 8-36. Thin-section and orientation diagrams of barite.

prominent cleavage or crystal outline, the nature of the extinction becomes known. Recognizable cleavage and crystal faces aid in examination. Good dispersion is useful.

When the positions of *a*, *b*, and *c* are once ascertained, the interference figure will furnish criteria for the relative fixation of *X*, *Y*, and *Z*. The position of the optic axes will also be ascertained at the same time. In practice each mineral presents a special problem in orientation, and data for the common minerals are included with the mineral descriptions in Part 2.

Barite furnishes a useful illustration of the problem involved in the optical orientation of an orthorhombic mineral. An idealized cleavage of barite is shown in Figure 8-36, together with a diagram of a thin section and three oriented cross sections. In thin section the barite grains exhibit cleavage in three directions, the cleavage parallel to {001} being more pronounced. The grain marked *R* in the thin section happens to be in a position in which the angles of cleavage measure 78°22′. The *c*-axis is perpendicular to this section. The planes {110} and {110} are parallel to the *c*-axis. In this grain the *a*-axis would bisect the obtuse angle of cleavage, and the *b*-axis would bisect the acute angle of cleavage. Between crossed nicols the extinction will be parallel to *a* and *b*, or symmetrical with respect to the cleavage. Grain S would have parallel extinction but might be normal to the *b*-axis and not in a position to give an interference figure of the acute bisectrix type. An interference figure is oriented with respect to the cleavage as shown in grain Q. A test with the quartz wedge will confirm the fact that the mineral is positive; hence $Bx_\alpha = Z$. The optic normal is Y, and $Bx_0 = X$. If one refers again to the

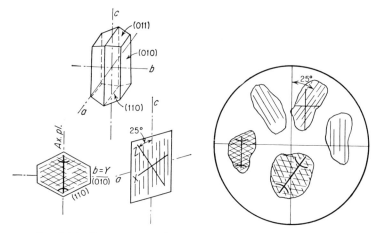

Fig. 8-37. Thin-section and orientation diagrams of hornblende.

figures illustrating the cleavage form, the following orientation is apparent:

$$a = Z$$
$$b = Y$$
$$c = X$$

The angle 2V as estimated with the microscope is approximately equal to the recorded angle 37°30′. Therefore the optic axes make an angle of 18°45′ with the *a*-axis.

The orientation in the case of orthorhombic crystals is not always so simple as in the case of barite. The principles and procedure, however, are essentially the same, and it is always fundamental to be able to fix the position of X, Y, and Z with respect to *a*, *b*, and *c*.

Monoclinic System. In monoclinic crystals, X, Y, or Z correspond to the *b*-axis. If Y corresponds to *b*, which is often the case, X and Z will occupy any position at 90° to each other in the plane of *a* and *c*.

Hornblende furnishes a good illustration of the problem of orientation of a monoclinic crystal. The mineral has two prominent directions of cleavage parallel to the rhombic prism {110}. The c-axis is parallel to the edge between the cleavages, and the b-axis bisects the angle between (100) and (1$\bar{1}$0) (Figure 8-37). In thin sections either one or two sets of cleavage lines appear, depending upon the orientation. Grains with two cleavage directions are symmetrical in extinction and yield biaxial negative interference figures. The axial plane bisects the obtuse angle of the cleavage, and Y bisects the acute angle. The position of Z may be obtained from a section parallel to the plane of the axes a and c. Light vibrating parallel to Z is the slow ray; the angle of maximum extinction for the slow ray may be determined with the mica plate. The maximum extinction angle for the single cleavage trace is the angle between Z and the c-axis. In hornblende this angle is about 25°. When Z is determined, the angle of X is known since it lies at 90° to Z. Y is perpendicular to the plane of Z and X.

Triclinic System. Each triclinic crystal constitutes an individual case in optical orientation. The center of the optical system must coincide with the center of the crystallographic system; otherwise there is no agreement.

REFERENCES

Grout, F. F.: "Petrography and Petrology," McGraw-Hill Book Company, Inc., New York, 1932.

Harker, A.: "Petrology for Students," 7th ed., Cambridge University Press, London, 1935.

Heinrich, E. W.: "Microscopic Petrography," McGraw-Hill Book Company, Inc., New York, 1956.

Johannsen, A.: "Rock-forming Minerals in Thin Sections," John Wiley & Sons, Inc., New York, 1908.

Kraus, E. H., W. F. Hunt, and L. S. Ramsdell: "Mineralogy," 3d ed., McGraw-Hill Book Company, Inc., New York, 1936.

Larsen, E. S., and H. Berman: Microscopic Determination of Non-opaque Minerals, *U. S. Geol. Survey Bull.* 848, 1934.

Luquer, L. M.: "Minerals in Rock Sections," 4th ed., D. Van Nostrand Company, Inc., Princeton, N.J., 1913.

Rogers, A. F.: "Introduction to the Study of Minerals," 3d ed., McGraw-Hill Book Company, Inc., New York, 1937.

Weinschenck, E.: "Petrographic Methods," trans. by R. W. Clark, McGraw-Hill Book Company, Inc., New York, 1912.

Williams, H., F. J. Turner, and C. M. Gilbert: "Petrography," W. H. Freeman & Co., San Francisco, 1954.

Winchell, A. N.: "Elements of Optical Mineralogy. Part II: Descriptions of Minerals," John Wiley & Sons, Inc., New York, 1927.

CHAPTER 9

Mineral Fragments

Crushed Fragments. The principles of microscopic observation with polarized light apply equally whether minerals are studied in thin sections or in crushed fragments. However, differences in mounting, cleavage development, or the distribution and orientation of the minerals in the mount enable the student to make optical determinations more accurately and conveniently with fragments than with thin sections. As a result, supplementary studies of fragments are often advisable.

A small amount of material suffices for a complete examination of crushed fragments; no preliminary grinding is necessary; a minimum of equipment is used (polarizing microscope and set of index liquids); cleavage fragments break according to form and assist greatly in establishing orientation; and individual crystals may be isolated for independent examination. Nevertheless, in spite of the utility of fragment methods, it should be kept in mind that this type of examination fails to yield the splendid exhibit of mineral association and texture observable in thin sections.

The practical utilization of crushed fragments in mineral identification was first attempted by Maschke in 1872, although it was not until years later that the method was sufficiently developed to be widely used. In 1898, Schroeder van der Kolk assembled a list of fluids suitable for use as immersion liquids; in 1906, his publication of a list giving a more extensive series of liquids, together with the refractive indices of 300 minerals determined by comparison with these liquids, was a great step forward. A. F. Rogers, E. S. Larsen, H. E. Merwin, C. S. Ross, F. E. Wright, H. Berman, and others have accumulated data that have greatly increased the application of the method. Perhaps the greatest stimulus was brought about by Larsen's "Microscopic Determination of the Nonopaque Minerals."

Methods of Mounting. Permanent mounts are prepared with Canada balsam. In the preparation, fragments are sprinkled on a slide and covered with balsam; then the balsam is cooked by placing the slide on a hot plate, and the mount is covered with a cover glass. This may be done in a few minutes, and the slide may be marked for purposes of filing.

Temporary mounts are made by utilizing the various inert liquids used for determining the indices of refraction. Screened fragments are preferable for routine work. If screens are not available, fragments of suitable size may be obtained by placing small lumps of a mineral between two glass slides and rubbing the slides together until the glass surfaces slide smoothly over each other on the mineral powder. On a clean glass slide, place about as many fragments as can be picked up on the tip of a small knife blade. By tapping the edge of the slide with the knife, distribute the fragments evenly over an area approximately ¼ inch in diameter. Then place a cover glass over the grains. With a small glass rod, apply a drop of oil at the edge of the cover glass. The oil will flow in and around the grains by capillary action (Figure 9-1). If one drop of oil is not sufficient, a second and a third may be applied until the fragments are completely immersed. Care should be taken, however, not to apply an excess of oil for this may cause the grains to float, thus hindering observations and measure-

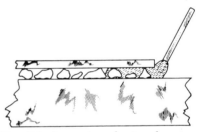

Fig. 9-1. Immersion of mineral grains.

ments. With sufficient care, two or three mounts may be made on a single slide. After use, the glass slides may be cleaned with alcohol, followed by rinsing in water and drying.

Temporary mounts are by no means restricted to fine powders. Small, well-formed crystals, detrital grains, coarse fragments, and oriented cleavages or sections are representative of materials that may be examined in a variety of positions under the microscope. A slight movement of the cover glass on a temporary mount frequently suffices to turn a fragment. This is somewhat easier if powdered glass slightly coarser than the fragments being studied is mixed with the sample. The glass fragments being free from cleavage lie in random positions and are easily turned, moving the fragments of the sample at the same time. The glass is easily distinguished by its isotropic character and index of refraction.

A binocular microscope of low power is extremely useful for the purpose of isolating small crystals or mineral grains (Figure 9-2). While looking through the binocular small crystals may be pried loose from a specimen with a needle and these form ideal samples for examination with the polarizing microscope, in either temporary or permanent mounts.

Immersion Method. In immersion, mineral fragments are placed under the microscope in a liquid of known index, and the refraction of light observed at the edges of the fragments may be utilized in index comparison.

The fragments examined may range widely in size. Ordinarily, fragments that pass through a standard 100-mesh screen and are caught on a 120-mesh screen are satisfactory. Refractive index determinations of minerals follow a routine procedure. Since the index of refraction of the liquid is known, the method of central illumination or that of oblique illumination may be used to compare the indices of refraction of the

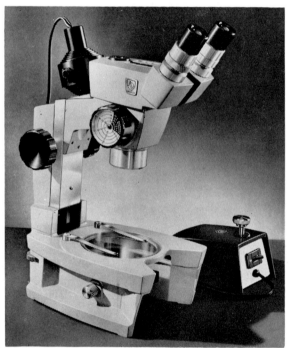

Fig. 9-2. A binocular microscope. (*Courtesy of American Optical Co.*)

mineral fragments with the index of refraction of the liquid. As soon as the index of the mineral is determined to be greater or less than the liquid, the slide is placed in a cleaning jar, and another mount is prepared, using a liquid with a different index. By utilizing a number of liquids and making repeated comparisons the indices of refraction of a mineral may be ascertained within reasonably narrow limits. In case the mineral is isotropic, having only one index of refraction, it is customary to determine the index of the mineral to within two or three in the third place of decimals. When minerals are anisotropic, having indices of refraction that vary with direction, equal accuracy is possible, but more comparisons are necessary to determine different values. It is customary to prepare a set of liquids with indices of refraction of 1.450, 1.455, 1.460, 1.465 . . . etc., up to a limit of 1.740. A considerable number of bottles are required for such a group of liquids. These are usually kept in a dark place and are painted black on the outside to keep out the light. A less elaborate set of liquids with values 1.50, 1.51, 1.52, 1.53 . . . etc., is frequently used. Such a set requires half the number of bottles, is more quickly standardized, and with careful mixing of drops on a slide will yield results accurate to ±0.003.

It is not always advisable to place the cover glass over dry fragments and allow the liquid to be drawn around each grain by capillary attraction, as explained above. To cite a specific instance, it may be desired to find the index of refraction of a mineral with a value between two liquids such as 1.555 and 1.560. In this case a drop of liquid 1.555 is placed upon a slide, and a drop of liquid 1.560 of the same size is placed near by but not quite touching the first drop. The mineral powder is then sprinkled between the drops, and both the drops and the powder are mixed with a needle, small wire, or small stirring rod. A small cover glass is then placed over the mixture, pressed down to remove air globules, and the mount is ready for microscopic examination. The index of the mixed liquid should be about 1.5575.

Index Determinations by Immersion. For hexagonal or tetragonal minerals n_ε and n_ω are determined; for orthorhombic, monoclinic, or triclinic minerals n_α, n_β, and n_γ. In these determinations it should be remembered that each mineral grain in the field of the microscope is doubly refracting with values n_2 and n_1. Furthermore, when a crystal is in the position of extinction, the planes of vibration of n_2 and n_1 are parallel to the vibration planes of the nicols.

The determination of n_ε and n_ω, or n_α and n_γ, usually resolves itself into a search with successive liquids until both the upper and lower limits of n_2 and n_1 for a given mineral are located. The difference between the two values equals the maximum double refraction of the mineral. It should be remembered, however, that cleavage or structure may limit the positions in which minerals will come to rest on the slide. In such cases the two extremes may not be obtained unless fragments are turned by moving the cover glass or interference figures are used to check the orientation.

The determination of n_β in biaxial minerals may be carried out in two ways. If interference figures on or near a bisectrix or an optic axis can be obtained for several grains in different liquids, the determination of n_β is simple. This is due to the fact that the index of the ray vibrating at right angles to the axial plane is n_β. It is also convenient to remember that any gain in a position to give an optic-axis figure yields rays with the index n_β in all directions. If such interference figures are not obtainable, and specific information concerning the position of n_β in fragments is not known, the value can still be determined by a process of elimination as explained below.

For each fragment shown in the field of the microscope, somewhere between n_2 and n_1 is the value n_β. In certain fragments either n_2 or n_1 may equal n_β, but from the consideration of biaxial crystals it can be shown that both n_2 and n_1 will approach but never pass beyond the value of n_β in the same fragment. Thus n_β may be located by varying the liquids and observing both n_2 and n_1 in a number of fragments. In Figure 9-3 assume the vertical lines to indicate the measured grains of a certain mineral. The horizontal lines cover the range in indices of refraction for different grains having different values of n_2 and n_1. It will

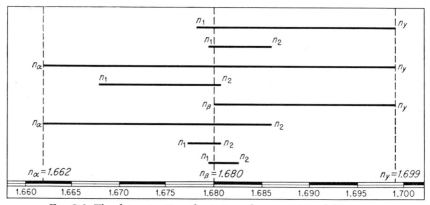

FIG. 9-3. The determination of n in irregular non-oriented fragments.

be observed that all lines cross or meet 1.680, this being the value of n_β; also, that no lines exceed 1.699, which is the value of n_γ; and that no lines are less than 1.662, which is the value of n_α. If fragments with weak double refractions are tried in successive liquids, testing both n_2 and n_1 in each case, the value of n_β can soon be approximated within narrow limits.

It is convenient as a confirmation of the determination of optic sign to remember that when $(n_\beta - n_\alpha)$ is decidedly greater than $(n_\gamma - n_\beta)$, the mineral is optically negative. If on the other hand, $(n_\beta - n_\alpha)$ is decidedly less than $(n_\gamma - n_\beta)$, the mineral is positive.

Form of Mineral Fragments. Mineral fragments often exhibit distinctive forms under the microscope that are extremely useful in their identification. Such forms may be due to cleavage of the crystals of the mineral or may be due to a characteristic growth that causes peculiar fragments, or the crystals may be so small that they appear as individuals beneath the microscope.

Form of minerals in crushed fragments is probably most frequently related to the cleavage. Since cleavage is the ability of a mineral to break into smaller and smaller particles with smooth surfaces that are parallel to possible crystal faces, it follows that this characteristic will be as evi-

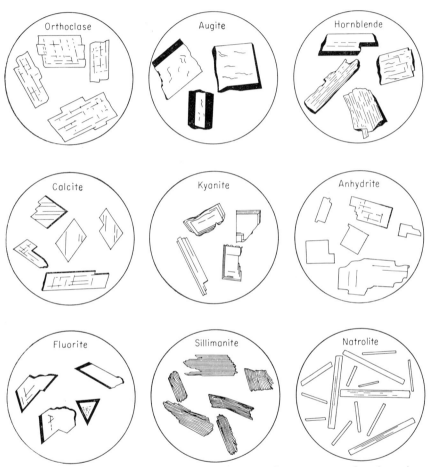

FIG. 9-4. Cleavage and fracture fragments. (a) One direction—irregular plates (not illustrated). (b) Two directions—orthoclase, augite, and hornblende. (c) Three directions—kyanite, anhydrite (rectangular), calcite (rhombohedral). (d) Four directions—fluorite (octahedral). (e) Prismatic sillimanite. (f) Acicular—natrolite.

dent in fragments as in a hand specimen. Minerals may exhibit cleavage in one, two, three, or even four and six directions (Figure 9-4). The identification of cleavage planes in mineral fragments is aided by the fact that the fragments normally orient themselves with one of the cleavage surfaces parallel to the surface of the slide. Thus, if a mineral has one direction of prominent cleavage, it will normally yield flat-lying fragments, with ragged or broken edges. Under crossed nicols, if the mineral is anisotropic, the flat surface may exhibit a single interference color, and the narrow edges will show color bands. If the mineral has two directions of cleavage, one direction will probably be the surface on which it lies, and the other direction will show as either inclined or vertical parallel edges. If the cleavage is developed at right angles, the edge may be vertical. If, however, the cleavage develops at an inclined angle, the edge will appear beveled.

The influence of cleavage or other directional separation along smooth planes is shown in Figure 9-4. The diagrams showing the cleavage fragments are idealized. In a field containing many broken fragments, a few will usually be found unmistakably representing the idealized shape. The majority, however, show only portions of the maximum cleavage development. Even minerals known to possess excellent cleavage are likely to yield a considerable number of irregular fragments when broken.

In addition to the flat-lying, inclined, or vertical planes of cleavage that modify mineral fragments, shapes due to original characteristics of crystallization may be observed. Asbestos, for example, produces thread-like fibers. Acicular or needlelike mineral structures will frequently yield fragments made up of bundles of elongated, thin, parallel crystals. Fine mica flakes may exhibit both flat-lying flakes and needlelike forms when the flakes are on edge. When the flakes are inelastic, wavy or curved plates are likely to result.

Knowledge of cleavage in fragments is necessary in using the immersion method for determining refractive indices.

Immersion Media. Liquids for use as immersion media should be colorless, as odorless as possible, chemically stable, and miscible in all proportions with each other. They should have low dispersion, low volatility, and moderate viscosity. Liquids should be inert and not react with or dissolve the substances to be tested.

Although many different liquids have been suggested as satisfactory immersion media, it has been found that a few well-chosen liquids are preferable to a wide range of complicated compounds.[1]

Common liquids for immersion media are as shown in the table on page 149.

In the preparation of the liquids, isoamyl isovalerate and kerosene may be mixed to form liquids up to 1.466 in indices of refraction. Kerosene and halowax oil may be used for mixtures between 1.466 and 1.63. Halowax oil and methylene iodide may be mixed to form liquids with indices

----

[1] Liquids suitable for index refraction determinations by the immersion method may be secured from R. P. Cargille Laboratories, Inc., 117 Liberty St., New York, N. Y.

Liquid	Approximate index of refraction
Water	1.333
Isoamyl isovalerate[1]	1.428
Kerosene[2]	1.466
Petroleum oil	1.475
α-monobromnaphthalene[3]	1.658
Methylene iodide[4]	1.740
Solution of methylene iodide and sulfur up to	1.794

[1] Eastman Kodak Co., Rochester, N.Y.

[2] A clear, highly refined product, called *government oil*, having the value given above is sold by Leeds & Northrup Co.

[3] Monochlornaphthalene, or "halowax oil" ($n = 1.63$), has been found by a number of workers to be equally satisfactory and more economical. It is sold by the Bakelite Corp.

[4] Edcan Laboratories, 12 Pine St., South Norwalk, Conn.

of refraction between 1.63 and 1.74. For indices below 1.43, some difficulty has been encountered in finding suitable liquids. With more than forty minerals and many inorganic substances having indices below 1.43, liquids in this range are desirable. Water and the alcohols are impractical because of their solvent action. Experiments with petroleum distillates have shown that fractionation of two ligroins, gasolene, and kerosene between narrow boiling-point limits results in stable liquids with indices between 1.3548 and 1.4593 at 22°C.

It has been found also that ethyl propionate and mesitylene are miscible in all proportions to form satisfactory index media between 1.385 and 1.43.

Satisfactory liquids with indices of refraction above 1.74 constitute a problem. Methylene iodide containing dissolved sulfur has been used for the range from 1.74 to 1.78. Phenyldiodoarsine ($n = 1.84$) mixed with methylene iodide has been used for the range from 1.78 to 1.84. A set of high-index liquids made up of phosphorus, sulfur, and methylene iodide covering the range 1.78–2.06 has been described by C. D. West. These liquids are practically stable, inexpensive, and safe to use with the proper precautions.

A set of high-index liquids, composed of arsenic bromide-arsenic sulfide-methylene iodide, has been described by L. H. Borgström. These liquids have a range from 1.78 to 1.95.

Mixed melts of sulfur and selenium (2.05 to 2.72) or piperine and arsenic and antimony triiodides (1.68 to 2.10) are used for high-index determinations. The melts are prepared in advance and arranged in a series of mixtures. The values of the indices of the mixtures are determined by the prism method. A small prism of the transparent melt is made and mounted on the stage of a goniometer. Both the angle of the prism and the angle of minimum deviation are measured. The index of refraction is then computed as previously explained for the prism method. The melt is molded into the form of a prism by using two cover glasses placed at an angle of 30° to each other. The melt is poured into the space between and allowed to cool. When cold, the cover glasses will break away, leaving a prism with smooth surfaces. Great care must be used not to overheat, or the indices of the piperine mixtures will vary greatly. When the index of the melt has been determined, the material is placed in a sealed tube and filed for future use. When applied, the ground-up material is melted around fragments of minerals, and the indices are compared by the method of central illumination.

Extensive investigation of high-index media suitable for work with minerals has been conducted by Larsen and Meyrowitz. Precipitated sulfur in arsenic tribromide has been used with methylene iodide in various proportions to form a series of high-index immersion liquids in the range 1.74 to 1.81. The liquids are stable and reasonably durable. The mixing curve is not a straight line but may be utilized. In the range 1.82 to 2.00 solutions have been prepared with end members as follows: (1) precipitated sulfur, 10 per cent, in arsenic tribromide, (2) precipitated sulfur, 20 per cent, and arsenic disulfide in arsenic tribromide, 60 per cent. The mixing curve is a straight line.

Standardization and Care of Liquids. Indices of refraction of standard liquids are determined according to the methods of refractive-index determination already mentioned. Standard refractometers are suitable for indices to 1.7; the goniometer and prism may be used for the entire range, including melts. Liquids should be standardized for the temperature at which they are to be used, since changes in the index of a liquid occur with temperature variations. Generally, increase in temperature lowers the index of a liquid. This change is approximately 0.0004 per degree centigrade for liquids with indices below 1.658, but for methylene iodide, it amounts to as much as 0.007 for each degree.

In preparing a liquid of a desired index by mixing two liquids of known indices, the following formula is convenient:

$$V_1 n_1 + V_2 n_2 = V_x n_x$$

where V represents volume, n the index, and $V_x n_x$ the volume and index desired. To illustrate, let the volume of $n_1 = V_1$ and the volume of $n_2 = V_2$, $n_1 = 1.4$, $n_2 = 1.65$ and $V_x n_x = 20$ cm^3 of index 1.5. Two equations may be written as follows:

$$1.4 V_1 + 1.65 V_2 = 30$$
$$V_1 + V_2 = 20$$

and, by solving,

$$V_2 = 8$$
$$V_1 = 12$$

Therefore, 8 cm³ of index liquid 1.65 and 12 cm³ of liquid 1.4 will make 20 cm³ of a liquid with an index of 1.5. For methylene iodide mixtures, it has been found that slightly more methylene iodide may be required than the formula indicates.

For accurate work it is important to protect liquids from light and evaporation. Black bottles (from 15 to 20 cm³) with glass applicator stoppers and glass caps are preferable for storage. A wooden box, fitted with a block recessed with round holes into which the bottles fit securely, makes a convenient and safe container for a complete set. While the liquids are in use, care should be taken to keep the bottles stoppered except when the applicator is actually being used.

REFERENCES

Borgström, L. H.: Contribution to the Development of the Immersion Method, *Bull. comm. géol. Finlande* 87, pp. 58–63, 1929.

Glass, J. J.: Standardization of Index Liquids, *Am. Mineralogist*, vol. 19, pp. 459–465, 1934.

Kaiser, E. P., and W. Parrish: Preparation of Immersion Liquids, *Ind. Eng. Chem.*, anal. ed., vol. 11, pp. 560–562, 1939.

Larsen, E. S., and H. Berman: The Microscopic Determination of the Non-opaque Minerals, *U. S. Geol. Survey Bull.* 848, 1934.

Larsen, Esper S., Jr., and Robert Meyrowitz: Immersion Liquids of High Refractive Index, *Am. Mineralogist*, vol. 36, pp. 746–750, 1951.

Maschke, O.: Über Abscheidung krystallisirter Kieselsäure aus wässrigen Lösungen, *Pogg. Ann.*, 5th ser., vol. 25, pp. 549–578, 1872.

Merwin, H. E.: Media of High Refraction, etc., *Am. J. Sci.*, vol. 34, pp. 42–47, 1912.

———: Media of Lower Refraction, *J. Wash. Acad. Sci.*, vol. 3, pp. 35–40, 1913.

Meyrowitz, Robert: A Compilation and Classification of Immersion Media of High Index of Refraction, *Am. Mineralogist*, vol. 40, pp. 398–409, 1955.

———: A New Series of Immersion Liquids, *Am. Mineralogist*, vol. 37, pp. 853–856, 1952.

———: Solvents and Solutes for the Preparation of Immersion Liquids of High Index of Refraction, *Am. Mineralogist*, vol. 41, pp. 49–59, 1956.

Rogers, A. F.: The Determination of Minerals in Crushed Fragments by Means of the Polarizing Microscope, *Quart., Columbia School Mines*, vol. 27, pp. 340–359, 1906.

Schroeder van der Kolk, J. L. C.: "Tabellen zur mikroskipischen Bestimmung der Mineralien nach ihrem Brechungsindex," Wiesbaden, 1906.

Switzer, George: Butyl "carbitol" as an Immersion Liquid, *Am. Mineralogist*, vol. 29, pp. 389–391, 1944.

West, C. D.: Immersion Liquids of High Refractive Index, *Am. Mineralogist*, vol. 21, pp. 245–249, 1936.

Wright, F. E.: The Methods of Petrographic-microscopic Research, *Carnegie Inst. Pub.* 158, 1911.

CHAPTER 10

Systematic Identification

Tables. The identification of mineral species involves procedures which must be repeated many times in the examination of even a few thin sections. Much wasted effort may be avoided if a systematic procedure is adopted. Tables 10-1 to 10-10 are arranged in a progressive sequence which requires simple observations first and more involved manipulations later. An outline follows:

KEY TO MINERAL TABLES

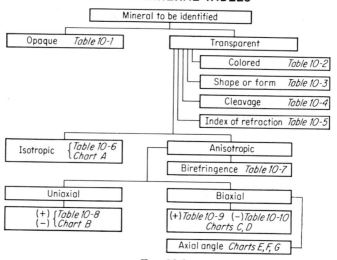

FIG. 10-1.

Opaque Minerals (Table 10-1). As a first step, it is desirable to observe whether a mineral is opaque or transparent. Occasionally, areas of opaque minerals are found. These should be illuminated from above the stage and may be identified by reference to Table 10-1. However, for opaque minerals, recourse must frequently be had to conventional mineralogical methods beyond the scope of this text.

Transparent Minerals (Tables 10-2 to 10-10). The tables are designed primarily for transparent minerals in thin section. With two exceptions (Tables 10-1 and 10-3) the tables also will be found suitable in most instances for mineral fragments as well as thin sections.

A systematic order of observation for each transparent mineral is (1) color, (2) shape or form, (3) cleavage, (4) index refraction, and (5) anisotropism. Should any of these features appear significant the appropriate table should be consulted.

If the mineral is colored, note also whether it is pleochroic or nonpleochroic; if pleochroic, note the colors of pleochroism. Should the mineral occur in some significant shape it should be compared with forms and shapes listed. Elongated crystals may be tested for positive or negative elongation. The presence of cleavage should lead to comparison with the cleavage types listed in the tables. If some knowledge of orientation may be gained from the cleavage, it should be applied.

Isotropic Minerals (Table 10-6). The group of isotropic minerals is small, and perhaps the mineral may be recognized directly if color, cleavage, and the relative index of refraction are taken into account.

Birefringent Minerals (Table 10-7). Anisotropic minerals range in double refraction through wide limits. In general, however, the order of the highest observed interference color for an unknown mineral in thin section can be of considerable assistance in determining a mineral. Since properly ground thin sections are about 0.03 to 0.035 mm in thickness, the double refraction may be estimated from the interference colors and reference to the interference color chart (see page 168).

Optical Character (Tables 10-8, 10-9, and 10-10). As a final stage in systematic identification, an attempt should be made to determine whether a mineral is uniaxial or biaxial, positive or negative. Interference figures aid in this identification. If a mineral proves to be biaxial, it is desirable to ascertain the axial angle and if possible the nature of the dispersion. These features are summarized in Tables 10-8, 10-9, and 10-10 and Charts B, C, D, E, F, and G.

Conclusion. The identification on the basis of optical properties will depend upon the possibilities suggested by each of the tables consulted. Frequently several possibilities remain after the criteria covered by the tables have been considered. These may be investigated further by reference to the mineral descriptions in Part 2 where more complete data are available. Mineral fragments may be used for refractive index determinations as described in Chapter 9 and the data applied to Table 10-5. Mineral associations and environment as described under occurrence are often helpful.

Experience has shown that the tables are adequate for routine identification of most common minerals encountered in thin sections. As a further aid in systematic identification, an outline procedure suggested for anisotropic transparent minerals is included.

OUTLINE FOR IDENTIFICATION
(Transparent Minerals*)

Mineral description
    Color....................... Pleochroic colors.............................
    Shape...
    Cleavage.................... Elongation................................
                               Extinction...............................
    Index of refraction   Relief in balsam..... ....
      + or − balsam............. Compared to other minerals
    Birefringence................. in the section...............................
Mineral possibilities as suggested by Tables 10-2, 10-3, 10-4, 10-5, and 10-7
    10-2.................... 10-3................... 10-4....................
    10-5........................... 10-7.................................
Optical character
    Uniaxial + ...   − ....   Biaxial + ...   − ....   Estimated $2V$...........
                                                         Dispersion.............
Optical orientation data..
Mineral identification as suggested by Tables 10-8, 10-9, and Charts B, C, D, E, F, and G...
Associated minerals..
Conclusion (verified by reference to mineral descriptions in Part 2)..............
....

  * Opaque minerals may be identified by reference to Table 10-1.

TABLE 10-1. OPAQUE MINERALS

Color with reflected light	Mineral	Comment
Black	Graphite, C	Frequently occurs in thin flakes or scattered specks with micaceous cleavage. Carbonaceous matter may occur as fine black inclusions.
Brass yellow	Pyrite, FeS_2	Euhedral crystals are common with square, triangular, or rectangular sections. Cleavage indistinct or absent. High relief due to hardness.
Bronze to copper red	Pyrrhotite, FeS(S)	Found in masses or bladed crystals. Basal parting ‖ to {0001}. Darker color than pyrite.
Strong brass yellow	Chalcopyrite, $CuFeS_2$	Found in masses and occasionally in euhedral crystals. Deeper yellow than pyrite and lower relief.
Steel blue, red, or black.	Hematite, Fe_2O_3	Blood red on translucent edges. Occasionally shows parting. Found in euhedral crystals and masses.
Violet black	Ilmenite, $FeTiO_3$	More violet or purple than hematite. Basal parting and flakelike crystals common. Often found with magnetite.
Steel blue black	Magnetite $Fe^{II}Fe_2^{III}O_4$	Octahedral (occasionally dodecahedral) crystals are common. The mineral may have octahedral parting. Frequently a primary mineral.
Iron black to brownish black.	Chromite $(Fe,Mg)(Cr,Al,Fe)_2O_4$	Usually brown on thin edges. Frequently found with serpentine.
Yellow brown	Limonite, $H_2Fe_2O_4(H_2O)_x$	Colloform, pisolitic, porous, and massive aggregates common. Thin, transparent edges are dark between crossed nicols.
White	Leucoxene, TiO_2, etc.	A white, fine-grained opaque alteration product of primary titanium minerals.

TABLE 10-2. COL

		Red	Pink rose	Orange	Brown	Yellow
Isotropic non-pleochroic	Isometric	*Sphalerite* *Spinel* Cliachite Perovskite	*Sodalite* *Fluorite* Perovskite Garnet	Perovskite	Sphalerite *Fluorite* Spinel Collophane Cliachite Perovskite Garnet	*Sodalite* Sphalerite *Fluorite* *Spinel* Collophane *Garnet*
Anisotropic pleochroic[1]	Uniaxial (+)	Rutile			Zircon Cassiterite Rutile	Zircon *Cassiterite* *Rutile* [*Chloritoid*]
	Uniaxial (−)		*Tourmaline* *Corundum*		[*Biotite*] Dravite Stilpnomelane Tourmaline *Apatite*	[*Biotite*] Dravite Stilpnomelane Schorlite *Tourmaline* Jarosite
	Biaxial (+)	Piedmontite Perovskite	*Piedmontite* Titanite *Staurolite* *Clinochlore* Perovskite	*Piedmontite* *Staurolite* Perovskite	*Titanite* *Monazite* Aegirine-augite Chondrodite Perovskite	Piedmontite Titanite Staurolite Monazite Chloritoid *Clinochlore* Aegirine-augite Chondrodite
	Biaxial (±)	Iddingsite			Iddingsite	
	Biaxial (−)	*Allanite*	Hypersthene Andalusite Dumortierite		Biotite Allanite Phlogopite Basaltic Hornblende *Aegirine* *Hypersthene* Hornblende	Biotite Epidote *Glaucophane* Allanite Phlogopite Actinolite *Glauconite*

Note: Italics indicate lesser examples; brackets, occasional examples. Colored minerals, although

ORED MINERALS

Green	Blue	Violet	Gray	Black
	Sodalite		*Sodalite*	
Fluorite	Fluorite	Fluorite		
Spinel	Spinel			Spinel
			Cliachite	
Perovskite		*Perovskite*	*Perovskite*	
Garnet				*Garnet*
	Lazurite			
			Zircon	
			Cassiterite	
Rutile	*Rutile*	*Rutile*	*Rutile*	
[*Chloritoid*]	[*Chloritoid*]			
[*Chlorite*]	[*Chlorite*]			
[*Biotite*]				
Stilpnomelane				
Schorlite	Schorlite	Schorlite	Schorlite	Schorlite
Tourmaline				
	Corundum	Corundum		
Apatite	*Apatite*		Apatite	
		Piedmontite		
Sphene			*Sphene*	*Sphene*
Chloritoid	Chloritoid			
Chlorite				
Aegirine-augite				
Perovskite		*Perovskite*	*Perovskite*	
Crocidolite	Crocidolite	*Crocidolite*		
Chlorite	Chlorite			
Riebeckite	Riebeckite			
Biotite				
Epidote	*Epidote*			
	Glaucophane	Glaucophane	*Glaucophane*	
Lamprobolite				
Aegirine				*Aegirine*
Hypersthene				
Actinolite				
Glauconite				*Glauconite*
	Dumortierite	Dumortierite		
Hornblende				
	Cordierite			
	Lazulite			

normally pleochroic, may fail to vary in color with rotation under exceptional circumstances.

TABLE 10-3. FORM[1]

Minerals Found in Euhedral Crystals

cc = very common   c = common   r = rare   rr = very rare

Isometric	Tetragonal	Hexagonal	Orthorhombic	Monoclinic	Triclinic
Pyrite c	Rutile c	Quartz c	Celestite r	Gibbsite r	Microcline r
Fluorite r	Cassiterite c	Corundum c	Forsterite c	Monazite r	Plagioclase c
Spinel r	Melilite c	Calcite r	Olivine c	Lazulite rr	
Magnetite c	Idocrase c	Dolomite r	Fayalite c	Orthoclase c	
Perovskite c	Zircon c	Jarosite rr	Monticellite c	Sanidine cc	
Leucite cc	Scapolite r	Alunite rr	Topaz r	Adularia c	
Sodalite c		Apatite cc	Andalusite r	Aegirine-augite c	
Haüyne c		Dahllite c	Staurolite c	Spodumene c	
Garnet cc		Cancrinite r	Lawsonite r	Jadeite rr	
Analcime r		Tourmaline r	Dumortierite r	Lamprobolite cc	
		Chabazite c		Sphene c	
		Nepheline r		Epidote c	
				Pyroxene c	
				Amphibole c	

Form of Individual Crystals

Equant grains	Acicular	Lathlike	Columnar
Fluorite	Rutile	Ilmenite	Quartz
Quartz	Aragonite	Aragonite	Corundum
Periclase	Sillimanite	Barite	Orthoclase
Rutile	Dumortierite	Celestite	Sanidine
Cassiterite	Tourmaline	Gypsum	Microcline
Spinel	Stilbite	Aegirine	Anorthoclase
Magnetite	Natrolite	Mullite	Plagioclase
Chromite		Dumortierite	Nepheline
Anhydrite		Tourmaline	Cancrinite
Apatite		Epidote	Pyroxene
Leucite		Piedmontite	Spodumene
Sodalite		Prehnite	Wollastonite
Haüyne		Pyrophyllite	Amphibole
Melilite		Kyanite	Glaucophane
Forsterite			Beryl
Olivine			Scapolite
Fayalite			Idocrase
Chondrodite			Topaz
Garnet			Kyanite
Zircon			Zoisite
Topaz			Clinozoisite
Andalusite			Staurolite
Axinite			Micas
Allanite			Chlorites
Cordierite			Barite
Sphene			
Lawsonite			
Glauconite			
Analcime			

[1] As observed in thin section.

TABLE 10-3. FORM (*Continued*)

Forms of Crystal Aggregates

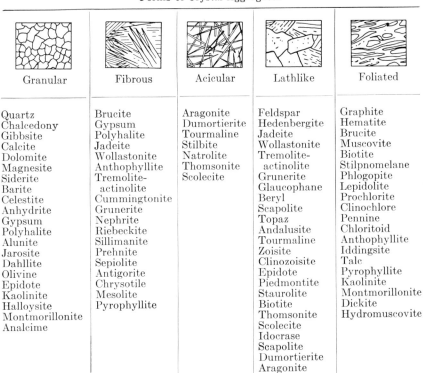

Granular	Fibrous	Acicular	Lathlike	Foliated
Quartz	Brucite	Aragonite	Feldspar	Graphite
Chalcedony	Gypsum	Dumortierite	Hedenbergite	Hematite
Gibbsite	Polyhalite	Tourmaline	Jadeite	Brucite
Calcite	Jadeite	Stilbite	Wollastonite	Muscovite
Dolomite	Wollastonite	Natrolite	Tremolite-	Biotite
Magnesite	Anthophyllite	Thomsonite	actinolite	Stilpnomelane
Siderite	Tremolite-	Scolecite	Grunerite	Phlogopite
Barite	actinolite		Glaucophane	Lepidolite
Celestite	Cummingtonite		Beryl	Prochlorite
Anhydrite	Grunerite		Scapolite	Clinochlore
Gypsum	Nephrite		Topaz	Pennine
Polyhalite	Riebeckite		Andalusite	Chlorite
Alunite	Sillimanite		Tourmaline	Anthophyllite
Jarosite	Prehnite		Zoisite	Iddingsite
Dahllite	Sepiolite		Clinozoisite	Talc
Olivine	Antigorite		Epidote	Pyrophyllite
Epidote	Chrysotile		Piedmontite	Kaolinite
Kaolinite	Mesolite		Staurolite	Montmorillonite
Halloysite	Pyrophyllite		Biotite	Dickite
Montmorillonite			Thomsonite	Hydromuscovite
Analcime			Scolecite	
			Idocrase	
			Scapolite	
			Dumortierite	
			Aragonite	

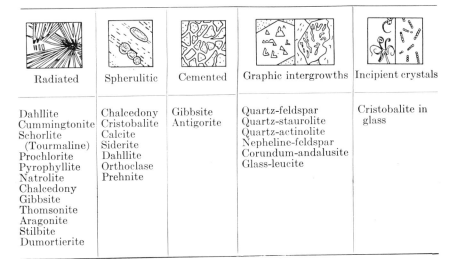

Radiated	Spherulitic	Cemented	Graphic intergrowths	Incipient crystals
Dahllite	Chalcedony	Gibbsite	Quartz-feldspar	Cristobalite in
Cummingtonite	Cristobalite	Antigorite	Quartz-staurolite	glass
Schorlite	Calcite		Quartz-actinolite	
(Tourmaline)	Siderite		Nepheline-feldspar	
Prochlorite	Dahllite		Corundum-andalusite	
Pyrophyllite	Orthoclase		Glass-leucite	
Natrolite	Prehnite			
Chalcedony				
Gibbsite				
Thomsonite				
Aragonite				
Stilbite				
Dumortierite				

TABLE 10-3. FORM (*Concluded*)

Structures

Shatter cracks	Shards	Perlitic cracks	Lithophysae	Flow (with phenocrysts)
Glass Halloysite Opal	Glass Montmorillonite	Glass	Tridymite	Lechatelierite Glass

Banded	Colloform	Oolitic	Pisolitic	Organic structures

Lechatelierite
Dahllite
Chalcedony
Opal
Calcite
Aragonite
Barite
Fluorite
	Opal
	Siderite
	Collophane
	Halloysite
		Limonite
		Calcite
		Siderite
		Collophane
		Chamosite
		Palagonite
			Cliachite
			Limonite
				Bone (*a*):
				  Collophane
				Cellular (*b*):
				  Chalcedony
				  Opal
				  Quartz
				
				Microfossil
				  replacement
				
				Opal
				Calcite
				Aragonite
				Dolomite
				Collophane
				Glauconite
				Chalcedony

TABLE 10-4. CLEAVAGE

P = perfect D = distinct

Minerals with Cleavage in One Direction

Index	Relief	Double refraction 0.01 or less	Double refraction 0.01–0.03	Double refraction 0.03 or greater
$n \vee$ balsam	Low	Stilbite (010)P Heulandite (010)P Thomsonite (010)D Gypsum (010)P	Montmorillonite (001)D	
$n \wedge$ balsam	Low	Kaolinite (001)D Dickite (001)D Chlorite (001)P	Cordierite (010)D Gibbsite (001)D Alunite (0001)D Brucite (0001)P Polyhalite (100)D	
	Low to moderate		Cancrinite (10$\bar{1}$0)D	Prehnite (001)D Pyrophyllite (001)P Talc (001)P Muscovite (001)P Lepidolite (001)P
	Moderate to high	Topaz (001)P Zoisite (010)P Clinozoisite (001)P Staurolite (010)D Chloritoid (001)P Corundum (0001) parting	Prehnite (001)D Glauconite (001)P Sillimanite (100)P Mullite (100)D Dumortierite (100)D	Phlogopite (001)P Biotite (001)P Stilpnomelane (001)P Chondrodite (001)P Epidote (001)P Piedmontite D Jarosite (0001)D Monazite (001) (parting)

Minerals with Cleavage in Two Directions

Index	Relief			
$n \vee$ balsam	Low	Mesolite (110)P(1$\bar{1}$0)P Scolecite (110)D Orthoclase (001)P(010)D Sanidine (001)P(010)D Anorthoclase (001)P(010)D Microcline (001)P(010)D Albite (001)P(010)D	Natrolite (110)P	
	Low	Plagioclase (001)P(010)D	Scapolite (110)D	
$n \wedge$ balsam	Moderate to high	Enstatite (110)P Andalusite (110)D Riebeckite (110)P	Tremolite-actinolite (110)P Anthophyllite (110) Glaucophane (110)P Wollastonite (100)P(001)D Hornblende (110)P Cummingtonite (110)P Jadeite (110)P Hedenbergite (110)P Augite (110)P Enstatite (110)P Hypersthene (110)P Aegirine-augite (110)P Spodumene (110)P	Diopside (110)P Grunerite (110)P Pigeonite (110)P Aegirine (110)P Lamprobolite (110)P Rutile (110)D Sphene (parting)

TABLE 10-4. CLEAVAGE (*Concluded*)

Minerals with Cleavage in Three or More Directions

Index	Relief	Double refraction 0.01 or less	Double refraction 0.01–0.03	Double refraction 0.03 or greater
		Three directions (miscellaneous types)		
$n >$ balsam	Low relief	Halite (100)P (isotropic)	Scapolite (100)P(110)D Ext. parallel or sym. Celestite (001)P(110)D	Anhydrite (001)(010)(100)P Ext. parallel
	Moderate to high relief	Axinite (001)(130)(010)D Inclined Ext. Corundum (1011) (parting)	Barite (001)(110)P Ext. parallel or sym. Lawsonite (010)P(110)D Kyanite (110)(010)P(001) parting; Inclined ext.	Diaspore (010)(210)P Ext. parallel or sym. Iddingsite (100)(010)(001)D Ext. parallel
	Extreme relief	Periclase (100)P(isotropic) Perovskite (100)P(isotropic)		Rutile (100)(110)D Ext. parallel or sym.

Three directions (rhombohedral carbonates)

Calcite Dolomite Magnesite Siderite	All minerals in this group exhibit the following: Variation in relief with direction moderate to high. Very high double refraction. 0.172 (calcite)–0.234 (siderite). Usually twinned. Uniaxial negative. Cleavage rhombohedral.

Special cases

Isotropic		$n <$ balsam $n >$ balsam	Fluorite (111) octahedral Spinel (111) octahedral parting Sphalerite (110)P dodecahedral cleavage
Anisotropic	$n >$ balsam	Relief low	Nepheline (10$\bar{1}$0)D (hexagonal)

TABLE 10-5. INDICES OF REFRACTION

The indices of refraction n, n_α, n_γ, n_ϵ, and n_ω are abbreviated n, α, γ, ϵ, and ω.

Index		Mineral	Index		Mineral
1.40–1.46	n	Opal	1.525–1.530	γ	Microcline
1.434	n	Fluorite	1.525–1.532	α	Albite
1.458–1.462	n	Lechatelierite	1.526	γ	Orthoclase
1.469	α	Tridymite	1.527–1.543	ϵ	Nepheline
1.47–1.63	n	Palagonite	1.527–1.541	γ	Anorthoclase
1.473–1.480	α	Natrolite	1.529	γ	Gypsum
1.473	γ	Tridymite	1.530	α	Aragonite
1.478–1.485	α	Chabazite	1.530–1.547	ω	Nepheline
1.48–1.61	n	Volcanic glass	1.531	α	Chalcedony
1.480–1.490	γ	Chabazite	1.532–1.545	α	Oligoclase
1.483–1.487	n	Sodalite	1.532–1.552	α	Cordierite
1.484	α	Cristobalite	1.533	γ	Palygorskite
1.485–1.493	γ	Natrolite	1.535–1.570	α	Hydromuscovite
1.486	ϵ	Calcite	1.536–1.541	γ	Albite
1.487	n	Analcime	1.538–1.545	α	Talc
1.487	γ	Cristobalite	1.539	γ	Chalcedony
1.490–1.506	α	Sepiolite	1.539–1.570	γ	Cordierite
1.492	α	Montmorillonite	1.540–1.571	ϵ	Scapolite
1.493–1.546	α	Chrysotile	1.541–1.552	γ	Oligoclase
1.494–1.500	α	Stilbite	1.541–1.579	α	Biotite
1.496–1.499	α	Heulandite	1.544	n	Halite
1.496–1.500	ϵ	Cancrinite	1.5442	ω	Quartz
1.496–1.510	n	Haüyne	1.545–1.555	α	Andesine
1.500–1.508	γ	Stilbite	1.548	α	Polyhalite
1.500–1.526	ϵ	Dolomite	1.549–1.561	n	Halloysite
1.50–1.57	n	Antigorite (Serpophite)	1.550–1.607	ω	Scapolite
1.501–1.505	γ	Heulandite	1.551–1.562	α	Phlogopite
1.505	α	Mesolite	1.552	α	Pyrophyllite
1.505–1.526	γ	Sepiolite	1.552–1.562	γ	Andesine
1.506	γ	Mesolite	1.5533	ϵ	Quartz
1.507–1.524	ω	Cancrinite	1.554–1.567	ω	Gibbsite
1.508	α	Leucite	1.555–1.563	α	Labradorite
1.509	γ	Leucite	1.555–1.564	α	Antigorite
1.509–1.527	ϵ	Magnesite	1.556–1.570	α	Muscovite
1.510	α	Palygorskite	1.560	α	Lepidolite
1.512	α	Scolecite	1.560	α	Dickite
1.512–1.530	α	Thomsonite	1.561	α	Kaolinite
1.513	γ	Montmorillonite	1.562–1.571	γ	Labradorite
1.517–1.520	α	Sanidine	1.562–1.573	γ	Antigorite
1.517–1.557	γ	Chrysotile	1.563–1.571	α	Bytownite
1.518	α	Orthoclase	1.564–1.590	ϵ	Beryl
1.518–1.522	α	Microcline	1.565–1.605	γ	Hydromuscovite
1.518–1.542	γ	Thomsonite	1.566	ω	Brucite
1.519	γ	Scolecite	1.566	γ	Dickite
1.520	α	Gypsum	1.566	γ	Kaolinite
1.522–1.536	α	Anorthoclase	1.567	γ	Polyhalite
1.524–1.526	γ	Sanidine	1.568–1.598	ω	Beryl

TABLE 10-5. INDICES OF REFRACTION (*Continued*)

Index		Mineral	Index		Mineral
1.570	α	Anhydrite	1.628–1.658	ϵ	Schorlite (Tourmaline)
1.57–1.61	n	Cliachite	1.629–1.640	α	Andalusite
1.57–1.62	n	Collophane	1.630–1.651	ϵ	Apatite
1.571–1.575	α	Anorthite	1.631	γ	Celestite
1.571–1.582	γ	Bytownite	1.632–1.634	ω	Melilite
1.571–1.588	α	Clinochlore	1.632–1.655	ω	Dravite (Tourmaline)
1.572	ω	Alunite	1.633–1.655	ω	Apatite
1.574–1.638	γ	Biotite	1.633–1.701	γ	Hornblende
1.575–1.582	α	Pennine	1.634	γ	Wollastonite
1.575–1.590	γ	Talc	1.635	n	Chamosite
1.576–1.583	γ	Pennine	1.635–1.640	α	Forsterite
1.576–1.589	γ	Gibbsite	1.635–1.655	ω	Elbaite (Tourmaline)
1.576–1.597	γ	Clinochlore	1.636	α	Barite
1.582–1.588	γ	Anorthite	1.639–1.642	γ	Lazulite
1.585	ϵ	Brucite	1.639–1.647	γ	Andalusite
1.588–1.658	α	Prochlorite	1.639–1.657	α	Cummingtonite
1.590–1.612	α	Glauconite	1.639–1.668	γ	Glaucophane
1.592	ϵ	Alunite	1.64–1.77	α	Allanite
1.592–1.643	α	Chondrodite	1.641–1.651	α	Monticellite
1.593–1.611	γ	Muscovite	1.642	α	Mullite
1.596–1.633	ϵ	Siderite	1.645–1.665	γ	Prehnite
1.598–1.606	γ	Phlogopite	1.648	γ	Barite
1.598–1.652	α	Anthophyllite	1.650–1.665	α	Enstatite
1.599–1.667	γ	Prochlorite	1.650–1.698	α	Diopside
1.600	γ	Pyrophyllite	1.651–1.668	α	Spodumene
1.600–1.628	α	Nephrite	1.651–1.681	α	Olivine
1.600–1.628	α	Tremolite-actinolite	1.652–1.698	ω	Schorlite (Tourmaline)
1.603–1.604	α	Lazulite	1.654	γ	Mullite
1.605	γ	Lepidolite	1.655–1.666	α	Jadeite
1.607–1.629	α	Topaz	1.655–1.669	γ	Monticellite
1.610–1.644	γ	Glauconite	1.657–1.661	α	Sillimanite
1.612–1.634	α	Stilpnomelane	1.657–1.663	α	Grunerite
1.613–1.628	ϵ	Dravite (Tourmaline)	1.658	ω	Calcite
1.614	γ	Anhydrite	1.658–1.674	γ	Enstatite
1.614–1.675	α	Hornblende	1.659–1.678	α	Dumortierite
1.615–1.629	ϵ	Elbaite (Tourmaline)	1.66–1.80	γ	Allanite
1.615–1.635	α	Prehnite	1.664–1.686	γ	Cummingtonite
1.617–1.638	γ	Topaz	1.665	α	Lawsonite
1.619–1.626	ϵ	Dahllite	1.667–1.688	γ	Jadeite
1.620	α	Wollastonite	1.670–1.680	γ	Forsterite
1.621–1.655	α	Glaucophane	1.670–1.692	α	Lamprobolite
1.621–1.670	γ	Chondrodite	1.673–1.715	α	Hypersthene
1.622	α	Celestite	1.674–1.730	α	Iddingsite
1.623–1.635	ω	Dahllite	1.677–1.681	γ	Spodumene
1.623–1.676	γ	Anthophyllite	1.677–1.684	γ	Sillimanite
1.625–1.655	γ	Nephrite	1.678–1.684	α	Axinite
1.625–1.655	γ	Tremolite-actinolite	1.680–1.716	ω	Dolomite
1.626–1.629	ϵ	Melilite	1.680–1.718	α	Pigeonite

TABLE 10-5. INDICES OF REFRACTION (*Concluded*)

Index		Mineral	Index		Mineral
1.680–1.745	α	Aegirine-augite	1.736–1.763	n	Grossularite
1.681–1.727	γ	Diopside	1.738–1.760	n	Periclase
1.683–1.731	γ	Hypersthene	1.741–1.760	n	Pyrope
1.684	γ	Lawsonite	1.745–1.758	α	Piedmontite
1.686	γ	Aragonite	1.745–1.777	α	Aegirine
1.686–1.692	γ	Dumortierite	1.746–1.762	γ	Staurolite
1.688–1.696	γ	Axinite	1.750	γ	Diaspore
1.688–1.712	α	Augite	1.751–1.757	γ	Hedenbergite
1.689–1.718	γ	Olivine	1.759–1.763	ε	Corundum
1.693	α	Riebeckite	1.767–1.772	ω	Corundum
1.693–1.760	γ	Lamprobolite	1.778–1.815	n	Almandite
1.696–1.700	α	Zoisite	1.782–1.836	γ	Aegirine
1.697	γ	Riebeckite	1.786–1.800	α	Monazite
1.699–1.717	γ	Grunerite	1.792–1.820	n	Spessartite
1.700–1.726	ω	Magnesite	1.805–1.835	α	Fayalite
1.700–1.745	γ	Stilpnomelane	1.806–1.832	γ	Piedmontite
1.701–1.726	ε	Idocrase	1.820	ω	Jarosite
1.702	α	Diaspore	1.830–1.875	ω	Siderite
1.702–1.718	γ	Zoisite	1.837–1.849	γ	Monazite
1.705–1.732	ω	Idocrase	1.838–1.870	n	Uvarovite
1.709–1.782	γ	Aegirine-augite	1.847–1.886	γ	Fayalite
1.710–1.723	α	Clinozoisite	1.857–1.887	n	Andradite
1.712	α	Kyanite	1.887–1.913	α	Sphene
1.713–1.737	γ	Augite	1.925–1.931	ω	Zircon
1.715	ε	Jarosite	1.979–2.054	γ	Sphene
1.715–1.724	α	Chloritoid	1.985–1.993	ε	Zircon
1.718–1.768	γ	Iddingsite	1.996	ω	Cassiterite
1.719–1.734	γ	Clinozoisite	2.00–2.10	n	Limonite
1.719–1.744	γ	Pigeonite	2.07–2.16	n	Chromite
1.72–1.78	n	Spinel	2.093	ε	Cassiterite
1.720–1.734	α	Epidote	2.34–2.38	n	Perovskite
1.728	γ	Kyanite	2.37–2.47	n	Sphalerite
1.731–1.737	γ	Chloritoid	2.603–2.616	ω	Rutile
1.732–1.739	α	Hedenbergite	2.889–2.903	ε	Rutile
1.734–1.779	γ	Epidote	2.94	ε	Hematite
1.736–1.747	α	Staurolite	3.22	ω	Hematite

TABLE 10-6. ISOTROPIC MINERALS

Relief	Mineral	Index
Moderate relief	Opal	1.40 –1.46
	Fluorite	1.434
	Lechatelierite	1.458–1.462
	Sodalite	1.483–1.487
	Analcime	1.487
	Haüyne	1.496–1.510
	Balsam = 1.537	
Low relief	Halite	1.544
	Halloysite	1.549–1.561
	Antigorite (Serpophite)	1.50 –1.57
	Cliachite	1.57 –1.61
	Collophane	1.57 –1.62
Moderate to strong relief	Periclase	1.738–1.760
	Grossularite ⎱	1.736–1.763
	Pyrope ⎰	1.741–1.760
	Almandite ⎱ *Garnet group*	1.778–1.815
	Spessartite ⎰	1.792–1.820
	Uvarovite ⎱	1.838–1.870
	Andradite ⎰	1.857–1.887
Very high relief	Limonite	2.00 –2.10
	Spinel	1.72 –1.78
	Chromite	2.07 –2.16
	Perovskite	2.34 –2.38
	Sphalerite	2.37 –2.47
	Volcanic glass (mineraloid)	1.48 –1.61
	Palagonite (mineraloid)	1.47 –1.63

TABLE 10-7. BIREFRINGENCE

Birefringence	Mineral	Birefringence	Mineral
0.00 –0.002	Analcime (possibly)	0.009	Quartz
0.00 –0.002	Perovskite	0.009–0.010	Topaz
0.00 –0.003	Antigorite (Serpophite)	0.009–0.011	Albite
0.00 –0.004	Haüyne (occas.)	0.010–0.012	Axinite
0.001	Leucite	0.010–0.015	Staurolite
0.001	Mesolite	0.010–0.016	Hypersthene
0.001	Halloysite	0.01–0.03	Allanite
0.001–0.004	Pennine	0.010–0.036	Scapolite
0.001–0.011	Prochlorite	0.011–0.013	Anorthite
0.002–0.010	Chabazite	0.011–0.014	Chrysotile
0.003	Cristobalite	0.011–0.020	Dumortierite
0.003–0.004	Apatite	0.012	Barite
0.003–0.004	Nepheline	0.012	Mullite
0.004	Tridymite	0.012–0.013	Natrolite
0.004	Riebeckite	0.012–0.023	Jadeite
0.004–0.006	Idocrase	0.013–0.016	Chloritoid
0.004–0.008	Beryl	0.013–0.018	Glaucophane
0.004–0.009	Dahllite	0.013–0.027	Spodumene
0.004–0.011	Clinochlore	0.014	Wollastonite
0.005	Collophane	0.014–0.018	Monticellite
0.005	Kaolinite	0.014–0.045	Epidote
0.005–0.006	Melilite	0.015–0.020	Sepiolite
0.005–0.007	Anorthoclase	0.015–0.023	Elbaite (Tourmaline)
0.005–0.011	Clinozoisite	0.016	Kyanite
0.006	Dickite	0.016–0.025	Anthophyllite
0.006–0.008	Stilbite	0.018–0.019	Hedenbergite
0.006–0.012	Thomsonite	0.019	Brucite
0.006–0.018	Zoisite	0.019	Lawsonite
0.007	Sanidine	0.019	Polyhalite
0.007	Heulandite	0.019–0.025	Dravite (Tourmaline)
0.007	Andesine	0.019–0.026	Hornblende
0.007	Scolecite	0.020	Alunite
0.007	Microcline	0.020–0.023	Sillimanite
0.007–0.008	Chamosite	0.020–0.032	Glauconite
0.007–0.008	Labradorite	0.020–0.033	Prehnite
0.007–0.009	Antigorite	0.021	Montmorillonite
0.007–0.009	Oligoclase	0.021–0.025	Augite
0.007–0.011	Andalusite	0.021–0.033	Pigeonite
0.007–0.011	Cordierite	0.022	Gibbsite
0.007–0.028	Cancrinite	0.022–0.027	Nephrite
0.008	Chalcedony	0.022–0.027	Tremolite-actinolite
0.008	Orthoclase	0.022–0.040	Schorlite (Tourmaline)
0.008–0.009	Corundum	0.023	Palygorskite
0.008–0.009	Enstatite	0.025–0.029	Cummingtonite
0.008–0.011	Bytownite	0.026–0.072	Lamprobolite
0.009	Celestite	0.027–0.035	Chondrodite
0.009	Gypsum	0.029–0.031	Diopside

TABLE 10-7. BIREFRINGENCE (*Concluded*)

Birefringence	Mineral	Birefringence	Mineral
0.029–0.037	Aegirine-augite	0.045	Lepidolite
0.030–0.035	Hydromuscovite	0.048	Diaspore
0.030–0.050	Talc	0.048	Pyrophyllite
0.030–0.119	Stilpnomelane	0.049–0.051	Monazite
0.033–0.059	Biotite	0.060–0.062	Zircon
0.035–0.040	Forsterite	0.061–0.082	Piedmontite
0.036–0.038	Lazulite	0.092–0.141	Sphene
0.037–0.041	Olivine	0.097	Cassiterite
0.037–0.041	Muscovite	0.105	Jarosite
0.037–0.059	Aegirine	0.156	Aragonite
0.038–0.044	Iddingsite	0.172	Calcite
0.042–0.051	Fayalite	0.180–0.190	Dolomite
0.042–0.054	Grunerite	0.191–0.199	Magnesite
0.044	Anhydrite	0.234–0.242	Siderite
0.044–0.047	Phlogopite	0.286–0.287	Rutile

TABLE 10-8. UNIAXIAL MINERALS

Mineral	n_ϵ	n_ω	Sign	Birefringence
Calcite	1.486	1.658	−	0.172
Cancrinite	1.496–1.500	1.507–1.524	−	0.007–0.028
Dolomite	1.500–1.526	1.680–1.716	−	0.180–0.190
Magnesite	1.509–1.527	1.700–1.726	−	0.191–0.199
Nepheline	1.527–1.543	1.530–1.547	−	0.003–0.004
Scapolite	1.540–1.571	1.550–1.607	−	0.010–0.036
Beryl	1.564–1.590	1.568–1.598	−	0.004–0.008
Siderite	1.596–1.633	1.830–1.875	−	0.234–0.242
Stilpnomelane	1.612–1.634	1.700–1.745	−	0.030–0.119
Dravite (Tourmaline)	1.613–1.628	1.632–1.655	−	0.019–0.025
Elbaite (Tourmaline)	1.615–1.629	1.635–1.655	−	0.015–0.023
Dahllite	1.619–1.626	1.623–1.635	−	0.004–0.009
Melilite	1.626–1.629	1.632–1.634	−	0.005–0.006
Schorlite (Tourmaline)	1.628–1.658	1.652–1.698	−	0.022–0.040
Apatite	1.630–1.651	1.633–1.655	−	0.003–0.004
Idocrase	1.701–1.726	1.705–1.732	−	0.004–0.006
Jarosite	1.715	1.820	−	0.105
Corundum	1.759–1.763	1.767–1.772	−	0.008–0.009
Hematite	2.94	3.22	−	

Mineral	n_ω	n_ϵ	Sign	Birefringence
Quartz	1.5442	1.5533	+	0.009
Brucite	1.566	1.585	+	0.019
Alunite	1.572	1.592	+	0.020
Zircon	1.925–1.931	1.985–1.993	+	0.060–0.062
Cassiterite	1.996	2.093	+	0.097
Rutile	2.603–2.616	2.889–2.903	+	0.286–0.287

TABLE 10-9. BIAXIAL POSITIVE MINERALS

Mineral	n_α	n_β	n_λ	Birefringence
Tridymite	1.469	1.469	1.473	0.004
Natrolite	1.473–1.480	1.476–1.482	1.485–1.493	0.012–0.013
Chabazite	1.478–1.485		1.480–1.490	0.002–0.010
Chrysotile	1.493–1.546	1.504–1.550	1.517–1.557	0.011–0.014
Heulandite	1.496–1.499	1.497–1.501	1.501–1.505	0.007
Mesolite	1.505	1.505	1.506	0.001
Thomsonite	1.512–1.530	1.513–1.532	1.518–1.542	0.006–0.012
Gypsum	1.520	1.522	1.529	0.009
Albite	1.525–1.532	1.529–1.536	1.536–1.541	0.009–0.011
Oligoclase	1.532–1.545	1.536–1.548	1.541–1.552	0.007–0.009
Cordierite	1.532–1.552	1.536–1.562	1.539–1.570	0.007–0.011
Andesine	1.545–1.555	1.548–1.558	1.552–1.562	0.007
Gibbsite	1.554–1.567	1.554–1.567	1.576–1.589	0.022
Labradorite	1.555–1.563	1.558–1.567	1.562–1.571	0.007–0.008
Dickite	1.560	1.562	1.566	0.006
Anhydrite	1.570	1.576	1.614	0.044
Clinochlore	1.571–1.588	1.571–1.588	1.576–1.597	0.004–0.011
Pennine	1.575–1.582	1.576–1.582	1.576–1.583	0.001–0.004
Prochlorite	1.588–1.658	1.589–1.667	1.599–1.667	0.001–0.011
Chondrodite	1.592–1.643	1.602–1.655	1.621–1.670	0 027–0.035
Anthophyllite	1.598–1.652	1.615–1.662	1.623–1.676	0.016–0.025
Topaz	1.607–1.629	1.610–1.631	1.617–1 638	0.009–0.010
Prehnite	1.615–1.635	1.624–1.642	1.645–1 665	0.020–0.033
Celestite	1.622	1.624	1.631	0.009
Forsterite	1.635–1.640	1.651–1.660	1.670–1.680	0.035–0.040
Barite	1.636	1.637	1.648	0.012
Cummingtonite	1.639–1.657	1.645–1.669	1.664–1.686	0.025–0.029
Mullite	1.642	1.644	1.654	0.012
Enstatite	1.650–1.665	1.653–1.670	1.658–1.674	0.008–0.009
Diopside	1.650–1.698	1.657–1.706	1.681–1.727	0.029–0.031
Spodumene	1.651–1.668	1.665–1.675	1.677–1.681	0.013–0.027
Olivine	1.651–1.681	1.670–1.706	1.689–1.718	0.037–0.041
Jadeite	1.655–1.666	1.659–1.674	1.667–1.688	0.012–0.023
Sillimanite	1.657–1.661	1.658–1.670	1.677–1.684	0.020–0.023
Lawsonite	1.665	1.674	1.684	0.019
Iddingsite	1.674–1.730	1.715–1.763	1.718–1.768	0.038–0.044
Aegirine-augite	1.680–1.745	1.687–1.770	1.709–1.782	0.029–0.037
Pigeonite	1.680–1.718	1.698–1.725	1.719–1.744	0.021–0.033
Augite	1.688–1.712	1.701–1.717	1.713–1.737	0.021–0.025
Zoisite	1.696–1.700	1.696–1.703	1.702–1.718	0.006–0.018
Diaspore	1.702	1.722	1.750	0.048
Clinozoisite	1.710–1.723	1.715–1.729	1.719–1.734	0.005–0.011
Chloritoid	1.715–1.724	1.719–1.726	1.731–1.737	0.013–0.016
Hedenbergite	1.732–1.739	1.737–1.745	1.751–1.757	0.018–0.019
Staurolite	1.736–1.747	1.741–1.754	1.746–1.762	0.010–0.015
Piedmontite	1.745–1.758	1.764–1.789	1.806–1.832	0.061–0.082
Monazite	1.786–1.800	1.788–1.801	1.837–1.849	0.049–0.051
Sphene	1.887–1.913	1.894–1.921	1.979–2.054	0.092–0.141

TABLE 10-10. BIAXIAL NEGATIVE MINERALS

Mineral	n_α	n_β	n_λ	Birefringence
Sepiolite	1.490–1.506	....	1.505–1.526	0.015–0.020
Montmorillonite	1.492	1.513	1.513	0.021
Stilbite	1.494–1.500	1.498–1.504	1.500–1.508	0.006–0.008
Scolecite	1.512	1.519	1.519	0.007
Sanidine	1.517–1.520	1.523–1.525	1.524–1.526	0.007
Orthoclase	1.518	1.524	1.526	0.008
Microcline	1.518–1.522	1.522–1.526	1.525–1.530	0.007
Anorthoclase	1.522–1.536	1.526–1.539	1.527–1.541	0.005–0.007
Aragonite	1.530	1.682	1.686	0.156
Oligoclase	1.532–1.545	1.536–1.548	1.541–1.552	0.007–0.009
Cordierite	1.532–1.552	1.536–1.562	1.539–1.570	0.007–0.011
Hydromuscovite	1.535–1.570	....	1.565–1.605	0.030–0.035
Talc	1.538–1.545	1.575–1.590	1.575–1.590	0.030–0.050
Biotite	1.541–1.579	1.574–1.638	1.574–1.638	0.033–0.059
Andesine	1.545–1.555	1.548–1.558	1.552–1.562	0.007
Polyhalite	1.548	1.562	1.567	0.019
Phlogopite	1.551–1.562	1.598–1.606	1.598–1.606	0.044–0.047
Pyrophyllite	1.552	1.588	1.600	0.048
Antigorite	1.555–1.564	1.562–1.573	1.562–1.573	0.007–0.009
Muscovite	1.556–1.570	1.587–1.607	1.593–1.611	0.037–0.041
Lepidolite	1.560	1.598	1.605	0.045
Kaolinite	1.561	1.565	1.566	0.005
Bytownite	1.563–1.571	1.567–1.577	1.571–1.582	0.008–0.011
Anorthite	1.571–1.575	1.577–1.583	1.582–1.588	0.011–0.013
Pennine	1.575–1.582	1.576–1.582	1.576–1.583	0.001–0.004
Glauconite	1.590–1.612	1.609–1.643	1.610–1.644	0.020–0.032
Tremolite-actinolite	1.600–1.628	1.613–1.644	1.625–1.655	0.022–0.027
Nephrite	1.600–1.628	1.613–1.644	1.625–1.655	0.022–0.027
Lazulite	1.603–1.604	1.632–1.633	1.639–1.642	0.036–0.038
Hornblende	1.614–1.675	1.618–1.691	1.633–1.701	0.019–0.026
Wollastonite	1.620	1.632	1.634	0.014
Chamosite	....	1.635	....	0.007–0.008
Glaucophane	1.621–1.655	1.638–1.664	1.639–1.668	0.013–0.018
Andalusite	1.629–1.640	1.633–1.644	1.639–1.647	0.007–0.011
Allanite	1.640–1.770	1.650–1.770	1.660–1.800	0.010–0.030
Monticellite	1.641–1.651	1.646–1.662	1.655–1.669	0.014–0.018
Olivine	1.651–1.681	1.670–1.706	1.689–1.718	0.037–0.041
Grunerite	1.657–1.663	1.684–1.697	1.699–1.717	0.042–0.054
Dumortierite	1.659–1.678	1.684–1.691	1.686–1.692	0.011–0.020
Lamprobolite	1.670–1.692	1.683–1.730	1.693–1.760	0.026–0.072
Hypersthene	1.673–1.715	1.678–1.728	1.683–1.731	0.010–0.016
Iddingsite	1.674–1.730	1.715–1.763	1.718–1.768	0.038–0.044
Axinite	1.678–1.684	1.685–1.692	1.688–1.696	0.010–0.012
Riebeckite	1.693	1.695	1.697	0.004
Kyanite	1.712	1.720	1.728	0.016
Epidote	1.720–1.734	1.724–1.763	1.734–1.779	0.014–0.045
Aegirine	1.745–1.777	1.770–1.823	1.782–1.836	0.037–0.059
Fayalite	1.805–1.835	1.838–1.877	1.847–1.886	0.042–0.051

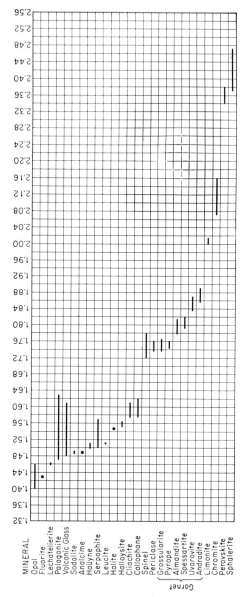

CHART A. Range of Refractive Indices—Isotropic Minerals.

172

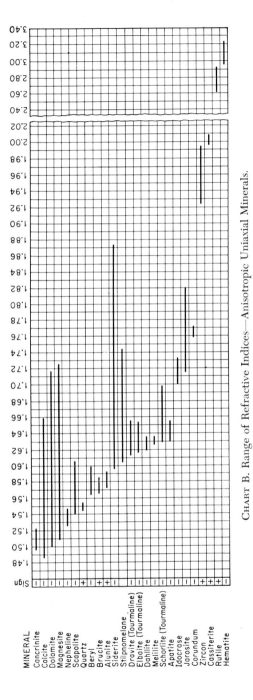

CHART B. Range of Refractive Indices—Anisotropic Uniaxial Minerals.

173

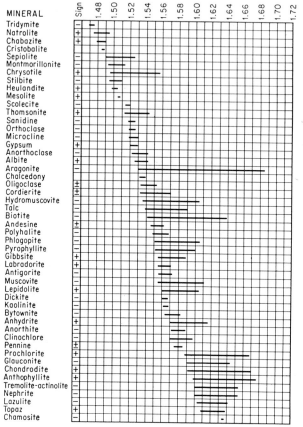

CHART C. Range of Refractive Indices—Anisotropic Biaxial Minerals.

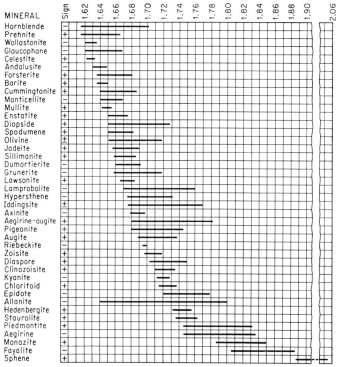

CHART D. Range of Refractive Indices—Anisotropic Biaxial Minerals.

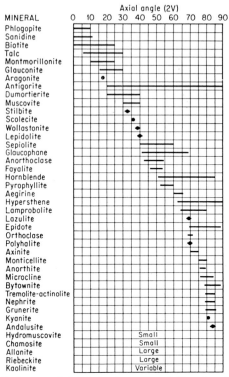

CHART E. Range of Axial Angles—Biaxial Negative Minerals.

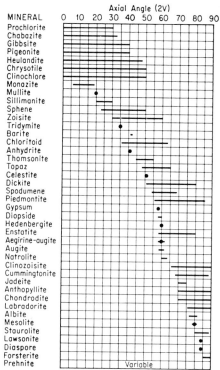

Axial Angle (2V)

MINERAL	0	10	20	30	40	50	60	70	80	90
Prochlorite										
Chabazite										
Gibbsite										
Pigeonite										
Heulandite										
Chrysotile										
Clinochlore										
Monazite										
Mullite										
Sillimanite										
Sphene										
Zoisite										
Tridymite										
Barite										
Chloritoid										
Anhydrite										
Thomsonite										
Topaz										
Celestite										
Dickite										
Spodumene										
Piedmontite										
Gypsum										
Diopside										
Hedenbergite										
Enstatite										
Aegirine-augite										
Augite										
Natrolite										
Clinozoisite										
Cummingtonite										
Jadeite										
Anthopyllite										
Chondrodite										
Labradorite										
Albite										
Mesolite										
Staurolite										
Lawsonite										
Diaspore										
Forsterite										
Prehnite					Variable					

CHART F. Range of Axial Angles—Biaxial Positive Minerals.

Axial Angle (2V)

MINERAL	0	10	20	30	40	50	60	70	80	90
Pennine										
Iddingsite										
Cordierite										
Olivine										
Andesine										
Oligoclase										

CHART G. Range of Axial Angles—Biaxial Positive/Negative Minerals.

PART TWO

Mineral Descriptions

Introduction to Part Two

Approximately 1700 mineral species are recognized. Rock-forming constituents ordinarily found in thin sections constitute a comparatively small proportion of the total. In the following pages descriptions of individual minerals, mineraloids, and mineral groups are given. The species listed include practically all the important transparent minerals found in igneous, sedimentary, and metamorphic rocks, together with the common vein minerals. Minerals other than those listed occasionally are encountered; then the larger reference books should be consulted.

For convenience, the microscopic and optical characteristics of the minerals are given under a uniform sequence of headings. *Color* refers to the color of the mineral in thin section. The term *neutral* is used for very pale colors of indeterminate hue. Pleochroism and absorption are included along with color, for ordinarily the polarizer is in place during the entire examination of the slide. *Relief* refers to ordinary thin sections mounted in Canada balsam or to fragments in immersion media of corresponding index. The interference colors listed are usually the maximum colors for thin sections of about 0.03-mm. thickness. If sections are thicker or thinner than this value, allowance must be made. The thickness may be determined fairly accurately if a known mineral such as quartz or plagioclase is present in the slide. Extinction angles measured clockwise are considered positive; and counterclockwise, negative. *Orientation* refers especially to the position of the faster and slower rays in characteristic sections. The complete optical orientation is given in the tabulation just below the name of the mineral. The size of the axial angle for biaxial crystals is indicated in a general way in the text. Exact values of this angle are given in the tabulation just mentioned. Approximate measurements of the axial angle can be made in favorable cases by the use of a micrometer ocular that has been calibrated by means of several biaxial crystals of known axial angles. The universal stage is useful for accurate determinations. Under the heading *Distinguishing Features* resemblances to, and differences from, similar minerals are pointed out as an aid in the determination. *Related Minerals* are the minerals similar in appearance and properties to the one under discussion.

Orientation diagrams for nearly all the biaxial minerals are given, and

181

for most of the monoclinic minerals plans combined with side views
are inserted in order to facilitate an understanding of their optical
properties. Photomicrographs of thin sections are included to aid in
identification.

MINERAL GROUPS

This text is devoted primarily to the examination of transparent minerals and particularly common minerals encountered in thin sections.
Thus practical considerations cause a number of deviations from accepted
classified mineral lists. The mineral groups listed for the chapters of Part
2 conform essentially to normal usage. However, examination of chapter
headings in Part 2 reveals a pronounced inequality in mineral distribution among the groups named.

The non-silicate minerals from elements to phosphates are covered
in two chapters, while five chapters are required for the silicates. This
reflects the importance of the silicates among rock-forming minerals.

The classification of the silicates is primarily structural. However, all
structures are not known with equal assurance. Also, a number of silicates apparently are amorphous when examined with the microscope,
although they may exhibit evidence of crystallinity in X-ray diffraction
patterns. These species are termed mineraloids. In the classification they
are placed close to chemically related minerals.

The silicates may be divided into six groups which depend upon the
structural arrangement of SiO_4 tetrahedra. A single SiO_4 group consists
of four larger oxygen atoms each at the corner of the tetrahedron with
one smaller silicon atom at the center. The structural groups arranged to
emphasize natural occurrence provide the skeleton of a useful silicate
classification.

Silicate Groups

1. Framework complexes—tectosilicates
    Silica minerals, Feldspars, Feldspathoids, Sodalite group, Zeolites
2. Chain structures—inosilicates
    Pyroxenes, Amphiboles, Epidote group
3. Single tetrahedral groups—nesosilicates
    Olivine group, Garnet group, Zircon, Humite group, Sillimanite
    group, Idocrase, Axinite
4. Multiple tetrahedral groups—sorosilicates
    Lawsonite
5. Ring groups with six units—cyclosilicates
    Beryl, Tourmaline, Cordierite, Wollastonite

6. Sheet structures—phyllosilicates
    Micas, Chlorites, Clay minerals, Talc, Pyrophyllite, Serpentine group

Group names follow the usage of Bragg (1930). The group order selected favors occurrence.

Isomorphous groups are common among minerals. Several species that crystallize in the same way may at the same time form a group that will exhibit a range in chemical composition. The chemical formulas of the group are analogous although each species will represent some chemical substitution. The calcite group is an example, with calcite $CaCO_3$, magnesite $MgCO_3$, siderite $FeCO_3$ and other carbonates alike in hexagonal crystallization but differing in the substitution of Ca, Mg, Fe and other cations in the chemical formulas.

Polymorphism is also frequently recognized among minerals. The same chemical substance as found in nature may crystallize in two or more ways. This applies to $CaCO_3$, which crystallizes in the hexagonal system to form calcite and in the orthorhombic system to form aragonite. Both minerals also belong to isomorphous groups, the calcite group as just indicated and the aragonite group, which in addition to aragonite includes witherite $BaCO_3$, strontianite $SrCO_3$, and cerussite $PbCO_3$.

The oxide TiO_2 is found in three types of crystallization which also illustrate polymorphism. Rutile and anatase are tetragonal but with different structural dimensions, while brookite is orthorhombic.

Both isomorphism and polymorphism will be encountered repeatedly among the minerals described in this text. Among isomorphous groups particular attention should be devoted to the range in optical properties exhibited by group members.

REFERENCES

Bragg, W. L.: The Structure of Silicates, Z. F. Krist., vol. 74, pp. 237–305, 1930.
Chudoba, K.: "Mikroskopische Charakteristik der gesteinsbildenden Mineralien," Herder u. Co., Freiburg, 1932.
————: "Die Feldspäte und ihre praktische Bestimmung," Schweizerbart Verlag, Stuttgart, 1932.
Freund, H.: Mikroskopie der Silikate, "Handbuch der Mikroskopie in der Technik," vol. 4, Umschau Verlag, Frankfurt, 1955.
Hatch, F. H., and A. K. Wells: "The Petrology of the Igneous Rocks," 9th ed., George Allen & Unwin, Ltd., London, 1937.
Iddings, J. P.: "Rock Minerals," 2d ed., John Wiley & Sons, Inc., New York, 1911.
Ingerson, E.: Methods and Problems of Geologic Thermometry, Econ. Geol., 50th ann. vol., pp. 341–410, 1955.

Johannsen, A.: "Essentials for the Microscopical Determination of Rock-forming Minerals and Rocks in Thin Sections," 2d ed., University of Chicago Press, Chicago, 1928.

Kennedy, G. C.: Charts for Correlation of Optical Properties with Chemical Composition of Some Common Rock-forming Minerals, *Am. Mineralogist*, vol. 32, pp. 561–573, 1947.

Larsen, E. S., and H. Berman: The Microscopic Determination of the Non-opaque Minerals, *U.S. Geol. Survey Bull.* 848, Washington, D.C., 1934.

Mason, Brian: "Principles of Geochemistry," John Wiley & Sons, Inc., New York, 1951.

Milner, H. B.: "Sedimentary Petrography," 3d ed., Thomas Murby & Co., London, 1940.

Rosenbusch, H.: "Mikroskopische Physiographie der petrographisch wichtigen Mineralien," rev. by O. Mügge, 5th ed., vol. 1, part 2, Schweizerbart Verlag, Stuttgart, 1927.

Tickell, F. G.: "The Examination of Fragmental Rocks," 2d ed., Stanford University Press, Stanford, Calif., 1940.

Wahlstrom, E. E.: "Petrographic Mineralogy," John Wiley & Sons, Inc., New York, 1955.

Weinschenk, E.: "Petrographic Methods," trans. by R. W. Clark, McGraw-Hill Book Company, Inc., New York, 1912.

Williams, H., F. J. Turner, and C. M. Gilbert: "Petrography," W. H. Freeman & Co., San Francisco, 1954.

Winchell, A. N.: "Elements of Optical Mineralogy," 4th ed., part 2, John Wiley & Sons, Inc., New York, 1951.

Elements to Hydroxides

ELEMENTS	MULTIPLE OXIDES
Graphite*	Spinel Group
SULFIDES	Spinel
Sphalerite*	Magnetite*
Pyrite*	Chromite*
Pyrrhotite*	Perovskite
Chalcopyrite*	HYDROXIDES
HALIDES	Brucite
Halite	Diaspore
Fluorite	Bauxite Minerals
OXIDES	Boehmite
Periclase	Gibbsite
Corundum	Cliachite
Hematite*	Limonite*
Ilmenite*	
Rutile	
Cassiterite	

Opaque Minerals. In the list of minerals included in Chapter 11 a number are either opaque or semitranslucent. These may be examined by directing a strong beam of light on the upper surface of the thin section or by transferring the slide to a binocular microscope. The ten opaque minerals listed are frequently found associated with transparent rock-forming minerals. Since these are among the most common minerals known the appearance of the mineral in reflected light usually is sufficient for an approximate identification.

ELEMENTS

Aside from graphite, elements are not ordinarily encountered in thin-section examination. A possible exception is sulfur, which is found in salt dome cap rock and is deposited around fumaroles.

* Minerals that are opaque or semi-transparent in ordinary thin sections.

GRAPHITE

C   Opaque   Hexagonal

Graphite is black with a metallic luster in reflected light and often occurs in thin flakes or disseminated scales. The crystals are tabular.

FIG. 11-1. (×20) Graphite (black) showing elongate sections cut normal to flakes.

The mineral is characteristic of metamorphic rocks such as schists, gneisses, slates, and metamorphic limestones. The gray color of many metamorphic limestones may be attributed to graphite. In some occurrences it is the only mineral present in addition to calcite.

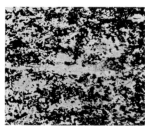

FIG. 11-2. (×15) Small crystals of graphite (black) disseminated through metamorphic limestone.

Carbonaceous Matter. In some rocks it is common to find finely divided opaque particles in which carbon is a major constituent but crystallization to a definite mineral has not occurred. Such carbonaceous matter has not been subjected to a temperature high enough to form graphite.

SULFIDES

Aside from sphalerite the few sulfides ordinarily observed in thin sections are opaque. Often these may be examined more effectively on polished surfaces with reflected light.

SPHALERITE

(Zn,Fe)S   Opaque to Transparent   Isometric
$$n = 2.37 \text{ to } 2.47$$
(n increases with Fe)

Sphalerite ordinarily occurs in irregular masses and anhedral crystals. It is gray to yellow or brown in thin sections but may not be uniform.

Cleavage occurs in six directions (dodecahedral) forming an intricate pattern. The relief is very high and the mineral shows an adamantine luster in reflected light. Transparent crystals are isotropic.

Sphalerite is a common and widely distributed mineral in veins and replacement deposits. The usual associates are pyrite, galena, marcasite,

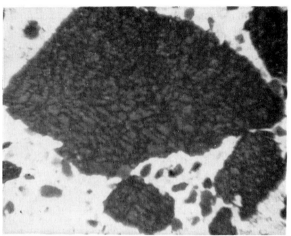

FIG. 11-3. (×20) Sphalerite partly translucent with complex dodecahedral cleavage.

and the gangue minerals: quartz, chalcedony, calcite, dolomite, and siderite.

PYRITE

FeS_2	Opaque	Isometric

Pyrite is the most common sulfide mineral. It is brass yellow with a metallic luster in reflected light. In thin section it may be distinguished from chalcopyrite, which is darker yellow, and pyrrhotite, which is a dark bronze. In thin section pyrite may resemble marcasite in color and supplementary methods may be required to distinguish the two.

Pyrite is common in euhedral crystals. These are often cubes which yield square, rectangular, triangular, or even hexagonal outlines. It also occurs in irregular grains, masses, and veinlets.

Pyrite is an unusually common and widely distributed mineral. It occurs in many rock types, in veins, and in replacement deposits. Where oxidation has been present pyrite may be altered to limonite.

PYRRHOTITE

$Fe_{1-x}S$	Opaque	Hexagonal

Pyrrhotite is bronze with a metallic luster in reflected light. It usually occurs in grains and irregular masses. Parting parallel to (0001) is fairly common.

The mineral occurs in igneous rocks as a late magmatic mineral. It is also found in veins, and in some metamorphic rocks. It forms at higher temperatures than pyrite.

CHALCOPYRITE

$CuFeS_2$ Opaque   Tetragonal

Chalcopyrite is one of the most widely distributed copper minerals. It is deep brass yellow with a metallic luster in reflected light. It is found

FIG. 11-4. ($\times$60) Chalcopyrite (black) surrounding quartz and muscovite.

in anhedral grains and veinlets but only occasionally in euhedral crystals.

The mineral is common in veins and ore deposits with several metals. It is occasionally found in igneous, sedimentary, and metamorphic rocks.

HALIDES

The study of the halides and related species is a special problem. Halite and fluorite are included in this text. Halite is an evaporite mineral. Fluorite is a vein mineral and an accessory in many rock types.

Evaporite minerals are numerous and worthy of more attention than is possible in an introductory text. They include carbonates, sulfates, and borates in addition to halides. It seems appropriate to call attention to this group in connection with the halides.

Evaporite Minerals. At periods in geologic time sedimentary basins have accumulated large bodies of halite, gypsum, dolomite, anhydrite, and other salts. The great basin of northern Germany and the basin which covers adjacent portions of New Mexico, Texas, Kansas, and Oklahoma are outstanding examples. Among the basins recognized are isolated marine remnants, shallow basins with intermittent oceanic connections, and isolated desert basins.

As sea water evaporates in isolated basins such as the Caspian Sea, the concentration of salts increases and eventually NaCl, KCl, $CaSO_4$, $CaSO_4.2H_2O$, and complex salts which contain Mg, Ca, K, and Na are precipitated as minerals. Fluctuations in salinity due to intermittent streams have often occurred with the result that salts have been deposited in layers which are rhythmically repeated. The accumulation of evaporites in enclosed basins may exceed the saline content of the original marine body.

COMMON EVAPORITE MINERALS

Mineral	System and composition	Index of refraction n_α	n_β	n_γ	Interference figure	Cleavage
Sylvite	I KCl		$n = 1.4903*$			{100}
Halite†	I NaCl		$n = 1.5443*$			{100}
Carnallite	O $KMgCl_3.6H_2O$	1.4665	1.4753	1.4937*	B_x +	indistinct
Kainite	M $KMg(SO_4)Cl.3H_2O$	1.494	1.505	1.516	B_x −	{001}
Langbeinite	I $K_2Mg_2(SO_4)_3$		$n = 1.5347*$			none
Polyhalite†	T $K_2Ca_2Mg(SO_4)_4.2H_2O$	1.547	0.560	1.567	B_x −	{10$\bar{1}$}
Thenardite	O Na_2SO_4	1.464	1.474	1.485	B_x +	{010},{100},{001}
Anhydrite†	O $CaSO_4$	1.5698	1.5754	1.6136*	B_x +	{010},{100},{001}
Gypsum†	M $CaSO_4.2H_2O$	1.5207	1.5299	1.5230*	B_x +	{010},{100},{011}
Kieserite	M $MgSO_4.H_2O$	1.520	1.533	1.584	B_x +	{110},{111},{$\bar{1}$11}, {$\bar{1}$01},{011}
Calcite†	H $CaCO_3$	$n_\epsilon = 1.4863$ $n_\omega = 1.6583*$			U −	{10$\bar{1}$1}
Aragonite†	O $CaCO_3$	1.5300	1.6810	1.6854*	B_x −	{010},{110},{011}
Dolomite†	H $Ca(Mg.Fe)(CO_3)_2$	$n_\epsilon = 1.500$ $n_\omega = 1.679$			U −	{10$\bar{1}$1}
Kernite	M $Na_2B_4O_7.4H_2O$	1.454	1.472	1.488	B_x −	{100},{001}
Borax	M $Na_2B_4O_7.10H_2O$	1.4466	1.4687	1.4717*	B_x −	{100},{110}
Ulexite	T $NaCaB_5O_9.8H_2O$	1.491	1.504	1.520	B_x +	{010},{1$\bar{1}$0},{110}
Colemanite	M $Ca_2B_6O_{11}.5H_2O$	1.5863	1.5920	1.6140*	B_x +	{010},{001}

* (Na-light).
† See text descriptions.

Partly isolated basins may contain abundant anhydrite and dolomite but are deficient in soluble salts. Desert basins yield borates and less extensive accumulations of soluble salts.

Thin sections of evaporites may be made by grinding in glycol. Studies of the textures and relationships of these materials have been made by Stewart (1949), Shaller and Henderson (1932), and others. Common evaporate minerals are listed. More complete descriptions will be found in the references at the end of the chapter.

HALITE

NaCl   Isometric

$$n = 1.544$$

Color. Colorless but may contain inclusions.

Form. Halite is not found in thin sections prepared in the ordinary way, but the sections may be ground in glycol. The halite usually appears in anhedral crystals (Fig. 11-5).

Cleavage. Perfect cubic.

Relief. Very low, n being about the same as balsam or clove oil.

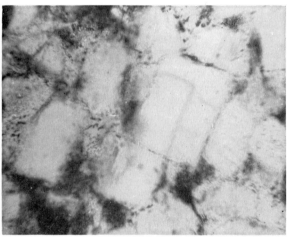

FIG. 11-5. (×60) Halite with cubic outlines accentuated by silty inclusions along crystal boundaries.

Birefringence. Nil. Dark between crossed nicols. Halite from the highly compressed salt of salt domes may be anisotropic in thick sections.

Distinguishing Features. The very low relief, cubic cleavage, and solubility are characteristic. About the only mineral that is likely to be mistaken for halite is sylvite, but the latter has appreciable relief and an index less than balsam (for sylvite $n = 1.490$).

Occurrence. Halite occurs in sedimentary beds of rock salt that are often accompanied by anhydrite and gypsum. Sylvite and polyhalite are characteristic associates.

Fluorite

CaF_2 Isometric

$$n = 1.434$$

Color. Colorless or purple in bands or spots.

Form. Fluorite is sometimes found in euhedral crystals with square outline, but it is usually anhedral and often fills the spaces between other minerals.

Cleavage. Perfect octahedral {111}. The cleavage usually appears as two intersecting lines at oblique angles of 70° and 110°, occasionally at three intersecting lines of 60° and 120° (Figure 8-35).

Relief. Fairly high, $n <$ balsam. According to Merwin, the index of refraction is remarkably constant (1.4338 for sodium light). Dispersion of fluorite is very low; hence the use of fluorite for apochromatic objectives.

Fig. 11-6. (×18) Fluorite showing zonal structure.

Birefringence. Nil. Dark between crossed nicols.

Distinguishing Features. The rather high relief, perfect cleavage, and isotropic character distinguish fluorite from practically all other minerals. The purple spots or bands (see Figure 11-6) are very characteristic.

Occurrence. Fluorite is a common vein mineral, but it is rather rare in rocks in general. It is found in some granites, occasionally in sandstones, limestones, and phosphorites. In the western United States and in West Germany, radioactive black fluorite is associated with uranium.

OXIDES

At least six simple oxides are frequently encountered in thin sections. Ilmenite, hematite, and at times rutile are translucent or opaque. Otherwise the oxides yield distinctive optical properties.

PERICLASE

PERICLASE

MgO   Isometric

$$n = 1.738 \text{ to } 1.760$$

Periclase is a rare but widely distributed mineral.

Color. Colorless in thin sections.

Form. Periclase occurs in small crystals or anhedral crystal aggregates.

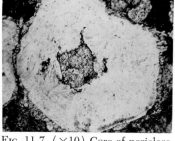

Individual anhedra may be recognized by cleavage traces.

Cleavage. Cubic. Parting, dodecahedral.

Relief. High, $n >$ balsam.

Birefringence. Nil. Dark between crossed nicols.

Distinguishing Features. The cubic cleavage, high relief, and isotropic character taken together are distinctive.

FIG. 11-7. (×10) Core of periclase surrounded by brucite in metamorphic limestone.

Alteration. Periclase is usually altered to brucite which, in turn, may be altered to hydromagnesite.

Occurrence. The most common occurrence of periclase is in metamorphic limestones. It is found as cores within brucite spots that are formed by hydration of the periclase.

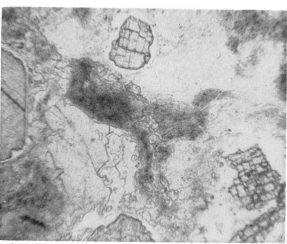

FIG. 11-8. (×60) Periclase in brucite-bearing rock showing cubic cleavage.

Artificial Periclase. Artificial periclase, now prepared on a commercial scale from selected magnesite, is more familiar than the natural mineral. It is used as a high-grade electrical insulator.

CORUNDUM

Al_2O_3 Hexagonal
                                                (Rhombohedral subsystem)

$$n_\epsilon = 1.759 \text{ to } 1.763$$
$$n_\omega = 1.767 \text{ to } 1.772$$
$$\text{Opt. } (-)$$

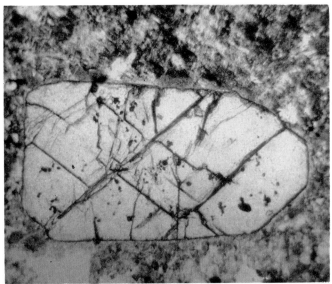

FIG. 11-9. ($\times 40$) Corundum crystal with rhombohedral parting in corundum syenite.

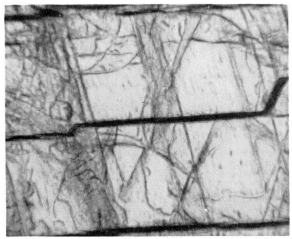

FIG. 11-10. ($\times 50$) Corundum crystal with well-developed parting.

Color. Usually colorless, sometimes with blue or pink areas that are not uniformly colored. Zoned crystals are not uncommon. In thick sections corundum may be pleochroic.

Form. Euhedral crystals are common. The habit varies from tabular to prismatic; cross sections are six-sided and may show zonal structure. Skeleton crystals are often encountered.

Cleavage. Parting often parallel to the unit rhombohedron $\{10\bar{1}1\}$ or the pinacoid $\{0001\}$ or both.

Relief. Very high, $n >$ balsam.

Birefringence. Weak, $n_\omega - n_\varepsilon = 0.008$–$0.009$. Sections are usually thicker than normal on account of the extreme hardness of the corundum. For this reason the maximum interference color of most thin sections runs up into the second order.

Extinction. Parallel to the crystal outlines or symmetrical to the rhombohedral parting.

Orientation. Sections of tabular crystals are length-slow, and sections of prismatic crystals are length-fast since the optic sign of the mineral is negative.

Twinning. Twinning lamellae or twin seams with $\{10\bar{1}1\}$ as the twin-plane are rather common.

Interference Figure. The figure obtained in basal sections is uniaxial negative usually with one ring. Some figures are biaxial with 2V as high as 30°.

Distinguishing Features. The combination of very high relief with weak birefringence, parting, and twinning lamellae is distinctive.

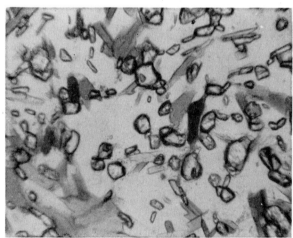

Fig. 11-11. (×60) Small corundum crystals disseminated through quartz and interspersed with biotite.

Occurrence. Corundum is especially characteristic of corundum syenites, contact-metamorphic limestones, and metamorphosed shales. It may also be found in schists and as a sporadic detrital mineral. It is one of the principal constituents of emery, which is probably a metamorphosed bauxite or laterite. In igneous rocks it never occurs with original quartz.

HEMATITE

Fe_2O_3 Opaque to translucent   Hexagonal

(Rhombohedral subsystem)

$$n_\epsilon = 2.94$$
$$n_\omega = 3.22$$
$$\text{Opt. } (-)$$

Steel-gray black with metallic luster in reflected light, with a tendency to a marginal red. Some occurrences are red and translucent.

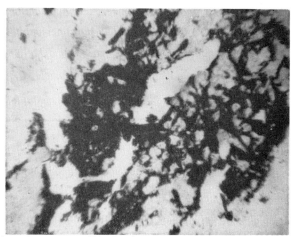

Fig. 11-12. ($\times 20$) Hematite (black) filling the interstices between quartz veins and following fractures in a quartzite.

Hematite occurs in anhedral crystals, grains, masses and occasionally in minute scales. Pseudocubic rhombohedral parting may be observed.

The mineral occurs as the main constituent of hematite schist. It is a secondary mineral in many rock types. Hematite is rare as an original constituent of igneous rocks.

ILMENITE

$FeTiO_3$ Opaque   Hexagonal

(Rhombohedral subsystem)

Ilmenite is blue-gray black with metallic luster in reflected light. It may show a white or yellowish border alteration to leucoxene.

The mineral occurs in disseminated tabular crystals which may be cut into elongate sections. Skeleton crystals frequently occur. It is also found in irregular grains and masses.

Ilmenite is a widely distributed mineral in some types of igneous rocks, more especially diabases and dolerites. It is an important constituent of titanium-bearing sands. It is often associated with magnetite in iron ore.

Leucoxene. An opaque white substance called *leucoxene* is common as an alteration product of titanium minerals in various rocks. It occurs on

Fig. 11-13. (×18) Skeleton crystal of ilmenite.

the surface and around the borders of ilmenite and is also disseminated through various rocks and is probably the result of hydrothermal alteration. Leucoxene has sometimes been identified with sphene. Leucoxene in a detrital deposit in Oklahoma is amorphous hydrous titanium dioxide, according to Coil.

RUTILE

TiO_2 Tetragonal

$$n_\omega = 2.603 \text{ to } 2.616$$
$$n_\epsilon = 2.889 \text{ to } 2.903$$
$$\text{Opt. } (+)$$

Color. Yellowish to reddish brown in thin sections. In reflected light it shows adamantine luster.

Form. Rutile usually occurs in small prismatic to acicular crystals and in grains. Knee-shaped twins with {101} as the twin-plane are characteristic. Capillary crystals are common, especially in quartz.

Cleavage. Parallel to the length of the crystals {110}.

Relief. Very high, $n >$ balsam. Adamantine luster by reflected light.

Birefringence. Extreme, $n_\varepsilon - n_\omega = 0.286$–$0.287$; interference colors are very high but do not show well on account of total reflection.

Extinction. Parallel.

Twinning. Common (see Form).

Distinguishing Features. The mineral most likely to be mistaken for rutile is probably baddeleyite (ZrO_2), which sometimes occurs in corundum syenites. The color, together with very high relief, is distinctive.

Related Minerals. Two polymorphs of rutile, anatase (also tetragonal), and brookite (orthorhombic) are of importance as detrital minerals.

Occurrence. Rutile is a rather widely distributed accessory mineral in various metamorphic rocks. It occasionally occurs in igneous rocks such as the albitite of Kragerö, Norway. Rutile also occurs as a detrital mineral. Sphene is a common associate.

CASSITERITE

SnO_2 Tetragonal

$$n_\omega = 1.996$$
$$n_\epsilon = 2.093$$
$$\text{Opt. } (+)$$

Color. Colorless to gray, yellowish, reddish, or brown in thin sections. It often shows zones of varying color.

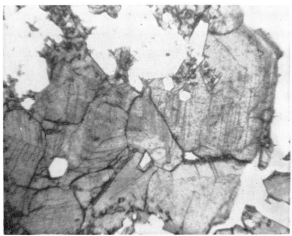

Fig. 11-14. ($\times 20$) Cassiterite showing zonal growth lines in a section cut from a quartz vein.

Form. Cassiterite is usually found in subhedral crystals. Veinlets are rather common.

Cleavage. Prismatic, parallel to the length.

Relief. Very high, $n >$ balsam. Adamantine luster in reflected light.

Birefringence. Extreme, $n_\varepsilon - n_\omega = 0.097$; the interference colors are high order but are usually masked by the color of the mineral.

Extinction. Parallel to the cleavage, oblique to the twin-plane.

Twinning. Twinned crystals are common; the twin-plane is {101}.

Distinguishing Features. Cassiterite resembles sphalerite, but the latter is isotropic. From rutile it is distinguished by lower birefringence.

Occurrence. Cassiterite occurs in granite pegmatites, in greisen, and in high-temperature veins. The usual associates are quartz, muscovite, schorlite, and topaz. The wood-tin variety occurs in rhyolites.

MULTIPLE OXIDES

The spinel group and perovskite have been selected as the members of this division most likely to be encountered in thin-section study.

The Spinel Group

The spinels are aluminates, ferrites, and chromites of dyad metals magnesium and iron. They occur in isometric crystals, usually octahedrons, and are optically isotropic.

In addition to the common spinels described here—spinel, magnetite, and chromite—there are hercynite ($FeAl_2O_4$), magnesioferrite, ($MgFe_2O_4$), galaxite ($MnAl_2O_4$), franklinite [$(Zn,Mn)Fe_2O_4$], and gahnite ($ZnAl_2O_4$).

SPINEL

$(Mg,Fe)(Al,Cr)_2O_4$ Isometric

$$n = 1.72 \text{ to } 1.78$$

Color. Colorless to green (pleonaste), olive green, or brown (picotite) in thin sections.

Form. Spinel practically always occurs in euhedral or subhedral crystals or in equant grains. Crystals are octahedra, and the most common sections are rhombic in outline.

Cleavage. Imperfect octahedral, but it may not show.

Relief. High, $n >$ balsam.

Birefringence. It is one of the few isometric minerals that is invariably isotropic.

Twinning. Twinning according to the spinel law with {111} as twin-plane is rather common, but it does not usually show in the slide.

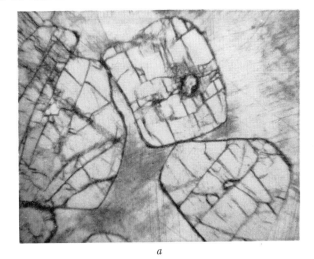

a

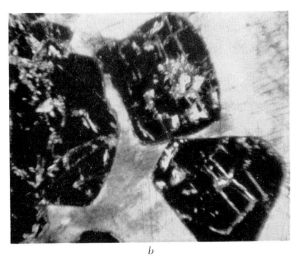

b

FIG. 11-15. (×20) Two views of a spinel section. (*a*) Ordinary illumination showing spinel in dolomite. (*b*) The same crystals between crossed nicols. (Streaks and patches of birefringence in the spinel are caused by alteration.)

Distinguishing Features. Pleonaste, iron-bearing variety of spinel, is much like hercynite.

Spinel is distinguished from garnet by its octahedral form.

Related Minerals. A related mineral, hercynite $FeAl_2O_4$, is a prominent constituent of certain types of emery. Picotite is intermediate between spinel and chromite. It resembles chromite but is more transparent. Galaxite is manganese spinel with the formula $MnAl_2O_4$. It occurs with alleghanyite.

Occurrence. Spinel occurs in metamorphic limestone with phlogopite and chondrodite, in other metamorphic rocks, and also in various igneous rocks. It is rare as a detrital mineral.

Picotite is common in peridotites, dunites, and derived serpentines.

MAGNETITE

$Fe^{II}Fe_2^{III}O_4$ Opaque   Isometric

Black with a metallic luster in reflected light. If present in abundance the thin section is magnetic. Crystals may be octahedra which yield triangular, square, or rhombic sections. A triangular pattern due to octahedral parting may be present.

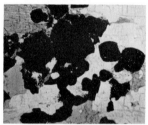

Fig. 11-16. (×7) Euhedral to anhedral magnetite (black) in norite.

Magnetite is common in nearly all igneous and metamorphic rocks. In igneous rocks it is a late magmatic mineral. It is a common detrital mineral in sands accumulated along modern or ancient strand lines.

CHROMITE

$(Fe,Mg)(Cr,Al,Fe)_2O_4$ Opaque to translucent   Isometric
$$n = 2.07 \text{ to } 2.16$$

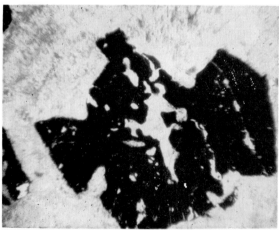

Fig. 11-17. (×20) Chromite (black) with rounded outlines.

Black with a submetallic luster in reflected light. The mineral is often translucent and brown on thin edges. It occurs in subhedral crystals, grains, or aggregates. Minute octahedra occasionally are found.

The chromite of meteorites approaches the composition $FeCr_2O_4$, but terrestrial chromite always contains appreciable amounts of magnesium and aluminum.

Chromite occurs for the most part in peridotites, pyroxenites, dunites, and derived serpentines. It is at times a late magmatic mineral. In most serpentines it is a relict mineral but at times it may be formed during serpentinization at the expense of picotite.

PEROVSKITE

$CaTiO_3$ Pseudoisometric

$$n = 2.34 \text{ to } 2.38$$

Color. Yellow to brown in thin sections.

Form. Perovskite is usually found in minute cubic crystals.

Cleavage. Cubic, noticed only in the larger crystals.

Relief. Very high, $n >$ balsam. It is difficult to make the Becke test on account of total reflection. In reflected light it shows adamantine luster.

Birefringence. Nil to 0.002. Minute crystals are dark between crossed nicols; larger crystals show very weak birefringence.

Twinning. The larger crystals show complicated polysynthetic twinning.

Distinguishing Features. Perovskite resembles melanite (garnet) and picotite (spinel), but it has a much higher refractive index than either of these.

Occurrence. Perovskite is a rare, but widely distributed, mineral in basic igneous rocks, especially melilite basalts and peridotites. It is also found in chlorite and talc schists and in some metamorphic limestones.

HYDROXIDES

All members of this group lose water on ignition. Thus the term hydrous oxide has been frequently applied.

DIASPORE

$AlO(OH)$ Orthorhombic

$$n_\alpha = 1.702$$
$$n_\beta = 1.722$$
$$n_\gamma = 1.750$$
$$2V = 84°; \text{ Opt. } (+)$$
$$a = \gamma \text{ or } Z, \ b = \beta \text{ or } Y, \ c = \alpha \text{ or } X$$

Color. Colorless to pale blue in thin sections. Sometimes pleochroic in thick sections.

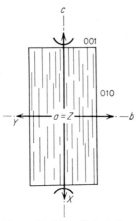

Fig. 11-18. Orientation diagram of diaspore. Section parallel to (100).

Form. Diaspore occurs in tabular crystals parallel to {010}. The crystals may be rather large to very minute. The mineral also occurs in minute aggregates.

Cleavage. Perfect in one direction {010}.

Relief. High, $n >$ balsam.

Birefringence. Strong, $n_\gamma - n_a = 0.048$; so the maximum interference color is about upper third order.

Extinction. Parallel.

Orientation. The crystals are length-fast.

Interference Figure. The figure is biaxial positive with a very large axial angle. The axial plane is {010}. Dispersion, $r < v$ weak.

Distinguishing Features. Diaspore associated with flint clay resembles clay particles in dimensions but has stronger birefringence. More coarsely crystalline diaspore may resemble anhydrite but has higher relief and only one cleavage direction.

Related Minerals. Boehmite is dimorphous with diaspore.

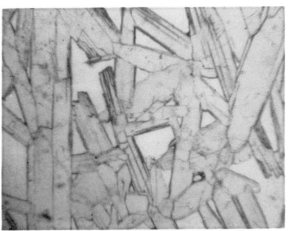

Fig. 11-19. ($\times$20) Interlocking laths of diaspore.

Occurrence. Diaspore occurs in metamorphic rocks such as schists and emery. It occurs in a few altered igneous rocks associated with alunite. It is also a prominent constituent of the highly aluminous flint clays.

BRUCITE

$Mg(OH)_2$
Hexagonal
(Rhombohedral subsystem)

$$n_\omega = 1.566$$
$$n_\epsilon = 1.585$$
$$\text{Opt. } (+)$$

Color. Colorless in thin sections.

Form. Brucite usually occurs in plates or scaly aggregates that appear fibrous in sections.

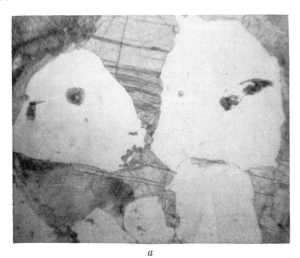

a

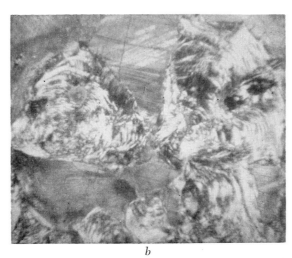

b

FIG. 11-20. (×20) Brucite in metamorphic limestone. (*a*) With ordinary illumination. (*b*) Between crossed nicols.

Cleavage. Perfect in one direction {0001} but may not show in thin sections.

Relief. Fair, $n >$ balsam.

Birefringence. Moderate, $n_\varepsilon - n_\omega = 0.019$. Some of the interference colors are anomalous; a peculiar reddish brown hue takes the place of the yellow and orange of the first order. If the section is too thin, the anomalous colors do not show.

Extinction. Parallel.

Orientation. The scaly aggregates, which are apparently fibrous, are length-fast.

Interference Figure. The interference figure is uniaxial positive with the first ring anomalous (see Birefringence). At times the figure may be biaxial with a small axial angle.

Distinguishing Features. It resembles alunite but has better cleavage and anomalous interference colors.

Alteration. Brucite is often altered to hydromagnesite, $Mg_4(OH)_2\text{-}(CO_3)_3.3H_2O$.

Occurrence. The most common occurrence of brucite is in metamorphic calcite-brucite rocks as an alteration of periclase, MgO. It is sometimes found in serpentine.

Bauxite Minerals

The term *bauxite* is widely used for aluminum ore. It was originally applied (Berthier, 1821) to aluminous material believed at that time to be a single mineral but since shown to contain at least two constituents. Bauxite is properly a generic term for rocks rich in hydrous aluminum oxides. Such rocks are frequently formed by weathering in warm, humid regions where organic acids derived from heavy vegetation are abundant. The process is frequently called lateritization. The product *laterite*, often both ferruginous and aluminous, is a widespread intermediate stage in the formation of bauxite. Aluminum minerals common in bauxite are gibbsite, boehmite, and cliachite.

BOEHMITE

AlO(OH)   Orthorhombic

$$n_\alpha = 1.638$$
$$n_\beta = 1.645$$
$$n_\gamma = 1.651$$
$$2V = \text{moderate; Opt. } (-)?$$
$$a = \alpha \text{ or } X; b = \gamma \text{ or } Z; c = \beta \text{ or } Y$$

Form. Crystals are minute and tabular.

Cleavage. In one direction parallel to {010}.

Birefringence. Moderate, $n_\gamma - n_\alpha = 0.013$.

Distinguishing Features. Closely resembles gibbsite in thin section, but the refractive indices are higher and the birefringence is less.

Occurrence. Widely distributed in bauxite where at times it may be the main mineral.

GIBBSITE

Al(OH)$_3$ (Hydrargillite)   Monoclinic
                                                                         $\angle\beta = 85°29'$

$$n_\alpha = 1.554 \text{ to } 1.567$$
$$n_\beta = 1.554 \text{ to } 1.567$$
$$n_\gamma = 1.576 \text{ to } 1.589$$
$$2V = 0° \text{ to } 40°; \text{ Opt. } (+)$$
$$b = \alpha \text{ or } X, a \wedge \gamma \text{ or } Z = 26°$$

Color. Colorless to pale brown in thin sections.

Form. Gibbsite (called *hydrargillite* by European mineralogists) occurs in minute pseudohexagonal euhedral crystals in cavities and in fine

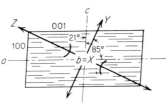

Fig. 11-21. Orientation diagram of gibbsite. Section parallel to (010).

crystalline aggregates that are often pseudomorphous after feldspars. Reticulate structure is common.

Cleavage. In one direction parallel to {001}, but it may be difficult to see.

Relief. Moderate, $n > $ balsam.

Birefringence. Moderate, $n_\gamma - n_\alpha = 0.022$. The maximum interference colors are bright upper first-order or lower second-order colors.

Extinction. Oblique extinction angles, up to a maximum of 26° for $a \wedge \gamma$ or Z in sections parallel to {010}.

Orientation. Since the crystals are tabular parallel to {001}, elongate sections with twinning are length-slow.

Twinning. Polysynthetic twinning with {001} as twinplane is often sharp and well defined.

Interference Figure. The crystals are usually too small to give an interference figure. In most crystals the axial plane is normal to (010), but in some it is parallel to (010).

Distinguishing Features. On account of the aggregate structure gibbsite resembles chalcedony, but the relief is higher and the birefringence much stronger. It also resembles dahllite, but the latter mineral has weak birefringence.

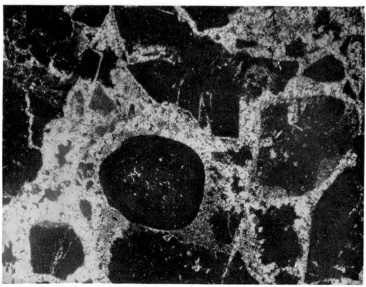

FIG. 11-22. (×25) (× nicols) Gibbsite surrounds and penetrates pisolites and broken areas of cliachite (black).

Occurrence. Some bauxites (bauxite is used as a rock name) are made up largely of gibbsite, others largely of amorphous cliachite with crystalline gibbsite in cavities.

CLIACHITE

$Al_2O_3(H_2O)_x$ (Bauxite in part)   Mineraloid
                                $n = 1.57$ to 1.61

Color. Colorless to deep brown or red in thin sections. Translucent to nearly opaque.

Form. Cliachite is pisolitic or massive without any indication of crystalline structure.

Relief. Moderate, $n >$ balsam. It is difficult to test the relief and refractive index unless the mineral is powdered.

Birefringence. Nil. In favorable spots or in a powdered form the mineral is isotropic.

Distinguishing Features. The pisolitic structure (Figure 8-3) and association with gibbsite are distinctive. Contraction cracks due to shrinkage of the original spheroidal gel-form frequently appear in thin sections.

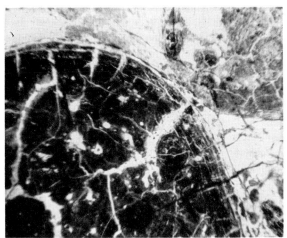

FIG. 11-23. (×20) Bauxite showing a segment of a pisolite. The dark area is cliachite. Contraction cracks are filled with gibbsite.

Occurrence. Cliachite is the main constituent of many bauxites. Common associates are gibbsite and siderite. There may also be relict minerals such as ilmenite and sphene, for in some cases bauxites are derived from nepheline syenites.

LIMONITE

$H_2Fe_2O_4(H_2O)_x$ Opaque to translucent   Mineraloid
$n = 2.0$ to 2.1

Limonite is brown in reflected light. It may be translucent in some masses and on thin edges. It frequently forms a stain or a border around other minerals, particularly those with a high iron content.

FIG. 11-24. (×9) Limonite cementing detrital fragments of quartz.

The mineral is usually isotropic but may show irregular birefringence due to strain. Goethite is similar to limonite but is distinctly crystalline with parallel extinction.

Limonite is a secondary mineral product ordinarily the result of oxidation or weathering. It may form a cement for sand grains. It is often present on the weathered surface of rocks. It occasionally forms pseudomorphs after other minerals especially pyrite.

REFERENCES

Evaporites

Schaller, W. T., and E. P. Henderson: Mineralogy of drill cores from the potash field of New Mexico and Texas, *U.S. Geol. Survey Bull.* 833, p. 124, 1932.
Stewart, F. H.: The Petrology of the Evaporites of the Eskdale No. 2 Boring, East Yorkshire, *Mineral. Mag.*, vol. 28, pp. 621–675, 1949.

Bauxite

"Problems of Clay and Laterite Genesis: A Symposium," pp. 1–244, AIME, New York, 1952.

Carbonates, Sulfates, and Phosphates

CARBONATES	SULFATES	PHOSPHATES
Calcite Group	Barite	Monazite
Calcite	Celestite	Apatite
Dolomite	Anhydrite	Dahllite
Magnesite	Gypsum	Collophane
Siderite	Polyhalite	Lazulite
Aragonite Group	Alunite	
Aragonite	Jarosite	

The minerals of Chapter 12 contain several isomorphous groups where the range in optical properties may provide inadequate criteria for positive identification between members. This applies particularly to several carbonate and sulfate groups. The textural information revealed by the thin sections will be found particularly useful but it may be necessary to resort to chemical and X-ray diffraction methods for precise identification.

The Calcite Group

The calcite group of rhombohedral carbonates consists of the minerals listed below, together with rhodochrosite ($MnCO_3$) and smithsonite

CALCITE GROUP

Mineral	Chemical composition	n_ϵ	n_ω	$n_\omega - n_\epsilon$
Calcite..........	$CaCO_3$	1.486	1.658	0.172
Dolomite........	$Ca(Mg,Fe)(CO_3)_2$	1.500–1.526	1.680–1.716	0.180–0.190
Magnesite........	$MgCO_3$	1.509–1.527	1.700–1.726	0.191–0.199
Siderite..........	$FeCO_3$	1.596–1.633	1.830–1.875	0.234–0.242

($ZnCO_3$). They are hexagonal (rhombohedral subsystem) with perfect rhombohedral cleavage and a cleavage angle of 73° to 75°. They are uniaxial and optically negative. All show change of relief when rotated; the higher relief is obtained when the long diagonal of the rhomb is parallel to the vibration plane of the lower nicol. The birefringence is extreme, and the maximum interference colors are high-order white.

Dolomite and magnesite may contain ferrous carbonate in isomorphous mixture, and this increases the value of the refractive indices.

Another member of the calcite group is rhodochrosite, $MnCO_3$. It is very similar to the other minerals in its optical properties. Rhodochrosite occurs in veins but is very rare as a rock-forming mineral. Still another member of the group is smithsonite. It usually occurs in the oxidized zone and is sometimes pseudomorphous after calcite and dolomite.

CALCITE

$CaCO_3$ Hexagonal
(Rhombohedral subsystem)

$$n_\epsilon = 1.486$$
$$n_\omega = 1.658$$
$$\text{Opt. } (-)$$

Color. Colorless in thin sections, but it is often cloudy.

Form. Fine to coarse aggregates, usually anhedral. Euhedral crystals in rock sections are rare. Calcite often shows organic structure of some kind. It is frequently oolitic or spherulitic.

Cleavage. Perfect rhombohedral $\{10\bar{1}1\}$, usually shows at two intersecting lines at oblique angles (75° if section is cut normal to the cleavage traces). In fine aggregates the cleavage may not show. There is sometimes parting parallel to $\{0\bar{1}12\}$ which is due to twin-gliding.

Relief. Varies with the direction. It is high when the long diagonal of the rhomb is parallel to the vibration plane of the lower nicol and low when the short diagonal is in this position. Occasional sections parallel to $\{0001\}$ have high relief in all positions.

Birefringence. Extreme, $n_\omega - n_\varepsilon = 0.172$. The maximum interference color is pearl gray or white of the higher orders. Thin edges of the slide usually show bright colors of the fourth and fifth orders and tints of higher orders. Thin films and twin lamellae of calcite usually show bright interference colors.

Extinction. Symmetrical to the cleavage traces. When a section is in one of the extinction positions, fine birefringent calcite dust formed by grinding is prominent.

Orientation. Is difficult to determine on account of the extreme birefringence.

Twinning. Polysynthetic twinning with $\{0\bar{1}12\}$ as twin-plane is very common, especially in the calcite of metamorphic limestone. The twin

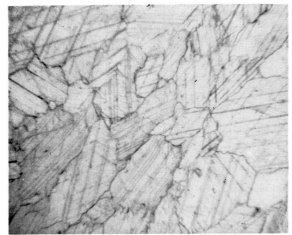

FIG. 12-1. (×20) Anhedral calcite crystals showing rhombohedral cleavage.

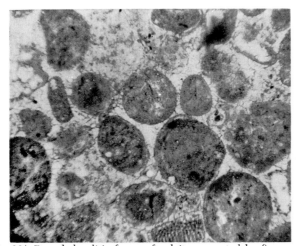

FIG. 12-2. (×60) Rounded oolitic forms of calcite cemented by fine granular calcite.

lamellae are mostly parallel to the long diagonal, but they also intersect at oblique angles depending upon how the section is cut. The twin lamellae are usually so thin that they show first-order interference colors.

Interference Figure. The interference figure is uniaxial negative with many rings. Cleavage flakes give a very eccentric figure. Occasionally calcite gives a biaxial figure with a small axial angle.

Distinguishing Features. Dolomite, magnesite, and siderite may all be mistaken for calcite. Dolomite is usually subhedral to euhedral and often has twin lamellae parallel to the short diagonal as well as to the long diagonal. Siderite usually has iron stains around the borders of the grains,

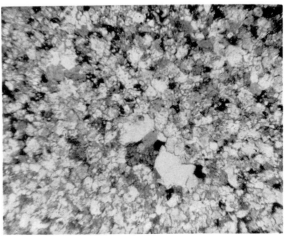

FIG. 12-3. (×60) Finely crystalline calcite containing coarser quartz. (× nicols.)

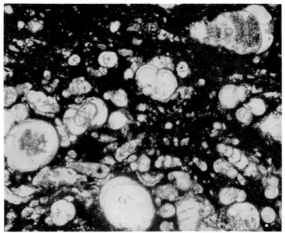

FIG. 12-4. (×25) Calcite forming casts of foraminifera distributed through carbonaceous shale.

and the relief is not low in any position. Since there is no distinctive feature for magnesite, it may be necessary to make microchemical tests. Aragonite is also similar to calcite but lacks the rhombohedral cleavage, and in no section is the refractive index distinctly less than that of balsam. Aragonite is also biaxial.

Alteration. Calcite is often replaced by quartz. This feature is often observed in quartz veins.

Occurrence. Calcite is the principal constituent of both sedimentary and metamorphic limestones, but it is found in many other rock types. It is a very common secondary mineral in cavities of igneous rocks, where it is often associated with zeolites. It is also a deuteric mineral in some igneous rocks. Next to quartz, calcite is the most common vein mineral.

DOLOMITE

$Ca(Mg,Fe)(CO_3)_2$ (inc. Ankerite)   Hexagonal
(Rhombohedral subsystem)

$$n_\epsilon = 1.500 \text{ to } 1.526$$
$$n_\omega = 1.680 \text{ to } 1.716$$
$$\text{Opt. } (-)$$

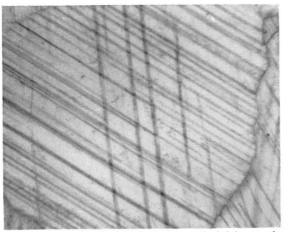

FIG. 12-5. (×20) A portion of a single anhedral crystal of dolomite showing rhombo-hedral cleavage.

Color. Colorless to gray.

Form. Fine to coarse grained and usually subhedral. Euhedral crystals of the unit rhombohedron $\{10\bar{1}1\}$ are rather common and the crystals are often curved. Zonal structure is frequent; this is due to variation in the iron content.

Cleavage. Perfect rhombohedral parallel to $\{10\bar{1}1\}$, which usually shows as two intersecting sets of lines at oblique angles. There also may be parting parallel to $\{02\bar{2}1\}$.

Relief. Varies with the direction. It is high when the long diagonal of the rhomb is parallel to the vibration plane of the lower nicol and low when the short diagonal is in this position. An occasional section parallel to $\{0001\}$ has high relief in all positions.

Birefringence. Extreme, $n_\omega - n_\epsilon = 0.180$ to 0.190; interference colors are pearl gray or white of the high order. Rather bright colors of the fourth and fifth orders may show on the edge of the slide.

Extinction. Symmetrical to outlines of crystals and to the cleavage traces. Curved crystals show wavy extinction.

Twinning. The dolomite of metamorphic rocks usually shows polysyn-thetic twinning with $\{02\bar{2}1\}$ as twin-plane. The twinning lamellae are parallel to both short and long diagonals of the rhombs. As in calcite, the twin lamellae are usually so thin that they show first-order interference colors.

Interference Figure. The interference figure is uniaxial negative with many rings.

Distinguishing Features. Dolomite closely resembles calcite, but in many cases it may be distinguished by its tendency to euhedral crystals, by zonal structure, and by twinning lamellae parallel to the short diagonal. It is even more like magnesite, and thus it may be necessary to rely on chemical or microchemical tests.

Occurrence. Dolomite is a very common mineral. It occurs in veins and replacement deposits, in sedimentary dolomite rocks and limestones, and in metamorphic dolomite rocks.

MAGNESITE

MgCO$_3$ Hexagonal
                                                    (Rhombohedral subsystem)

$$n_\epsilon = 1.509 \text{ to } 1.527$$
$$n_\omega = 1.700 \text{ to } 1.726$$
$$\text{Opt. } (-)$$

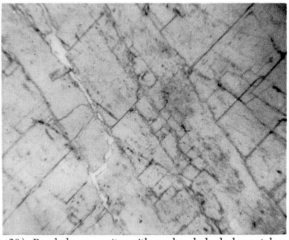

Fig. 12-6. (×20) Banded magnesite with a rhombohedral crystal pattern. A thin quartz vein cuts the magnesite.

Color. Colorless.

Form. Magnesite usually occurs in anhedral to subhedral crystal aggregates. The porcelain-like microcrystalline variety has a grain size on the order of 1μ. Euhedral crystals are exceedingly rare.

Cleavage. Perfect rhombohedral {10$\bar{1}$1} as in calcite, dolomite, and siderite except in the microcrystalline variety.

Relief. Changes on rotation like calcite and dolomite. It has high relief when the long diagonal of the rhomb is parallel to the vibration plane of the lower nicol and low relief when the short diagonal is in this position. An occasional section parallel to {0001} has high relief in all positions.

Birefringence. Extreme, $n_\omega - n_\varepsilon = 0.191$ to 0.199; interference colors are pearl gray (white of the high order).

Extinction. Symmetrical with respect to cleavage traces.

Twinning. Absent as far as known.

Interference Figure. The interference figure is uniaxial negative with many rings.

Distinguishing Features. Magnesite is very similar to dolomite and calcite and has no distinctive optical properties of its own aside from indices of refraction. For this reason chemical or microchemical tests may be necessary to distinguish it.

Occurrence. Metamorphic magnesite rocks are found in Stevens County, Washington. Magnesite is a common mineral in serpentine in both coarsely crystalline and microcrystalline varieties.

SIDERITE

$FeCO_3$ Hexagonal

(Rhombohedral subsystem)

$n_\varepsilon = 1.596$ to 1.633
$n_\omega = 1.830$ to 1.875
Opt. $(-)$

FIG. 12-7. ($\times 20$) Siderite crystals in quartz.

Color. In thin sections it is colorless to gray and may be yellowish or brown in spots on the edges. The brown spots are due to alteration.

Form. Siderite occurs in fine to coarse aggregates of anhedral to euhedral crystals and sometimes shows oolitic, spherulitic, or colloform structure.

Cleavage. Perfect rhombohedral $\{10\bar{1}1\}$ as in calcite, dolomite, and magnesite.

Relief. Varies somewhat on rotation. The relief is high when the long diagonal is parallel to the vibration plane of the lower nicol and moderate when the short diagonal is in this position. In both positions the index of refraction is greater than balsam.

Birefringence. Extreme, $n_\omega - n_\varepsilon = 0.234$ to 0.242. Interference colors are pearl gray (white of high order). Brighter colors may show on the edge of the slide.

Extinction. Symmetrical to cleavage traces.

Twinning. Twin lamellae parallel to the long diagonal [twin-plane = $\{01\bar{1}2\}$] are occasionally observed.

Interference Figure. The interference figure is uniaxial negative with numerous rings.

Distinguishing Features. Siderite very much resembles the other rhombohedral carbonates but may often be distinguished by the brown stain around the borders of the grains and along cleavage cracks. The index of refraction in all positions is greater than that of balsam; in calcite, dolomite, and magnesite the index of refraction n_ε is less than that of balsam.

Occurrence. The chief occurrence of siderite is in veins or replacement deposits with quartz as a common associate. Siderite also is a prominent mineral in some bauxites. It is the principal mineral of septarian clay ironstone concretions. Siderite is a prominent mineral in the oolitic ironstones of England as an associate of chamosite. It is a secondary mineral in the cavities of some basalts.

Aragonite Group

Orthorhombic carbonates of Ca, Ba, Sr, and Pb form an isomorphous group containing the minerals aragonite, witherite, strontianite, and cerussite.

ARAGONITE

$CaCO_3$ Orthorhombic
(Pseudohexagonal)

$$n_\alpha = 1.530$$
$$n_\beta = 1.682$$
$$n_\gamma = 1.686$$
$$2V = 18°; \text{Opt.} (-)$$
$$a = \beta \text{ or } Y, b = \gamma \text{ or } Z, c = \alpha \text{ or } X$$

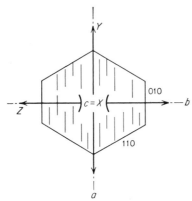

Fig. 12-8. Orientation diagram of aragonite. Section parallel to (001).

Color. Colorless in thin sections.

Form. Aragonite usually shows a columnar or fibrous structure. Cross sections are six-sided.

Cleavage. Imperfect parallel to the length of the crystals (010 face).

Relief. Varies with the direction; the relief is low when the columns or fibers are parallel to the vibration plane of the lower nicol and high when these are normal to this direction. Basal sections show no change of relief since n_β is about the same as n_γ.

Fig. 12-9. ($\times 22$) Euhedral aragonite with polysynthetic twinning. ($\times$ nicols.)

Birefringence. Extreme, $n_\gamma - n_\alpha = 0.156$. Interference colors pearl gray (white of the high order); brighter colors may show on thin edges and along cracks.

Extinction. Parallel to crystals or columns.

Twinning. Fairly common [twin-plane = {110}] both as twin lamellae and as contact and penetration twins.

Interference Figure. Basal {001} sections of aragonite give a negative biaxial interference figure with a small axial angle. The axial plane is {100}. Dispersion, $r < v$ weak.

Distinguishing Features. Aragonite greatly resembles calcite but lacks the rhombohedral cleavage. It is biaxial, whereas calcite is uniaxial.

Alteration. Aragonite alters easily to calcite, which is the stable form of calcium carbonate.

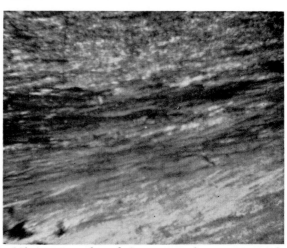

Fig. 12-10. (×20) A portion of a radial aggregate of aragonite crystals. (× nicols.)

Occurrence. The most common occurrence of aragonite is probably as a secondary mineral in cavities of basalts and andesites. It also occurs in seams of limestones, sandstones, and occasionally in veinlets. It was probably a widespread original constituent of sediments but has since been altered to calcite. It is also found in some metamorphic rocks.

SULFATES

About 150 sulfate compounds are found in nature. Among these a few common species have been selected for optical description. Descriptions of sulfates of less common occurrence should be sought in reference books.

BARITE

BaSO$_4$ Orthorhombic

$$n_\alpha = 1.636$$
$$n_\beta = 1.637$$
$$n_\gamma = 1.648$$
$$2V = 36° \text{ to } 37\frac{1}{2}°; \text{ Opt. } (+)$$
$$a = \gamma \text{ or } Z, \ b = \beta \text{ or } Y, \ c = \alpha \text{ or } X$$

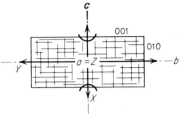

FIG. 12-11. Orientation diagram of barite. Section parallel to (100).

Color. Colorless in thin sections.

Form. Usually in granular aggregates, but the individual crystals may be elongate.

Cleavage. In three directions, parallel to {001} and {110} and therefore at angles of 90° and 78°.

Relief. Fairly high, $n >$ balsam.

Birefringence. Rather weak, $n_\gamma - n_\alpha = 0.012$, slightly greater than that of quartz. The maximum interference color is rarely above first-order yellow or orange. The interference colors are frequently mottled.

FIG. 12-12. (×45) Barite (bladed) with calcite in limestone.

Extinction. Parallel to the best cleavage {001}. The extinction in {001} sections is symmetrical.

Orientation. The direction of the best cleavage is the slower ray.

Twinning. Polysynthetic twinning with {110} as the twin-plane is occasionally found.

Interference Figure. Sections cut parallel to {100} give a positive biaxial interference figure with a moderate axial angle (Figure 8-36).

Cleavage plates parallel to {001} give an obtuse bisectrix figure. The axial plane is {010}. Dispersion, $r < v$ weak.

FIG. 12-13. (×20) Plumose pattern of barite crystals. (× nicols.)

Distinguishing Features. Barite greatly resembles celestite, but the axial angle is smaller. It may be necessary to determine refractive indices carefully or to make chemical tests in order to distinguish them.

Occurrence. Barite is a prominent vein mineral; the common associates are quartz and calcite. It also occurs in limestones and sandstones and is prominent in some concretions, but it is rare as a strictly rock-forming mineral.

CELESTITE

SrSO₄   Orthorhombic

$$n_\alpha = 1.622$$
$$n_\beta = 1.624$$
$$n_\gamma = 1.631$$
$$2V = 51°; \text{Opt.} (+)$$
$$a = \gamma \text{ or } Z, \ b = \beta \text{ or } Y, \ c = \alpha \text{ or } X$$

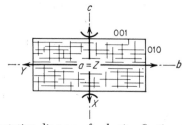

FIG. 12-14. Orientation diagram of celestite. Section parallel to (100).

Fig. 12-15. (×20) Interlocking crystals of celestite. (× nicols.)

Color. Colorless in thin sections.

Form. Euhedral to anhedral crystals, sometimes fine granular. Euhedral crystals are mostly tabular parallel to {001} and elongated in the direction of the b-axis [010].

Cleavage. Perfect parallel to {001}, imperfect parallel to {110}.

Relief. Fair, n > balsam.

Birefringence. Rather weak, $n_\gamma - n_\alpha = 0.009$, the same as that of quartz, so that the highest interference color is white or straw yellow.

Extinction. Parallel to the outlines and to the cleavage.

Orientation. The elongation of tabular crystals is parallel to the slower ray.

Interference Figure. Sections cut parallel to {100} give a positive biaxial interference figure with moderate axial angle. Cleavage plates parallel to {001} give an obtuse bisectrix figure. The axial plane is {010}. Dispersion, $r < v$.

Distinguishing Features. Celestite very much resembles barite, but the axial angle is larger.

Occurrence. Celestite usually occurs in sedimentary limestones, where it is probably more common than barite.

ANHYDRITE

CaSO$_4$ Orthorhombic

$$n_\alpha = 1.570$$
$$n_\beta = 1.576$$
$$n_\gamma = 1.614$$
$$2V = 42°; \text{ Opt. } (+)$$
$$a = \gamma \text{ or } Z, \ b = \beta \text{ or } Y, \ c = \alpha \text{ or } X$$

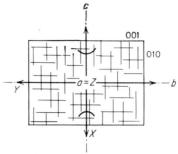

FIG. 12-16. Orientation diagram of anhydrite. Section parallel to (100).

Color. Colorless in thin sections.

Form. Usually fine to medium-grained aggregates or anhedral to subhedral crystals, which are sometimes elongate. Euhedral crystals are rare. It also occurs as inclusions in halite.

Cleavage. In three directions at right angles parallel to {100}, {010}, and {001}. It may also show parting parallel to {101} which is due to twinning.

Relief. Moderate, $n >$ balsam. Some sections show a slight change of relief when the stage is rotated.

Birefringence. Strong, $n_\gamma - n_\alpha = 0.044$. The interference colors range up to about third-order green.

Extinction. Parallel to the cleavage traces.

Twinning. Polysynthetic twinning with {101} as twin-plane is common. The twinning lamellae show best on the (010) face and make an angle of 42° and 48° with the cleavage traces. There may be two sets of twin lamellae (101) and (10$\bar{1}$) intersecting at angles of 83½° and 96½°.

Interference Figure. Cleavage fragments and sections parallel to {100} give a biaxial positive interference figure with a moderate axial angle. The axial plane is {010}. Dispersion, $r < v$.

Distinguishing Features. Anhydrite is distinguished from gypsum by higher relief and stronger birefringence. The rectangular pseudocubic cleavage is distinctive.

Alteration. Between grains and along veinlets anhydrite is often altered to gypsum, and anhydrite may be found as remnants within gypsum.

Occurrence. Anhydrite occurs in sedimentary beds. It is often encountered in deep drilling but near the surface is usually altered to gypsum. It often occurs with halite and is common in salt mines. In salt domes it is often found as cap rock. Metamorphic anhydrite rock is found at the Nevada-Douglas mine, Lyon County, Nevada. It is occasionally encountered in veins formed at depth.

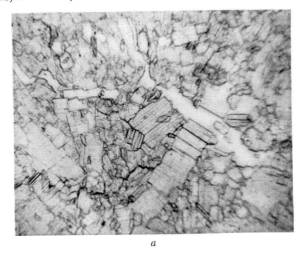

a

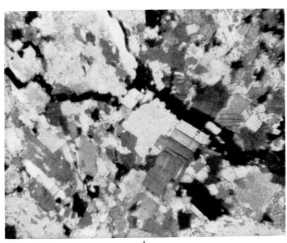

b

FIG. 12-17 *a,b*. (×20) A crystalline aggregate of anhydrite with rectangular cleavage. (*a*) Ordinary illumination. (*b*) × nicols.

GYPSUM

$CaSO_4.2H_2O$ Monoclinic
$\angle \beta = 80°42'$

$$n_\alpha = 1.520$$
$$n_\beta = 1.522$$
$$n_\gamma = 1.529$$
$$2V = 58°; \text{Opt. } (+)$$
$$b = \beta \text{ or } Y, c \wedge \alpha \text{ or } X = +37°28'$$

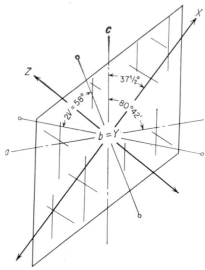

FIG. 12-18. Orientation diagram of gypsum. Section parallel to (010).

FIG. 12-19. (×18) Gypsum in gypsum rock. (× nicols.)

Color. Colorless in thin sections.

Form. Gypsum usually occurs in anhedral to subhedral aggregates and is often uneven grained. It sometimes shows a fibrous structure.

Cleavage. Perfect in one direction {010}, imperfect parallel to {100} and {$\bar{1}$11}. ($\bar{1}$00) $\wedge$ ($\bar{1}$01) = 66°10′.

Relief. Low, n slightly < balsam.

Birefringence. Rather weak, $n_\gamma - n_\alpha = 0.009$ (the same as that of quartz). The highest interference color is white or straw yellow. Sections with the highest interference color do not usually show any cleavage.

Extinction. Parallel to the best cleavage in sections normal to ($0\bar{1}0$).

Orientation. Cleavage traces are parallel to both slower and faster rays since $b = \beta$ or Y.

Twinning. The polysynthetic twinning often found in thin sections of gypsum is produced by heating the section.

Interference Figure. The interference figure is biaxial positive with a moderate axial angle. The axial plane is {010}. Dispersion, $r > v$. Sections parallel to (010) give a "flash figure."

Distinguishing Features. Gypsum is easily distinguished from anhydrite by lower relief and weaker birefringence.

Occurrence. Gypsum is the chief constituent of gypsum rock, which in most cases has been formed by the hydration of anhydrite. Anhydrite may occur in the gypsum as a relict mineral. Gypsum occurs in veinlets and between grains of anhydrite. Other commonly associated minerals are calcite, dolomite, and halite.

POLYHALITE

$K_2MgCa_2(SO_4)_4.2H_2O$ Triclinic

$$\angle\alpha = 92°29'$$
$$\angle\beta = 123°4'$$
$$\angle\gamma = 88°21'$$

$n_\alpha = 1.548$
$n_\beta = 1.562$
$n_\gamma = 1.567$
$2V = $ ca. $70°$; Opt. $(-)$
(Optical orientation unknown)

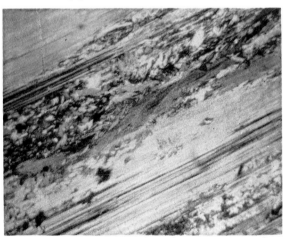

Fig. 12-20. ($\times 15$) Polyhalite showing polysynthetic twinning and variation in pigment. ($\times$ nicols.)

Color. Colorless to reddish in thin sections. The reddish color is due to hematitic pigment.

Form. Polyhalite shows granular or fibrous structure.

Cleavage. Parallel to (100) and parting parallel to (010).

Relief. Low, $n >$ balsam.

Birefringence. Moderate, $n_\gamma - n_\alpha = 0.019$. The interference colors range up to second-order blue.

Extinction. Oblique.

Twinning. Polysynthetic twinning with (010) as the twin-plane is very common.

Interference Figure. The interference figure is biaxial negative with a rather large axial angle, but it may be difficult to obtain on account of the small size of the crystals.

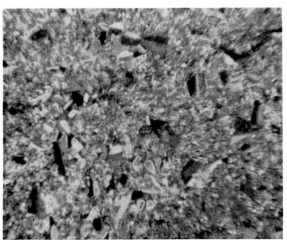

Fig. 12-21. ($\times$20) Twinned crystals of polyhalite in a granular aggregate. ($\times$ nicols.)

Distinguishing Features. Polyhalite may resemble gypsum, but both its refractive indices and birefringence are higher. It is decomposed by water with the separation of microchemical gypsum.

Occurrence. Polyhalite occurs in saline beds; the common associates are halite, sylvite, magnesite, and anhydrite. In the West Texas–New Mexico Permian basin it is an alteration product of anhydrite according to Schaller and Henderson.

ALUNITE

$KAl_3(OH)_6(SO_4)_2$ Hexagonal

(Rhombohedral subsystem)

$n_\omega = 1.572$

$n_\epsilon = 1.592$

Opt. (+)

Color. Colorless in thin sections.

Form. Alunite usually shows fine to coarse aggregates. Crystals vary from tabular to pseudocubic rhombohedral ($rr' = 90°50'$).

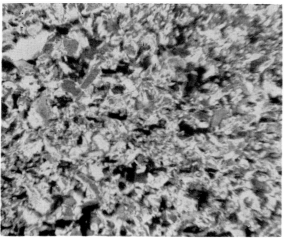

FIG. 12-22. (×60) Alunite in an alunite vein. (× nicols.)

Cleavage. Fair cleavage in one direction {0001}.

Relief. Fair, $n >$ balsam. When the stage is rotated there is a slight change of relief.

Birefringence. Moderate, $n_\varepsilon - n_\omega = 0.020$; the interference colors range up to second-order blue.

Extinction. Parallel or symmetrical in most sections. Basal sections are dark in all positions.

Orientation. Crystals and cleavage traces are length-fast.

Interference Figure. Basal sections give a positive uniaxial interference figure.

Related Minerals. Natroalunite, the sodium analogue of alunite, is very similar to alunite in its properties.

Occurrence. Alunite occurs as a hydrothermal alteration product of rhyolites, dacites, and andesites. It is also prominent as a vein mineral.

JAROSITE

$KFe_3^{III}(OH)_6(SO_4)_2$ Hexagonal

(Rhombohedral subsystem)

$n_\epsilon = 1.715$

$n_\omega = 1.820$

Opt. $(-)$

Color. Colorless to brown in thin sections.

Form. Jarosite occurs in crystal aggregates and occasionally in euhedral crystals, which are similar to those of alunite, for these two minerals are isomorphous.

Cleavage. Distinct cleavage in one direction {0001}.

Relief. Very high, $n >$ balsam.

Birefringence. Extreme, $n_\omega - n_\varepsilon = 0.105$.

Extinction. Parallel or symmetrical. Basal sections are dark in all positions.

Orientation. Difficult to test on account of the extreme birefringence.

Interference Figure. Tabular crystals give a negative uniaxial figure with many rings.

Related Minerals. Natrojarosite, $NaFe_3(OH)_6(SO_4)_2$; ammoniojarosite $NH_4Fe_3(OH)_6(SO_4)_2$; plumbojarosite $PbFe_6(OH)_{12}(SO_4)_4$; and argentojarosite $AgFe_3(OH)_6(SO_4)_2$ are all very similar to jarosite.

Alteration. Jarosite alters readily to limonite.

Occurrence. Jarosite is a rather common mineral in the lower oxidized zone of ore deposits. It is occasionally found in volcanic igneous rocks, perhaps as a late hydrothermal mineral.

PHOSPHATES

Many phosphate minerals are found in small concentrations in pegmatites, in metallic mineral deposits, and as minor rock constituents. The minerals described constitute the more abundant species.

MONAZITE

$(Ce,La,Nd,Pr)PO_4$ Monoclinic

$\angle\beta = 76°6'$

$$n_\alpha = 1.786 \text{ to } 1.800$$
$$n_\beta = 1.788 \text{ to } 1.801$$
$$n_\gamma = 1.837 \text{ to } 1.849$$
$$2V = 6° \text{ to } 19°; \text{ Opt. } (+)$$
$$b = \alpha \text{ or } X, c \wedge \gamma \text{ or } Z = -2° \text{ to } -10°$$

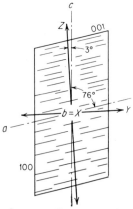

FIG. 12-23. Orientation diagram of monazite. Section parallel to (010).

Color. Nearly colorless to neutral in thin sections.

Form. Monazite occurs in euhedral crystals, which are usually very small.

Cleavage. Parting parallel to {001} is often prominent.

Relief. Very high, $n >$ balsam.

Birefringence. Strong to very strong, $n_\gamma - n_\alpha = 0.049$ to 0.051. The maximum interference color is upper third or lower fourth order. Cross sections of crystals have very weak birefringence since $n_\beta - n_\alpha = 0.001$ to 0.002. The mineral may be metamict with low birefringence.

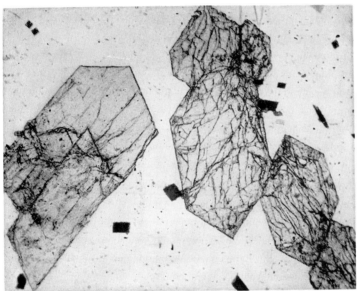

FIG. 12-24. ($\times 19$) Monazite crystals in quartz matrix.

Extinction. Longitudinal sections have a small extinction angle (2 to 10°). Sections parallel to {001} do not show complete extinction.

Orientation. Crystals are length-slow.

Interference Figure. The interference figure is biaxial positive with a small axial angle. The axial plane is normal to {010}. Dispersion strong, $r < v$.

Distinguishing Features. Monazite is more like sphene than any common mineral, but its birefringence is not so high. Since it usually contains thorium it is radioactive and even in thin section will affect a sensitive Geiger counter.

Occurrence. Monazite occurs in pegmatites, granite, and may be found in veins. It is a detrital mineral and may be found in ancient sedimentary strata or in younger sands.

APATITE

$3Ca_3(PO_4)_2.CaF_2$ Hexagonal
                                                    (Hexagonal subsystem)
$$n_\epsilon = 1.630 \text{ to } 1.651$$
$$n_\omega = 1.633 \text{ to } 1.655$$
$$\text{Opt. } (-)$$

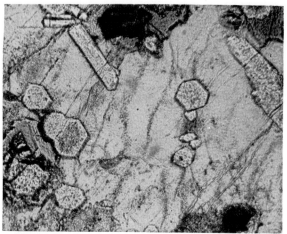

FIG. 12-25. (×30) Apatite crystals in igneous rocks.

Color. Colorless in thin sections.

Form. Apatite is usually found as minute six-sided prismatic crystals. It is a common and widely distributed mineral but usually occurs in small amounts. (See Figure 8-22.)

Cleavage. Imperfect basal {0001} shown as cross fractures. Larger crystals may show imperfect cleavage parallel to the length {10$\bar{1}$0}.

Relief. Moderate, $n >$ balsam.

Birefringence. Weak, $n_\omega - n_\varepsilon = 0.003$ to 0.004. The interference colors are first-order gray to white. Cross sections are dark between crossed nicols.

Extinction. Parallel.

Orientation. The crystals are usually length-fast, but crystals of tabular habit are length-slow.

Interference Figure. Basal sections are usually too small to give good interference figures.

Distinguishing Features. Apatite is distinctive. The only common mineral that closely resembles it is dahllite, which occurs as a secondary mineral in cavities and seams associated with collophane.

Related Minerals. Wilkeite, a rare mineral of the apatite group with the sulfate radical; voelckerite or oxy-apatite; fermorite, strontian apatite, and ellestadite are similar to apatite in physical properties.

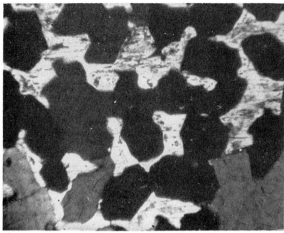

Fig. 12-26. (×20) Apatite crystals in approximately uniform orientation. (× nicols.)

Occurrence. Apatite is a common minor accessory mineral of practically all igneous rocks. In the opinion of Tolman and Rogers, it is a late magmatic mineral and not an early one. It also occurs in pegmatites, in some high-temperature veins, in metamorphic limestones and is also prominent in some iron ores.

DAHLLITE

$3Ca_3(PO_4)_2.CaCO_3$ Hexagonal

(Hexagonal subsystem)

$$n_\epsilon = 1.619 \text{ to } 1.626$$
$$n_\omega = 1.623 \text{ to } 1.635$$
$$\text{Opt. } (-)$$

Color. Colorless to pale brown or gray in thin sections.

Form. Dahllite occurs in minute hexagonal crystals, in crusts with banded subradiating structure, in spherulites, and in fine-grained aggregates forming concretions or sedimentary rocks.

Relief. Moderate, $n >$ balsam.

Birefringence. Weak, $n_\omega - n_\epsilon = 0.004$ to 0.009. Interference colors are bluish gray to white of the first order.

Extinction. Parallel. Cross sections are dark between crossed nicols, but occasionally they may show biaxial sectors.

Orientation. Prismatic crystals are length-fast like apatite. The columns of crusts and fibers of spherulites are also length-fast. Sections of tabular crystals are length-slow.

Interference Figure. Basal sections are usually too small to give good interference figures.

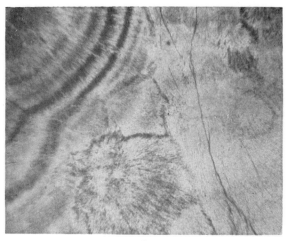

a

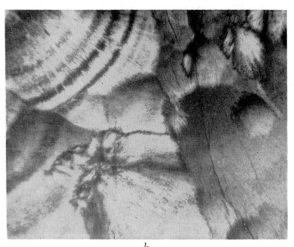

b

FIG. 12-27 *a,b.* (×60) A crust of dahllite showing banding and fiber texture. (*a*) Ordinary illumination. (*b*) The same view with × nicols.

Distinguishing Features. Dahllite is much like apatite, but it is always a secondary mineral. To make certain of its identity it may be necessary to try the solubility of isolated particles of the mineral.

Related Minerals. Francolite is a closely related mineral.

Occurrence. Dahllite occurs as a secondary mineral in phosphorite or so-called phosphate rock. The usual associate is collophane. The dahllite has probably been formed by the gradual crystallization of the collophane and by the migration of some of the calcium phosphate.

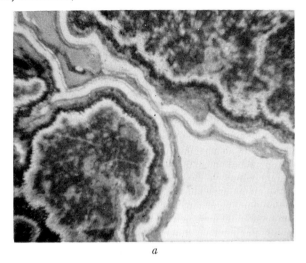

a

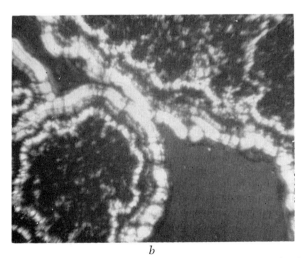

b

FIG. 12-28 *a,b*. ($\times$20) Dahlilite and collophane in phosphate rock. (*a*) Ordinary illumination. (*b*) Dahllite (white) and collophane (black) in the same view with $\times$ nicols.

COLLOPHANE

$$3Ca_3(PO_4)_2.nCa(CO_3,F_2,O)(H_2O)_x \qquad \text{Mineraloid}$$

$$n = 1.57 \text{ to } 1.62$$

Amorphous calcium carbonophosphate is usually considered to be a massive form of apatite, but it is distinctive and should be listed separately as a mineraloid.

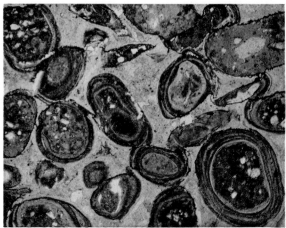

Fig. 12-29. (×18) Collophane in oolitic phosphorite. (Both the matrix and the ooliths are collophane.)

Color. Usually light to dark brown, yellowish brown, gray, etc., in thin sections, but occasionally it is colorless.

Form. Collophane is usually massive but may be oolitic or colloform, in grains and fragments. It often shows the organic structure of bones, molluscs, brachiopods, crinoids, bryozoans, or corals.

Cleavage. Absent. Irregular fracture may show on edges of the slide.

Relief. Moderate, $n >$ balsam. The index of refraction is variable, but it is usually 1.60 to 1.61.

Birefringence. Usually isotropic but may show weak form-birefringence (up to 0.005). Pseudospherulitic structure (concentric instead of fibrous elements) sometimes shows.

Orientation. Birefringent areas may be length-slow or length-fast.

Distinguishing Features. Some specimens of collophane resemble opal, but the refractive index of the latter is always less than that of balsam. Oolitic chamosite resembles oolitic collophane.

Alteration. Collophane is often more or less replaced by calcite. Replacement by quartz, chalcedony, or opal is very rare. In some specimens dahllite seems to be forming at the expense of collophane.

Occurrence. In sedimentary phosphatic limestones, in phosphorites or so-called phosphate rocks as the chief constituent, and in phosphate nodules. It is the dominant mineral of fossil bone, in which the microstructure of the original bone is usually preserved. In fossil bone it has been formed by phosphatic enrichment. In invertebrate fossils it has been formed by enrichment in the case of phosphatic brachiopods such as *Lingula,* but in most cases by the replacement of original calcareous organisms.

It also occurs as a detrital mineral in beach sands of the South Atlantic states according to J. H. C. Martens.

LAZULITE

$Al_2(Mg,Fe)(OH)_2(PO_4)_2$ Monoclinic
$\angle\beta = 88°$

$$n_\alpha = 1.603 \text{ to } 1.604$$
$$n_\beta = 1.632 \text{ to } 1.633$$
$$n_\gamma = 1.639 \text{ to } 1.642$$
$$2V = \text{ca. } 69°; \text{ Opt. } (-)$$
$$b = \beta \text{ or } Y, c \wedge \alpha \text{ or } X = +9°$$

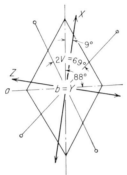

FIG. 12-30. Orientation diagram of lazulite. Section parallel to (010).

Color. Blue to colorless in thin sections. Some sections are pleochroic from blue to colorless. Axial colors: α or X = colorless; β or Y = azure blue; γ or Z = azure blue.

Form. Lazulite is occasionally found in euhedral crystals of bipyramidal habit but it usually occurs in anhedra.

Cleavage. Indistinct parallel to {110}.

Relief. Fairly high, $n >$ balsam.

Birefringence. Strong, $n_\gamma - n_\alpha = 0.036$ to 0.038, so that the maximum interference color is upper second or lower third order.

Extinction. Oblique.

Orientation. The long diagonal of the crystal sections is the faster ray.

Twinning. Polysynthetic twinning is common. Twin-axis = [001].

Interference Figure. The figure is biaxial negative with a large axial angle. The axial plane is {010}. Dispersion, $r < v$.

Distinguishing Features. Lazulite is practically the only blue pleochroic mineral with strong birefringence.

Occurrence. As far as known, lazulite is confined to metamorphic rocks. It occurs in quartzites and in quartz veins. The usual associates are quartz, rutile, corundum, pyrophyllite, kyanite, and andalusite.

CHAPTER 13

Silicates: Framework Structures (Tectosilicates)

SILICA GROUP	FELDSPARS	FELDSPATHOIDS
Quartz	Alkali Feldspars	Leucite
α-Quartz	Orthoclase	Nepheline
β-Quartz	Adularia	Cancrinite
Chalcedony	Sanidine	Sodalite
Opal	Microcline	Haüyne
Tridymite	Anorthoclase	Melilite
Cristobalite	Plagioclase	SCAPOLITE GROUP
Lechatelierite	Albite	ZEOLITES
Coesite	Oligoclase	Analcime
	Andesine	Heulandite
	Labradorite	Stilbite
	Bytownite	Chabazite
	Anorthite	Natrolite
		Mesolite
		Thompsonite
		Scolecite

The tectosilicates form the largest and probably the most important of the six-structural divisions among the silicates. The SiO_4 groups of this series form a continuous three-dimensional framework.

The silica group is frequently included among the oxides as listed in Chapter 11. However, quartz forms a large molecule in which each silicon has four single covalent bonds to oxygen. Each oxygen in turn is attached to two silicons. While the empirical formula is SiO_2 the term "silicon dioxide" is really a misnomer. Although quartz is classed structurally as a tectosilicate, several other members are included with quartz to avoid separation of the silica group.

SILICA GROUP

Silica occurs in nature in six distinct minerals and mineraloids as listed below. The first three are common; lechatelierite (silica glass) is rare, while tridymite and cristobalite are on occasion widely distributed in volcanic rocks.

In respect to physical properties the silica minerals may be placed in two groups. Quartz and chalcedony have refractive indices near balsam

THE SILICA MINERALS AND MINERALOIDS

Mineral	Crystal system	Indices of refraction
Quartz..........	Hexagonal	$n_\omega = 1.5442,\ n_\epsilon = 1.5533,\ n_\epsilon - n_\omega = 0.009$
Chalcedony.......	Aggregates	$n_\alpha = 1.531,\ \ n_\gamma = 1.539,\ \ n_\gamma - n_\alpha = 0.008$
Opal............	Mineraloid	$n = 1.40\text{--}1.46$
Tridymite........	Pseudohexagonal	$n_\alpha = 1.469,\ \ n_\gamma = 1.473,\ \ n_\gamma - n_\alpha = 0.004$
Cristobalite.......	Pseudoisometric	$n_\alpha = 1.484,\ \ n_\gamma = 1.487,\ \ n_\gamma - n_\alpha = 0.003$
Lechatelierite.....	Amorphous	$n = 1.458\text{--}1.462$

and birefringence of about 0.009; the other four have lower indices of refraction and weaker birefringence, which reaches nil in lechatelierite and usually in opal.

Chalcedony always occurs in aggregates of some sort, and consequently the optical properties are not completely known.

On heating quartz there is a sudden change in the properties and crystallization at about 573°C from the trigonal trapezohedral class to the hexagonal trapezohedral class. The low-temperature form is called α-quartz or *low quartz* and the high-temperature form β-quartz or *high quartz*. The quartz of some igneous rocks was β-quartz at the time of its formation but on cooling inverted to α-*quartz*. Similar changes take place on heating tridymite and cristobalite. The stability range of the various

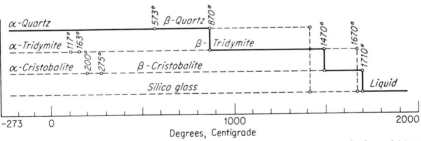

FIG. 13-1. Diagram to show the relations between the various forms of silica. (*After Sosman.*)

silica minerals is shown in the diagram of Figure 13-1. The inversion temperature of quartz by careful measurement has been shown by Tuttle (1949) to vary as much as 1.90°C. Lower inversion temperatures correlate with higher temperatures of formation.

Chalcedony and opal are low-temperature minerals. Quartz has a considerable temperature range. Tridymite and cristobalite also have a rather large temperature range. The two latter occur almost exclusively in volcanic igneous rocks and in all probability have been formed by hot gases at the close of the magmatic period.

Quartz crystals measuring several inches across may be grown on small seed crystals in an autoclave. A solution of sodium carbonate is employed in a sealed system at about 350°C to transfer silica from fragmented quartz in one chamber to the chamber containing seed crystals. The dissolving chamber is about 10°C higher in temperature.

Hale and Hurlbut (1949) grew a quartz crystal on a quartz sphere at temperatures of 376°C (top) and 397°C (bottom) in an autoclave. The pressure was estimated at 700 atm.

α-QUARTZ

SiO$_2$ (Low Quartz)   Hexagonal
                                                              (Rhombohedral subsystem)

$$n_\omega = 1.5442$$
$$n_\epsilon = 1.5533$$
$$\text{Opt. } (+)$$

 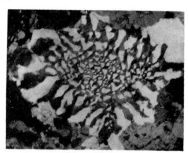

Fig. 13-2.   Fig. 13-3.

Fig. 13-2. ($\times 25$) Quartz grains in sandstone. ($\times$ nicols.)
Fig. 13-3. ($\times 10$) Graphic intergrowth of β-quartz and feldspar. ($\times$ nicols.)

Color. Colorless in thin sections. It often contains inclusions.

Form. Quartz occurs in euhedral prismatic crystals, in veinlets, disseminated grains, and as replacement anhedra. It may be intergrown with orthoclase or microcline (graphic granite) and with plagioclase in vermicular forms (myrmekite). It often occurs as a late interstitial mineral. Quartz is common as pseudomorphs after other minerals.

Cleavage. Usually absent, but it sometimes shows on the edge of the slide. The cleavage is imperfect rhombohedral {10$\bar{1}$1}, almost rectangular in favorable sections since $rr' = 85°46'$.

Relief. Very low, $n >$ balsam.

Birefringence. Rather weak, $n_\varepsilon - n_\omega = 0.009$; thin sections 0.03 mm thick show as a maximum, first-order white interference color with a slight tinge of yellow. Quartz is very useful in determining the thickness of any slide in which it occurs.

Extinction. Parallel in euhedral crystals and symmetrical to cleavage traces. Basal sections are dark in all positions. Irregular and wavy extinction due to strain is common. Vein quartz often shows peculiar structures such as flamboyant, feathered, lamellar, etc. Secondary enlargements of quartz grains are common in sandstones and quartzites.

Orientation. The position of the slower ray marks the trace of the c-axis. Euhedral crystals are therefore length-slow.

Twinning. Although twinning is common in quartz, it rarely shows in thin sections.

Interference Figure. Basal sections of ordinary thickness give a uniaxial positive figure without any rings. The interference figure of thick sections (greater than 1 mm) has a weak or hollow center on account of rotary polarization.

Fig. 13-4. ($\times 10$) Quartz crystals with graphic outlines surrounded by microcline. ($\times$ nicols).

Occasionally quartz gives a biaxial figure with 2V as high as 10°.

Distinguishing Features. Quartz is usually easy to determine on account of its lack of alteration, absence of cleavage except perhaps on the edge of the section, and absence of twinning. Cordierite may be mistaken for it, but cordierite is biaxial. Beryl resembles quartz in thin sections but is length-fast and optically negative. Some varieties of scapolite also resemble quartz, but they are optically negative, length-fast, and have cleavage. Chalcedony has aggregate structure.

Alteration. Quartz is less affected by alteration than almost any other mineral, but it sometimes shows slight replacement by sericite, by pyrophyllite, and rarely by talc.

Occurrence. Quartz is a ubiquitous mineral. It is found in many rock types as an essential, accessory, or secondary mineral. It is especially abundant in sandstones, arkoses, sands, quartzites, granites, rhyolites, and gneisses. In many igneous rocks it is a secondary mineral in seams and cavities. Quartz is the most common of all vein minerals. It occurs as a replacement of other minerals and as a replacement of wood and calcareous fossils.

Quartz is one of the most common detrital minerals.

β-QUARTZ

SiO₂   (High Quartz)   Hexagonal
                                                              (Hexagonal subsystem)

The quartz appearing as phenocrysts in rhyolites and quartz porphyries is the high-temperature form known as β-quartz. It has formed above 573°C.; and the low-temperature form called α-quartz below 573°C. On cooling, the β-quartz inverts to the α-form, so that all quartz examined in thin sections is now α-quartz. The habit of β-quartz is usually different from that of the α-form. A hexagonal dipyramid (the symmetry is $A_6.6A_2$) predominates, and the prism face is subordinate, whereas in the α-form the prism predominates.

As shown by Drugman, the twinning laws of β-quartz are different from those of α-quartz, but twinning rarely shows in thin sections.

CHALCEDONY

SiO₂   Aggregates
                                                              [Hexagonal (?)]

$$n_\omega = 1.531$$
$$n_\epsilon = 1.539$$

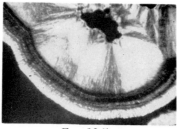   

FIG. 13-5.   FIG. 13-6.

FIG. 13-5. (×10) Radial chalcedony showing a portion of a polarization cross. (× nicols.)

FIG. 13-6. (×8) Banded chalcedony showing both salt and pepper structure and radial layers. (× nicols.)

Color. Colorless to pale brown in thin sections and often bluish white by reflected light.

Form. Chalcedony usually occurs as a cavity filling or lining that is often spherulitic as a replacement of fossils, as cementing material, and in massive form.

Relief. Low, n about the same as that of balsam, either slightly lower or slightly greater.

Birefringence. Rather weak, $n_\gamma - n_\alpha = 0.008$, practically the same as that of quartz. Chalcedony always shows aggregate structure between

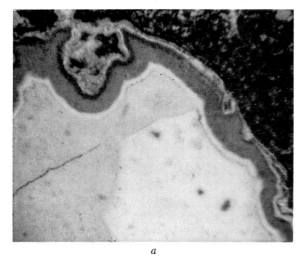

a

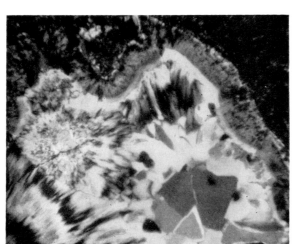

b

FIG. 13-7 *a,b*. (×20) A portion of a vesicle filled with silica: (*a*) ordinary illumination, and (*b*) the same area (× nicols) showing granular quartz surrounded by chalcedony aggregates.

crossed nicols. This often takes on a spherulitic form with the spherulitic cross prominent in many cases.

Extinction. Parallel to the length of the fibers.

Orientation. The fibers are usually length-fast, but in many cases they are length-slow. The fibers of concentric zones are often alternately slow and fast.

Distinguishing Features. The aggregate structure with optical properties very close to those of quartz is distinctive for chalcedony. The minerals most likely to be mistaken for chalcedony are probably gibbsite and dahllite, but in both of these the relief in balsam or clove oil is distinctly higher.

Occurrence. Chalcedony is a secondary mineral in the cavities of igneous rocks and is often associated with quartz, opal, and the zeolites. It also occurs in sedimentary limestone in nodules and bands and as a replacement of calcareous fossils. Chalcedony is the principal constituent of cherts and jaspers. It occurs in diatomite as a replacement of opal. The temperature range of chalcedony seems to be lower than that of quartz.

OPAL

$SiO_2(H_2O)_x$ Mineraloid

$$n = 1.40 \text{ to } 1.46$$
(usually ca. 1.45)

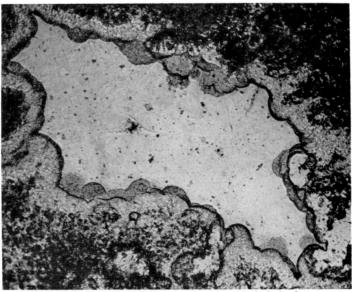

Fig. 13-8. (×65) Colloform opal with infilled chalcedony.

Like other mineraloids opal is variable in its properties.

Color. Colorless to pale gray or brown in thin sections.

Form. Opal is often found in colloform crusts, in veinlets, and as a cavity filling or lining. More often it is massive without any particular structure. It often occurs as a replacement of wood (Figure 8-4) and other organic materials. It is common as a replacement of feldspar and as the cementing material in sandstone.

Cleavage. Absent, but irregular fractures are found on the edges of thin sections.

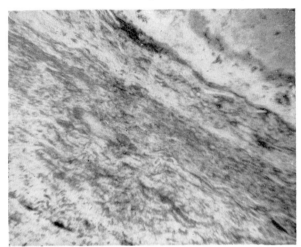

FIG. 13-9. (×20) Crenulated banding in opal.

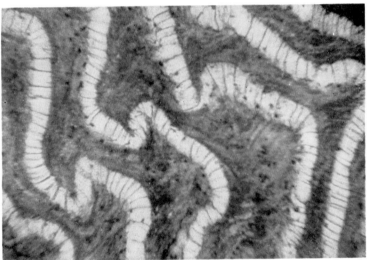

FIG. 13-10. (×25) Wood replacement by opal with contorted bands attributed to the gel-stage.

Relief. Rather high, but $n <$ balsam.

Birefringence. Usually nil, but some varieties, especially hyalite, may show very weak birefringence that is due to strain. Interference colors caused by exceedingly thin films show in sections of precious opal, especially in reflected light.

Distinguishing Features. The high relief and low index of refraction are distinctive. Lechatelierite (silica glass) is very similar, and it may be necessary to try the closed-tube test for water in order to distinguish them.

Occurrence. Opal is a secondary mineraloid in volcanic igneous rocks. It appears in cavities or seams and as a replacement of feldspars or other silicates. The more common associates are quartz, chalcedony, and tridymite. It is the principal constituent of diatomite (Figure 8-7) and geyserite and occasionally occurs as the cementing material in sandstone. It also occurs as the main constituent of opal shale and opal rock.

Lussatite. A fibrous variety of silica with a low index of refraction known as *lussatite* has been considered to be a variety of tridymite or even a distinct silica mineral, but it is probably a mixture of fibrous chalcedony and opal.

TRIDYMITE

SiO_2

Orthorhombic
(Hexagonal above 117°C)

$$n_\alpha = 1.469$$
$$n_\beta = 1.469$$
$$n_\gamma = 1.473$$
$$2V = 35°; \text{Opt.} (+)$$

Color. Colorless in thin sections.

Form. Tridymite usually occurs in minute euhedral crystals as a cavity lining. The crystals are six-sided, thin, tabular, and are often twinned. It also occurs as a porous crystalline aggregate.

Relief. Moderate, but $n <$ balsam.

Birefringence. Very weak, $n_\gamma - n_\alpha = 0.004$; best seen with a sensitive-violet test plate.

Twinning. Wedge-shaped twins made up of two or three individuals are characteristic. The twin plane is $\{10\bar{1}6\}$.

Interference Figure. Because of the small size of the crystals it is very difficult to obtain interference figures with tridymite.

Distinguishing Features. Tridymite very much resembles cristobalite, not only in its general appearance but also in its geologic occurrence. (In the experience of A. F. Rogers, the tile structure often said to be characteristic of this mineral is not at all common.) The twinning of tridymite and the wedge-shaped sections are characteristic; in their absence it may be necessary to determine the refractive index of isolated grains. (For tridymite $n < 1.480$; for cristobalite $n > 1.480$.)

Alteration. Paramorphs of cristobalite after tridymite have been found at several localities. Paramorphs of quartz after tridymite (the pseudo-tridymite of Mallard) are known from a number of localities.

Occurrence. The characteristic occurrence of tridymite is in the cavities of volcanic igneous rocks such as obsidian, rhyolite, andesite, etc. It is a late mineral formed by hot gases. Tridymite is not very abundant,

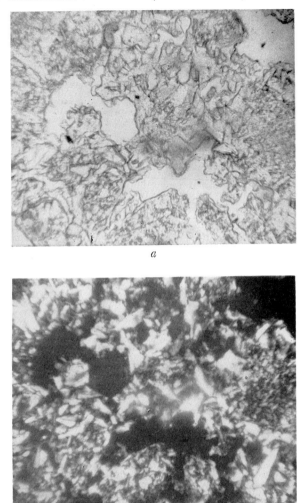

a

b

Fig. 13-11 *a,b*. (×60) (*a*) Tridymite surrounding vesicular cavities, and (*b*) the same area (× nicols) showing small twin crystals.

but it is common and widely distributed. A tridymite-feldspar rock formed by the action of hot gases upon rhyolitic obsidian has been studied by A. F. Rogers in Imperial County, California. In Texas tridymite occurs in a rhyolitic tuff (Gueydan formation of the southwestern Gulf Coastal Plain).

Artificial Tridymite. The principal constituent of silica brick is tridymite with cristobalite as an associate. The silica bricks are made by heating ground-up quartzites of low iron content. The best bricks are said to be those with the largest amount of tridymite.

CRISTOBALITE

SiO$_2$ Pseudoisometric
                                                              (Isometric above 230°C)

$$n_\alpha = 1.484$$
$$n_\gamma = 1.487$$

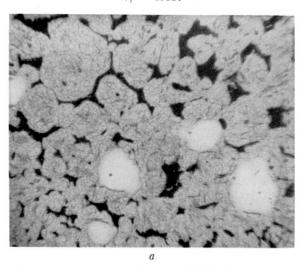

a

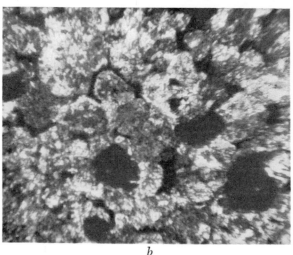

b

FIG. 13-12 *a,b*. (×60) (*a*) Cristobalite forming aggregates of small crystals, and (*b*) the same area (× nicols) showing minute anisotropic crystals.

Color. Colorless in thin sections.

Form. Cristobalite is found in minute square crystals or aggregates in the cavities of volcanic igneous rocks; it also occurs intergrown with the feldspar fibers of spherulites (see Figure 13-12).

Cleavage. Cristobalite has a peculiar curved fracture that is highly characteristic.

Relief. Moderate, $n <$ balsam.

Birefringence. Very weak, $n_\gamma - n_\alpha = 0.003$; best detected with a sensitive-violet test plate. Between crossed nicols it often shows a mosaic structure that is due in part to twinning.

Distinguishing Features. Cristobalite closely resembles tridymite, but the curved fracture usually distinguishes it. It may be necessary to determine the refractive index of detached fragments. (For cristobalite $n > 1.480$; for tridymite $n < 1.480$.)

Occurrence. Cristobalite is found in volcanic igneous rocks such as obsidian, rhyolite, andesite, auganite, and basalt. The fact that it usually occurs in cavities is evidence that it has been formed by hot gases at a late stage. Tridymite is a common associate, and at a number of localities paramorphs of cristobalite after tridymite have been noted.

Cristobalite has been found in some specimens of opal and hence has been formed at a temperature lower than its stability range.

Artificial Cristobalite. Cristobalite and tridymite are the constituents of silica bricks that are made by heating ground-up quartzites of low iron content.

LECHATELIERITE

SiO₂ (Silica Glass) Mineraloid

$$n = 1.458 \text{ to } 1.462$$

Color. Colorless in thin sections. The tendency toward opacity is due to minute bubbles.

Form. Lechatelierite is amorphous silica glass. It is usually vesicular and may also be banded and show flow structure.

Relief. Low, $n <$ balsam.

Birefringence. Nil. Dark between crossed nicols.

Distinguishing Features. From other glasses lechatelierite may be distinguished by its very low refractive index. It very much resembles opal except in its geologic occurrence. A closed-tube test may be necessary to make certain that the mineral is not opal.

Occurrence. Lechatelierite is the main constituent of fulgurites, which are hollow tubes of glass produced by the action of lightning upon quartzose sand.

An interesting occurrence of lechatelierite is that of Meteor Crater, Arizona. Here a highly vesicular silica glass has been produced from sandstone by the heat generated as a result of the explosive impact of a huge meteorite or meteorite swarm (Cañon Diablo meteorite).

Artificial Lechatelierite. Silica glass is now made artificially on a large scale for various kinds of chemical apparatus, lenses, and window panes to transmit ultraviolet light. It has a remarkably low coefficient of thermal expansion.

COESITE

SiO_2 Monoclinic
$\angle \beta = 120°$

$$n_\alpha = 1.599$$
$$n_\gamma = 1.604$$
$$2V = 54°; \text{Opt. } (+)$$

A dense (Sp. Gr. $= 3.01$) and extremely stable phase of silica is produced in the laboratory at 35,000 atm and 500–800°C by the reaction of equal parts of dry sodium metasilicate and diammonium phosphate. It forms both as extremely small aggregates and as crystals up to 0.6 mm in length. The material is colorless and transparent, and pseudohexagonal plates yield unsymmetrical extinction.

Normal quartz rather than dense silica forms below 35,000 atm in the range 500 to 800°C. Occasionally, near 35,000 atm both phases are observed. Above 800°C at 35,000 atm only normal quartz is produced. The conditions required for the formation of coesite, together with its great stability, may provide criteria for more closely estimating the conditions under which deep-seated rocks are crystallized.

FELDSPARS

The feldspar group (Figure 13-13a,b) approximates a tenary system and may be considered in terms of three components: orthoclase, Or $=$ $KAlSi_3O_8$; albite, Ab $=$ $NaAlSi_3O_8$; and anorthite, An $=$ $CaAl_2Si_2O_8$. Or and Ab form the *alkali feldspar group*, with An absent or a minor constituent. Ab and An form the *plagioclase group* where a range in composition may occur from 100 per cent Ab to 100 per cent An.

THE FELDSPAR MINERALS

Alkali feldspar		Plagioclase		
Monoclinic:	Composition	Triclinic:	Composition	
			Ab	An
Orthoclase	$(KNa)AlSi_3O_8$		100	0
		Albite		
Sanidine	$(KNa)AlSi_3O_8$		90	10
		Oligoclase		
Adularia	$(KNa)AlSi_3O_8$		70	30
		Andesine		
Triclinic:			50	50
		Labradorite		
Microcline	$(KNa)AlSi_3O_8$		30	70
		Bytownite		
Anorthoclase	$(NaK)AlSi_3O_8$		10	90
		Anorthite		
			0	100

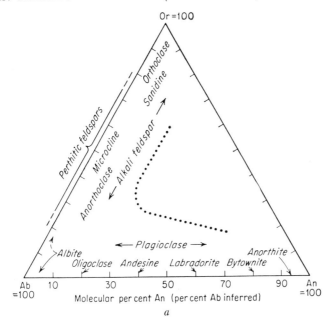

a

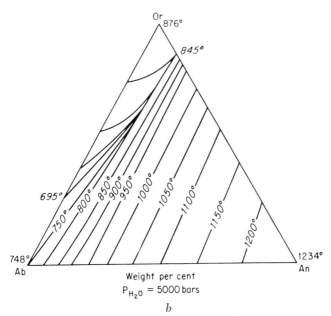

b

FIG. 13-13. (*a*) The approximate distribution of the feldspars in the ternary system Or-Ab-An. Anhydrous melts indicate an area of complete miscibility in the Or-An series at the right of the dotted line. (*Modified from Troger, 1955.*) (*b*) Temperatures of formation in the quaternary system Or-Ab-An-H₂O at 5,000 bars. (*After Yoder, Stewart, and Smith, 1957.*)

Among the feldspars, orthoclase, sanidine, and adularia are monoclinic while the other species—including some adularia—are triclinic. Although two systems of crystallization are represented throughout the feldspars, the crystal habits are somewhat similar, and the deviations in angular measurements of crystals are not large.

Temperature studies of feldspars include the examination of mineral associations, synthesis of pure feldspars at measured temperatures, melting point determinations, and synthesis in sealed bombs with H_2O. When products formed artificially are compared with natural feldspars, information concerning the temperatures of formation may be inferred.

The temperatures which prevail for plagioclase (Figure 13-14a) in the system Ab-An-H_2O show a higher range than the temperatures which prevail for the system Ab-Or-H_2O at 5,000 bars (Figure 13-14b). In the system Ab-Or-An-H_2O at 5,000 bars[1] Yoder, Stewart, and Smith (1957) have shown (Figure 13-13b) that anorthite, orthoclase, and albite will crystallize at 1234°C, 876°C, and 748°C, respectively.

In the series Ab-An-H_2O at 5,000 bars a solidus extends from 748°C to 1234°C (Figure 13-14a). Below the dotted line plagioclase crystals form at the composition indicated along the base of the diagram. Above the dotted line crystals and liquid exist together. Complete melting takes place above the solid line.

In the series Ab-Or-H_2O at 5,000 bars a range of feldspars may form. The minerals in general include adularia, orthoclase, sanidine, microcline, anorthoclase, and albite.

The system Or-Ab-An explains many of the features of the feldspars. A large miscibility gap (Figure 13-13a) lies between Or and An. Under anhydrous conditions crystals are unstable at temperatures in excess of 900°C. In the area of anorthoclase (and Na-sanidine) which borders the miscibility gap on the Or-Ab side of the diagram, crystals are stable at high temperatures and unstable at low temperatures.

The Or-Ab series is continuous at high temperatures, but on cooling exsolution develops. The homogenous material separates into two solid feldspar phases: one rich in soda, the other rich in potash. Where the potash-rich phase (microcline) predominates over the soda-rich phase (albite), the intergrowth is referred to as *perthite* (Figure 13-15). Where the soda-rich phase predominates, the intergrowth is described as *antiperthite* (Figure 13-16).

The name perthite is derived from the locality Perth, Quebec, Canada, where unusual examples of this type of exsolution were originally described. Perthitic intergrowth, known as *microperthite*, exhibits a characteristic pattern between crossed nicols. It develops in the Or-Ab series

---

[1] 1 bar = about 14.5 pounds per square inch.

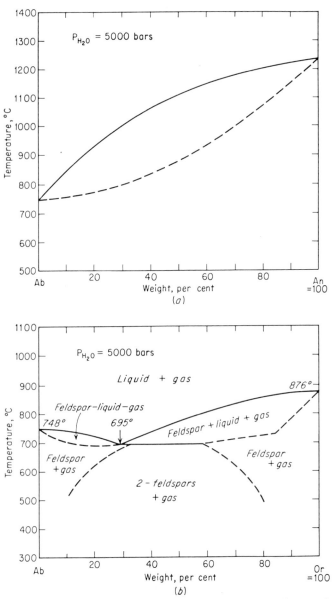

FIG. 13-14. Projections of the feldspar ternary systems at 5,000 bars H₂O pressure. (a) The plagioclase system Ab-An-H₂O. (b) The alkali feldspar system Ab-Or-H₂O. (After Yoder, Stewart, and Smith, 1957.)

with the fall in temperature below 660°C. X-ray study shows that Or-Ab feldspar which may appear beneath the microscope as a single phase is often made up of two phases. This may be called *cryptoperthite*.

The Ab-An series includes the plagioclase group from albite to anorthite. Köhler (1949) has shown that the optical properties of twinned plagioclase may reflect the thermal history of the material. A difference exists between the properties of plagioclase derived from high-temperature volcanic rocks and plagioclase from other sources.

Igneous Association. The alkali feldspars are widely distributed in igneous rocks, particularly among the granite and syenite clans. Plagioclase occurs in a range of compositions through the igneous rock classification from granite where Ab is predominant to peridotite where An

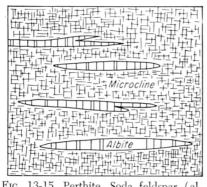 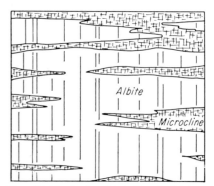

FIG. 13-15. Perthite. Soda feldspar (albite) crystallized in predominant potash feldspar (microcline) groundmass.

FIG. 13-16. Antiperthite. Potash feldspar (microcline) crystallized in a predominant soda feldspar (albite) groundmass.

predominates. Microscopic study in which the feldspars play a major role has contributed greatly to knowledge of igneous rocks.

The normal sequence and association of the feldspars with respect to the most common minerals derived from a magma was set forth by V. M. Goldschmidt (1916). The feldspars and quartz constitute the felsic products, while olivine, pyroxene, amphibole, and the associated metallic minerals form on the mafic side. The temperatures decline from the gabbroic to the granitic stages, but at the same time a sequence in the minerals formed is maintained according to the general outline of Figure 13-17.

The temperatures of formation of the feldspars are considered significant in the interpretation of the temperatures of rock crystallization. High- and low-temperature forms of several feldspars are recognized.

Potassium feldspar may crystallize as the high temperature modification sanidine, but it may be metastable and may invert later to microcline (MacKenzie, 1957). Three forms of albite are believed to exist as shown by internal structure: low temperature up to 450°C, intermediate temperature from 450°C to 1000°C, and high temperature above 1000°C.

Sanidine, albite, and other feldspars as formed in lavas or under other near surface conditions are indicative of high temperatures. On the other hand, orthoclase, albite, and other feldspars formed in well-crystallized

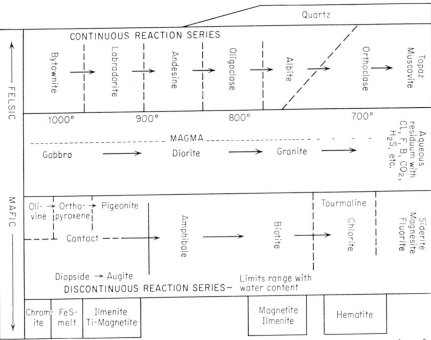

Fig. 13-17. The plagioclase sequence in igneous rocks. The approximate order of separation in the normal crystallization of a magma series. (*Modified from Tröger and V. M. Goldschmidt.*)

plutonic masses or in pegmatites are formed at lower temperatures. Adularia is frequently a vein mineral.

Numerous albite and oligoclase specimens (An_6 to An_{17}) from pegmatites and granites (Laves, 1954) have been shown to consist of two submicroscopically discrete phases. In microscopic study these appear as single phases. Yet X-ray studies show discontinuities in the progressive range of lattice dimensions with composition (Smith and Yoder, 1956). Until these are interpreted in terms of internal structure and more precise optical data are established, optical information now available must be utilized.

Crystallization. The optical properties of the feldspars are ordinarily oriented with respect to crystallographic directions. Monoclinic feldspar crystals may be illustrated by orthoclase (Figure 13-18). The significant interfacial angle (010) ∧ (001) and the angle between the two prominent cleavages is 90°. The angle β which measures the inclination of the a-axis is 63°57′. Triclinic members of the alkali feldspar group exhibit moderate but significant angular differences. The (010) ∧ (001) angle deviates from 90°.

The triclinic crystals of the plagioclase group may be illustrated by albite (Figure 13-19). Measurements for the significant angle (010) ∧

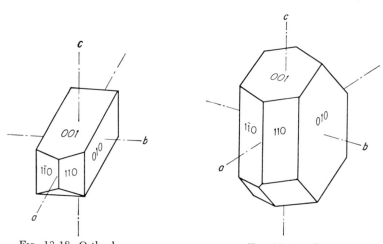

FIG. 13-18. Orthoclase.   FIG. 13-19. Albite.

(001) range from 90°3½′ (albite) to 83°54′ (anorthite). The angles between the crystal axes for plagioclase range as follows:

$\alpha(c \wedge b)$	$\beta(a \wedge c)$	$\gamma(a \wedge b)$
93°–94°30′	115°–116°30	87°–91°30

Both alkali feldspars and plagioclase have good cleavage in two directions parallel to (001) and (010). Cleavage fragments observed with the microscope often form small flat plates with two sides parallel. The best cleavage is parallel to (001), but (010) is also good (Figure 13-20). Fragments 0.1 to 0.4 mm thick and large enough to fill the field of the microscope yield interference figures which are readily measured. These are described by Tuttle as excellent mounts for determining the optic angle with the universal stage.

Feldspar frequently exhibits phase changes in what may appear externally as a single crystal but actually represents two or more individu..ls. The individuals show differences in birefringence between crossed nicols when examined in thin section. Several stages of growth in plagioclase may be shown by zonal structure. Complexity in growth at times may produce such an unusual development as a central crystal core of plagioclase enclosed in an envelope of orthoclase.

Twinning. Feldspars exhibit at least seven types of twinning. Symmetrical displacement is observed so frequently that twinning is widely used in study and identification.

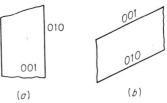

FIG. 13-20. Feldspar cleavage fragments. (*a*) Cleavage parallel to (001). (*b*) Cleavage parallel to (010).

Twins are described with reference to directions in the feldspar crystal. Description is given in terms of the axes around which twinning takes place, and the composition planes along which the twin individuals meet.

FELDSPAR TWINS

Type	Twin axis	Composition plane
Albite	$\perp$(010)	(010)
Manebach	$\perp$(001)	(001)
Baveno	$\perp$(021) or ($0\bar{2}1$)	(021) or ($0\bar{2}1$) (Right or Left)
Carlsbad	$\parallel$[001]	largely (010); partly (100)
Actine	$\parallel$[010]	(001)
Pericline	$\parallel$[010]	In zone (010); ranges
Ala	$\parallel$[100]	(001) or (010)

Twin crystals formed by simple repetition are represented by the Carlsbad, Baveno, and Manebach twin laws (Figure 13-21). Carlsbad twins are common in orthoclase, while Baveno and Manebach twins are occasionally observed. Carlsbad twins may also be present in plagioclase. In

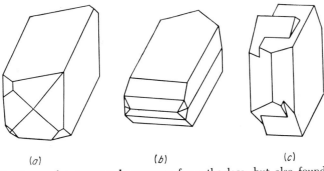

FIG. 13-21. Types of twin crystals common for orthoclase, but also found on other feldspars. (*a*) Baveno, (*b*) Manebach, (*c*) Carlsbad.

thin section, Carlsbad twins often exhibit two elongate individuals separated by a single composition plane (Figure 13-22a). The individuals differ in extinction between crossed nicols. Baveno twins may be separated by a diagonal plane (Figure 13-22b).

Multiple or polysynthetic twinning is abundant in plagioclase (Figure 13-23a). Albite twinning is widespread. It is recognized by the parallelism between the composition planes and the (010) cleavage (Figure 13-23b). Fragments showing albite twinning are useful in plagioclase identification.

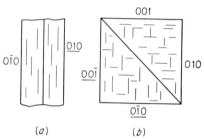

(a)   (b)

Fig. 13-22 a,b. Sections of twin crystals as illustrated by orthoclase: (a) Carlsbad and (b) Baveno.

According to Emmons and Gates (1943) polysynthetic twinning is formed late in the growth of the plagioclase crystal. A common force leading to polysynthetic twinning is the mutual interference of growing crystals. A phenocryst ordinarily suffers little twinning in a fine-grained groundmass. Donnay (1943) places greater weight on the role of internal factors in twinning.

Schuster's Method. In this identification, known as Schuster's Method, cleavage flakes are mounted on a glass slide. Fragments with slightly

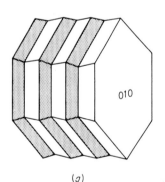
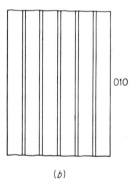

(a)   (b)

Fig. 13-23 a,b. (a) Polysynthetic twinning of the albite type as developed on a single plagioclase crystal. (b) A cleavage fragment showing albite twinning. Cleavage parallel to (001).

better cleavage will show composition planes parallel to cleavage edges. This is indicative of albite twins with composition planes normal to (001). Schuster's curves show the extinction angles corresponding to the complete range of plagioclase species (Figure 13-24). Reference to the curve for extinction on (001) should give the proper value of the albite twinning for the plagioclase under observation. The extinction angles for fragments on (010), also given, may yield more significant angles for plagioclase at the sodic end of the chart.

Michel-Lévy Method. Where albite twins are observed in thin sections no limitation in orientation prevails as in the case of the examination of fragments. Here Schuster's method is inapplicable. However, in such instances the statistical method of Michel-Lévy has been found useful.

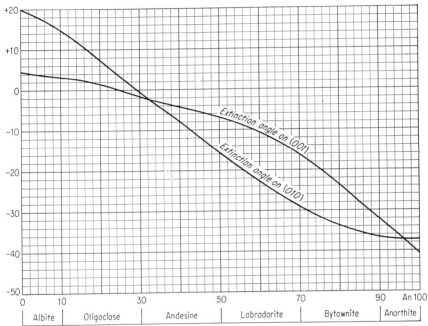

FIG. 13-24. Schuster's curves showing the extinction of albite twinning on (001) and (010) cleavages.

The method is dependent upon the presence of a satisfactory number of crystals in a section to provide a sufficiently representative identification. Sections of crystals cut normal to (010) are sought. These are recognized by three factors: (1) the sharpness of the composition planes with a slight change in focus, (2) uniformity of illumination of all lamellae when parallel to the vibration planes of the nicols, and (3) the equality of the extinction angles for twin sets rotated to the left or right.

A single measurement is shown in Figure 13-25. At least eight or ten different crystals should be measured to indicate the maximum extinction angle for a particular plagioclase. A difference of as much as 6° in *L* and *R* angles is allowable, but the average is used. Crystal sections in which the alternate *L* and *R* twin groups show uniform illumination yield satis-

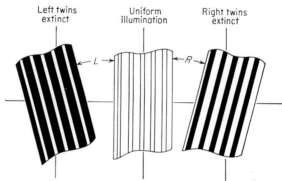

FIG. 13-25. Diagram showing the method of determining the extinction angles in albite twins cut normal to (010) for the plagioclase feldspars (the method of Michel-Lévy).

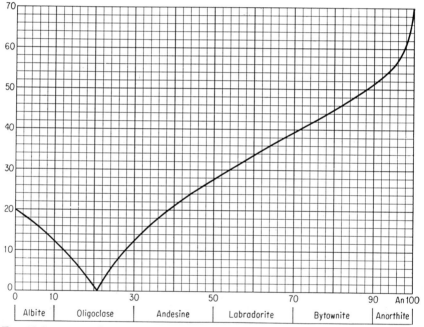

FIG. 13-26. Curve showing the maximum extinction angle of albite twins cut normal to (010) for the plagioclase feldspars (Michel-Lévy's method).

factory angles. In recording the extinction angle (Figure 13-26) the direction of the faster ray is used; otherwise no angle greater than 45° would be obtained. It will be noted that angles of $19\frac{1}{2}°$ or less appear twice on the curve. From An_0 to An_{21} the angle is negative, and for those above An_{21} it is positive. In the absence of the (001:100) edge—and this is rarely present—positive and negative angles cannot be distinguished.

FIG. 13-27. (×18) Combined Carlsbad-albite twinning in plagioclase. (× nicols.)

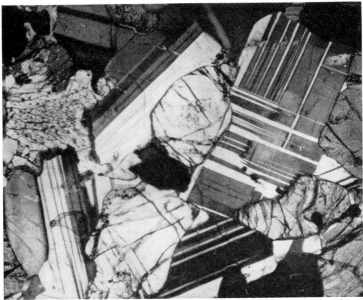

FIG. 13-28. (×24) Albite, Carlsbad, and pericline twinning in plagioclase. (× nicols.)

In order to identify plagioclase of the An_0-An_{21} range from plagioclase of the An_{21}-An_{38} range, indices of refraction or optical sign may be used. Most of the first group have indices of refraction less than balsam and are optically positive. The others have indices of refraction greater than balsam and are optically negative.

Extinction of Combined Carlsbad-Albite Twins. When Carlsbad and albite twinning are both present (Figures 13-27, 13-28), a single crystal section normal to (010) will suffice for the determination. Such sections (Figure 13-29) will in general yield four extinction positions for the crystal X_1, X_2 and Y_1, Y_2. Sections normal to (010), the composition face for both kinds of twins, may be recognized in the 45° position. Here the

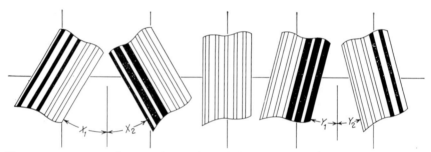

Fig. 13-29. Diagram showing the method of determining the two sets of extinction angles (X and Y) in sections of combined Carlsbad-albite twins cut normal to (010).

albite twinning disappears, and the crystal appears to be a simple Carlsbad twin. In the 0° position both the albite and Carlsbad twinning practically disappear.

The extinction angles X_1, X_2 and Y_1, Y_2 of the albite twins in each half of the section (Figure 13-29) are measured. The average of the two smaller (Y values) is given on the horizontal lines of Figure 13-30, and the average of the two larger (X values) on the curves. The intersection of the proper horizontal line with the appropriate curve gives a vertical line that indicates the relative amount of the anorthite molecule.

At a composition of about An_{20} Carlsbad twinning cannot be detected in thin sections, and the method is not readily applicable. In this case the maximum extinction angle for albite twins in sections normal to (010) is 0°.

Angle of the Rhombic Section. Pericline twinning when observed may provide useful information (Figure 13-31). It is polysynthetic and results in lathlike individuals which may resemble albite twins as observed with the microscope. However, pericline twin planes may be almost normal to the direction of the albite composition plane. Pericline

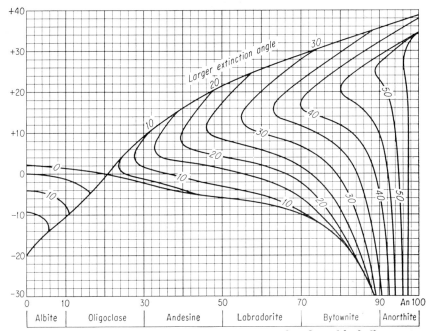

FIG. 13-30. Curves showing extinction angles of combined Carlsbad-albite twins normal to (010) for the plagioclase feldspars. (*After F. E. Wright.*)

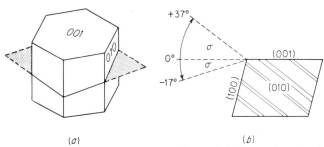

(a)   (b)

FIG. 13-31. The inclination of pericline twin planes. (a) One inclination of the composition plane projected to show the rhombic section. (b) Pericline twin planes on (010). The angle δ with (001) ranges from +37° to −17° (angle of the rhombic section).

twins are recognized by their inclination with reference to the (001) ∧ (010) edge (the angle of the rhombic section). A plagioclase crystal showing the projection of the rhombic section and the corresponding pericline composition plane is shown in Figure 13-31a. It is the inclination of the section rather than the shape that is significant. It ranges with the composition of the plagioclase from a positive angle of 37° for albite

(An_0) to a negative angle of 17° for anorthite (An_{100}). At about the intermediate composition of andesine (An_{40}) the angle of inclination is 0° (Figure 13-31b). The range in the angles for the various types of plagioclase as shown by Schmidt (1919) is given in Figure 13-32.

Combinations of albite and pericline twinning frequently appear in alkali feldspar—particularly in microcline. The combination produces a distinctive grid pattern between crossed nicols. In addition, tongues of

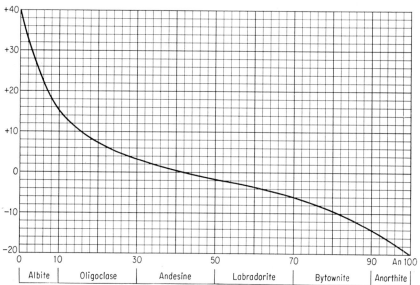

Fig. 13-32. A curve showing the range in angles of inclination of pericline twins from An_0 to An_{100}. (*After E. Schmidt.*)

albite often penetrate the grid structure at more or less regular intervals. The intergrowth forms the pattern known as perthite (Figure 13-15).

Alkali Feldspar Group

The alkali feldspar of volcanic rocks is frequently sanidine, while plutonic rocks yield orthoclase. Microcline is a common constituent of pegmatites while adularia may be a vein mineral.

High- and low-temperature groups of alkali feldspars have been distinguished by MacKenzie and Smith (1956). When correlated with X-ray data and composition, the optic angles for the alkali feldspars indicate a high-temperature division (Figure 13-33) containing anorthclase, two forms of sanidine and a high-temperature albite. Orthoclase, microcline, and low-temperature albite constitute a low-temperature

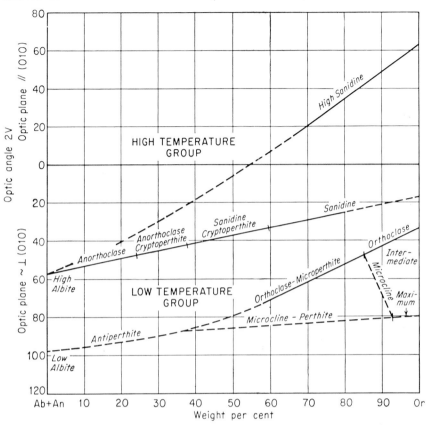

FIG. 13-33. The range in optic angles for the alkali feldspars. (*After Tuttle, 1952; MacKenzie and Smith, 1956.*)

group. The texture of the higher temperature group is cryptoperthitic while the lower temperature group is microperthitic.

ORTHOCLASE

$(K,Na)AlSi_3O_8$ Monoclinic
                                                        $\angle\beta = 63°57'$

$$n_\alpha = 1.518$$
$$n_\beta = 1.524$$
$$n_\gamma = 1.526$$
$$2V = 69° \text{ to } 72°; \text{ Opt. } (-)$$
$$b = \gamma \text{ or } Z, \ a \wedge \alpha \text{ or } X = +5° \text{ to } +12°,$$
$$c \wedge \beta \text{ or } Y = -14° \text{ to } -21°$$

Color. Colorless in thin sections, but may be cloudy on account of incipient alteration in contrast with quartz, which is clear.

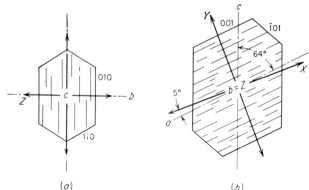

(a)   (b)
FIG. 13-34 *a,b*. Orientation diagrams of orthoclase. Sections (*a*) normal to the *c*-axis and (*b*) parallel to (010).

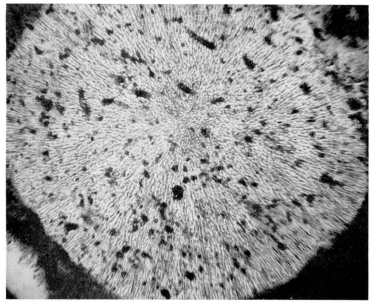

FIG. 13-35. (×160) Orthoclase-cristobalite spherulite in volcanic glass.

Form. Orthoclase occurs in phenocrysts, in subhedral and anhedral crystals, and in spherulites.

Cleavage. Perfect cleavage parallel to {001}, less perfect parallel to {010}, imperfect parallel to {110}.

Relief. Low, $n <$ balsam.

Birefringence. Weak, $n_\gamma - n_\alpha = 0.008$; so the interference colors are gray and white of the first order and the maximum a little lower than that of quartz in the same slide.

Extinction. On {001} parallel, on {010} from 5° to 12°, increasing with the soda content.

Orientation. Cleavage traces on {010} make a small angle with the faster ray.

Twinning. Twinning according to the Carlsbad law (*c*-axis or [001] = twin-axis). These are simple twins consisting of two individuals.

Interference Figure. The interference figure is biaxial negative with a large axial angle. The axial plane is normal to {010}. Dispersion, $r > v$.

Distinguishing Features. Orthoclase is distinguished from its dimorph sanidine by its large axial angle.

Occurrence. Orthoclase is a widely distributed mineral in persilicic igneous rocks such as granites and syenites. In spherulites of obsidian and rhyolite it is often intergrown with cristobalite or quartz. It is also common in detrital deposits and in sandstones and arkoses.

In rocks subjected to hydrothermal alteration orthoclase is ordinarily more resistant than plagioclase. Kaolinite often forms a weathering product at the expense of orthoclase.

ADULARIA

KAlSi$_3$O$_8$ Monoclinic

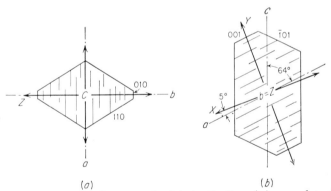

Fig. 13-36 *a,b*. Orientation diagrams of adularia. Sections (*a*) normal to the *c*-axis and (*b*) parallel to (010).

Adularia is probably a variety of orthoclase but is treated separately because of genetic significance.

The optical properties of adularia correspond to those of orthoclase, but the crystal habit is pseudo-orthorhombic with a rhombic cross section (110 ∧ 1̄10 = 61°13′). The (010) face is narrow or absent.

Adularia is a rather low-temperature feldspar found in veins and replacement deposits, and in some rocks of low-grade metamorphism. It is especially characteristic of Tertiary gold and silver ores of the bonanza

Fig. 13-37. (×20) Vein feldspar, probably adularia. (× nicols.)

type. The crystals are commonly minute and can be identified only with a rather high-power objective. X-ray study indicates a triclinic phase.

SANIDINE

$(K,Na)AlSi_3O_8$ Monoclinic

$$\angle\beta = 63°57'$$

$$n_\alpha = 1.517 \text{ to } 1.520$$
$$n_\beta = 1.523 \text{ to } 1.525$$
$$n_\gamma = 1.524 \text{ to } 1.526$$
$$2V = 0° \text{ to } 12°; \text{ Opt. } (-)$$

Orientation: (1) Ax. pl. {010}, $b = \beta$ or Y, $a \wedge \alpha$ or $X = +5°$ or (2) Ax. pl. $\perp$ {010}, $b = \gamma$ or Z, $a \wedge \alpha$ or $X = +5°$

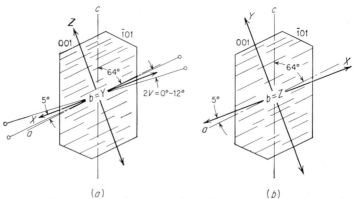

(a)   (b)

Fig. 13-38 a,b. Orientation diagrams of sanidine. Sections parallel to (010).

Color. Colorless in thin sections; clear in contrast with orthoclase, which is often cloudy.

Form. Sanidine usually occurs in distinct crystals as phenocrysts.

Cleavage. Perfect parallel to {001}, less perfect parallel to {010}. There may also be parting parallel to {100}.

Relief. Low, $n <$ balsam.

Birefringence. Weak, $n_\gamma - n_\alpha = 0.007$, so the interference colors are gray and grayish white of the first order.

Extinction. On (001) parallel, on (010) $+5°$. Sections normal to an optic axis remain practically dark since the axial angle is often very small.

Twinning. Usually according to the Carlsbad law (c-axis or $[001] =$ twin-axis). Twins are simple twins of two individuals and are rarely polysynthetic.

Interference Figure. Some sections give a negative biaxial interference figure with a small axial angle, but the angle may be so small that the figure is almost uniaxial. Dispersion, (1) $r < v$, (2) $r > v$.

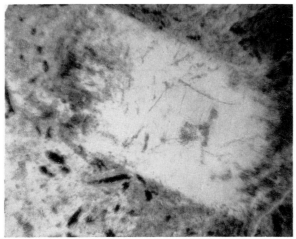

FIG. 13-39. ($\times 12$) A single crystal of sanidine which has suffered corrosion on each end.

Distinguishing Features. Sanidine is distinguished from orthoclase by the small axial angle and in some cases by a difference of orientation. Orthoclase is often cloudy on account of incipient alteration; sanidine, on the other hand, is clear.

Occurrence. Sanidine has been generally considered characteristic of volcanic rocks such as rhyolites and trachytes and the corresponding tuffs, but MacKenzie and Smith have suggested its occurrence in plutonic rocks as well.

MICROCLINE

KAlSi$_3$O$_8$ Triclinic

$$\angle\alpha = 89°53'$$
$$\angle\beta = 64°10'$$
$$\angle\gamma = 90°51'$$

$$n_\alpha = 1.518 \text{ to } 1.522$$
$$n_\beta = 1.522 \text{ to } 1.526$$
$$n_\gamma = 1.525 \text{ to } 1.530$$
$$2V = 77° \text{ to } 84°; \text{ Opt. } (-).$$

Ax. pl. or γ or Z are nearly $\perp$ (010). Angle
between trace of ax. pl. and edge (001): (010) $= +5°$

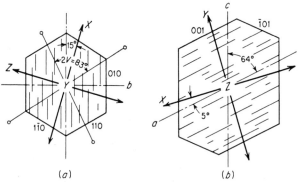

(a)   (b)

Fig. 13-40 a,b. Orientation diagrams of microcline. Sections (a) normal to the c-axis and (b) parallel to (010).

Color. Colorless in thin sections but may be cloudy on account of incipient alteration.

Form. Microcline is usually found in subhedral to anhedral crystals. Euhedral crystals are rarely seen in rock sections.

Cleavage. Perfect parallel to {001}, less perfect parallel to {010}, imperfect parallel to {110} and {1$\bar{1}$0}.

Relief. Low, $n <$ balsam.

Birefringence. Weak, $n_\gamma - n_\alpha = 0.007$, so interference colors are gray and white of the first order.

Extinction. Extinction angle on (001) $= +15°$, on (010) $= +5°$.

Orientation. Cleavage traces on (010) are about parallel to the faster ray.

Twinning. Polysynthetic twinning is almost universal in microcline. The twinning is in two directions, one according to the albite law ({010} $=$ twin-plane), and the other according to the pericline law (b-axis or [010] $=$ twin-axis). This usually gives the so-called *gridiron* or *quadrille* structure (Figure 13-41), the two sets of lamellae being at right angles. The twin lamellae are usually spindle shaped and the extinction usually wavy.

Intergrowth. Albite is commonly intergrown with microcline so that the (010) directions are parallel. This intergrowth is known as *perthite*.

Interference Figure. On account of the twinning it is usually difficult to obtain good interference figures. Dispersion, $r > v$.

FIG. 13-41. (×15) A microcline section cut parallel to (001). (× nicols.)

FIG. 13-42. (×12) Anhedral crystals of microcline in random orientations. (× nicols.)

Distinguishing Features. Microcline is distinguished from orthoclase by polysynthetic twinning and from orthoclase and albite by the extinction angle of 15° on (001) and by the spindle-shaped twin lamellae.

Occurrence. Microcline occurs in some granites, syenites, and gneisses. In *perthite* it is the principal feldspar of granite pegmatites. It is also a common mineral in sandstones, arkoses, etc., and is found as a detrital mineral in sands.

ANORTHOCLASE

$(Na,K)AlSi_3O_8$ (Soda Microcline)   Triclinic

$$\angle\alpha = 90°6'$$
$$\angle\beta = 63°42'$$
$$\angle\gamma = 90°17'$$

$$n_\alpha = 1.522 \text{ to } 1.536$$
$$n_\beta = 1.526 \text{ to } 1.539$$
$$n_\gamma = 1.527 \text{ to } 1.541$$
$$2V = 43° \text{ to } 54°; \text{ Opt. } (-).$$

Ax. pl. nearly $\perp$ to $\{010\}$

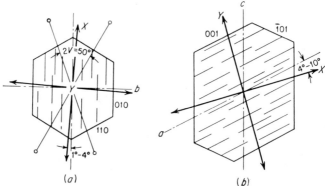

(a)   (b)

FIG. 13-43 a,b. Orientation diagram of anorthoclase. Sections (a) normal to the c-axis and (b) parallel to (010).

Color. Colorless in thin sections.

Form. Anorthoclase occurs in phenocrysts and in anhedral crystals; also in large cleavage masses.

Cleavage. Perfect parallel to $\{001\}$, less perfect parallel to $\{010\}$, as in the other feldspars.

Relief. Low, $n <$ balsam.

Birefringence. Weak, $n_\gamma - n_\alpha = 0.005\text{–}0.007$; the interference colors are gray and white of the first order.

Extinction. On (001) $= +1°$ to $+4°$, on (010) $= +4°$ to $+10°$.

Twinning. Polysynthetic twinning in two directions like that of microcline, but the lamellae are finer. It may be necessary to have an unusually thin section to detect the twinning.

Interference Figure. The figure is biaxial negative with a moderate axial angle. Dispersion, $r > v$.

Distinguishing Features. Anorthoclase may be distinguished from practically all other feldspars by the axial angle of about 50° (sanidine is lower and the others are higher). The small extinction angle on (001) distinguishes it from microcline and all the plagioclases except albite.

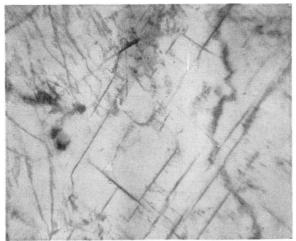

FIG. 13-44. (×30) A portion of a crystal of anorthoclase showing cleavage.

Occurrence. The characteristic occurrence of anorthoclase is in soda-rich igneous rocks such as rhomb porphyries. It is sometimes found in pegmatites. It is a comparatively rare mineral.

Plagioclase Group

The plagioclase minerals constitute an important group for which an unusual number of optical methods have been developed to aid in study and identification. These are illustrated in text figures and diagrams. For convenience the figures relating to the different methods are listed below:

PLAGIOCLASE METHODS

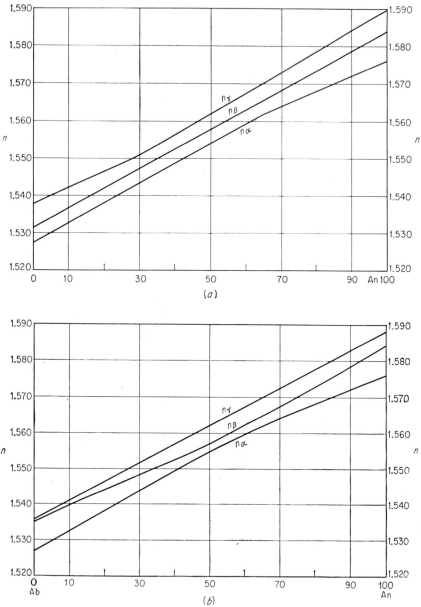

Fig. 13-45 a,b. (a) Indices of refraction of normal plagioclase. (Chayes, 1952.) (b) Indices of refraction of plagioclase inverted to high-temperature modifications by heating. (Smith, 1957.)

As studies of the group progress, a small but consistent distinction in optical properties develops between plagioclase of normal-temperature origin and high-temperature types. This is more noticeable in the range An_0 to An_{35} (albite and oligoclase). Fundamental optical data on the distinction between high- and low-temperature forms have not yet been established to the extent desirable for routine study. Data on the two types which may be applied with the universal stage are shown in Figure 13-50. Natural plagioclases have been converted to the high-temperature

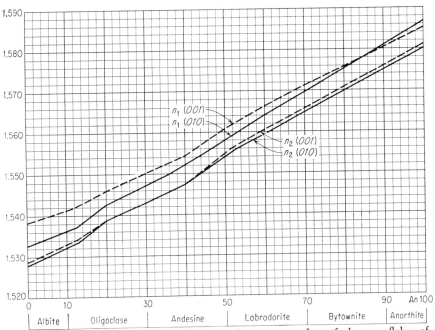

FIG. 13-46. Curves showing the indices of refraction n_1 and n_2 of cleavage flakes of the plagioclase feldspars. (*After Tsuboi*.)

forms and precise indices determined (Smith, 1957). These are given in Figure 13-45b.

The determination of the index of refraction of glass formed by the fusion of plagioclase has been utilized as a method of identification (Foster, 1955). Selected plagioclase fragments as free as possible from impurities are placed in platinum foil. The material is then heated to about 1500°C with the oxygen-gas blowpipe and quenched in water. The index of refraction of the glass formed is determined by the immersion method with index liquids. Refractive indices for plagioclase glass are significant of the original plagioclase (Figure 13-47).

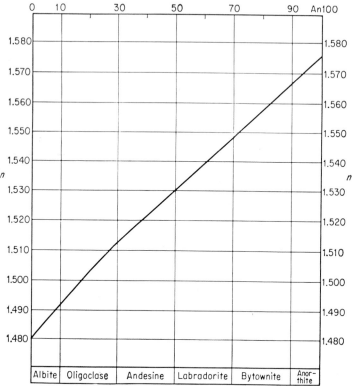

FIG. 13-47. Indices of refraction of plagioclase glass. (*After Foster, 1955.*)

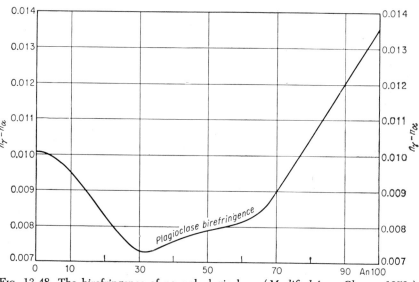

FIG. 13-48. The birefringence of normal plagioclase. (*Modified from Chayes, 1952.*)

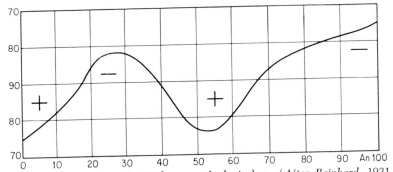

FIG. 13-49. The axial angle 2V for normal plagioclase. (*After Reinhard*, 1931.)

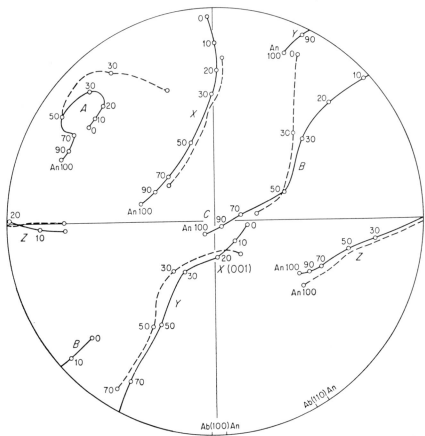

FIG. 13-50. A stereographic projection of X, Y, and Z and the optic axes A and B oriented with respect to (001) and the c-axis for both normal plagioclase (solid lines) and high-temperature plagioclase (broken lines). (*After Muir*, 1955.)

ALBITE

An$_{0-10}$ Triclinic

$$n_\alpha = 1.527 \text{ to } 1.533$$
$$n_\beta = 1.531 \text{ to } 1.537$$
$$n_\gamma = 1.538 \text{ to } 1.542$$
$$2V = 77° \text{ to } 82°; \text{ Opt. } (+)$$

Fig. 13-51. ($\times$12) Albite showing curved twin lamellae caused by deformation.

Color. Colorless in thin sections.

Form. Albite[2] occurs in plates or lath-shaped sections, rarely in phenocrysts. It may be intergrown with microcline.

Cleavage. {001} perfect, {010} less perfect, {110} and {1$\bar{1}$0} imperfect.

Relief. Low, $n <$ balsam. (For indices of cleavage flakes see Figure 13-46.)

Birefringence. Rather weak, $n_\gamma - n_\alpha = 0.009$ to 0.011; interference colors are pale yellow of the first order, about the same as quartz in the same section.

Extinction. The maximum extinction angle in albite twins (*i.e.*, twins according to the albite law) varies from 12° to 19°. In cleavage flakes parallel to (001) the extinction angle is 3° to 5°; on those parallel to (010), from 15° to 20°.

Twinning. Polysynthetic twinning according to the albite law ({010} = twin-plane) is rarely absent. There may also be twinning according to the Carlsbad law (*c*-axis or [001] = twin-axis) either alone or combined with albite twinning. Pericline twinning (*b*-axis or [010] = twin-axis) is sometimes present. The angle of the rhombic section is +15° to +37°.

---

[2] The word albite may be used in 3 ways (1) as a mineral name, (2) as a molecule, and (3) to describe polysynthetic twinning || to (010).

Interference Figure. The interference figure is biaxial positive with a large axial angle. Dispersion, $r < v$ weak.

Distinguishing Features. Albite is the only plagioclase with indices of refraction both equal to and considerably less than balsam. Extinction angles furnish significant criteria (Figure 13-26).

Occurrence. Albite occurs in some granites, in granite pegmatites, in veins, and in some metamorphic rocks. It is the only plagioclase that is at all common as a vein mineral. In some altered subsilicic igneous rocks

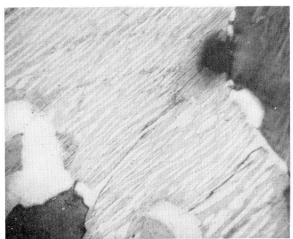

FIG. 13-52. ($\times 30$) Albite intergrown with microcline in a perthitic texture.

(spilites) it is formed at the expense of calcic plagioclase as a deuteric mineral.

OLIGOCLASE

An_{10-30} Triclinic

$$n_\alpha = 1.533 \text{ to } 1.543$$
$$n_\beta = 1.537 \text{ to } 1.548$$
$$n_\gamma = 1.542 \text{ to } 1.551$$
$$2V = 82° \text{ to } 90°; \text{ Opt. } (+) \text{ or } (-)$$

Color. Colorless in thin sections.

Form. Oligoclase occurs in euhedral, subhedral, and anhedral crystals. The appearance is the same as for the other feldspars.

Cleavage. {001} perfect, {010} less perfect, {110} and {1̄10} imperfect.

Relief. Low, n either less than, greater than, or about equal to that of balsam. (For indices of cleavage flakes see Figure 13-46.)

Birefringence. Weak or rather weak, $n_\gamma - n_\alpha = 0.008$ to 0.009; interference colors are gray or white of the first order.

Extinction. The maximum extinction angle in albite twins (twinning according to the albite law) varies from 0° to 12°. The extinction angle on a (001) cleavage flake varies from 0° to 3°; on {010} flakes, from 0° to + 15° (Figure 13-24).

Twinning. As in albite.

Interference Figure. The figure is biaxial, either positive or negative with a very large axial angle, or neutral ($2V = 90°$) for An_{17}. Dispersion, $r > v$ weak.

Distinguishing Features. Indices of refraction are slightly below balsam at one extreme, but are generally above. Extinction angles (Figure 13-26) are distinctive.

Occurrence. Oligoclase is very common in persilicic igneous rocks such as granites and rhyolites, also in syenites, trachytes, and other igneous rocks. It is occasionally found in granite pegmatites and also in some metamorphic rocks.

ANDESINE

An_{30-50} Triclinic

$$n_\alpha = 1.543 \text{ to } 1.554$$
$$n_\beta = 1.548 \text{ to } 1.558$$
$$n_\gamma = 1.551 \text{ to } 1.562$$
$$2V = 76° \text{ to } 90°; \text{ Opt. } (+) \text{ or } (-)$$

Color. Colorless in thin sections.

Form. Andesine is found in euhedral to anhedral crystals.

Cleavage. {001} perfect, {010} less perfect, {110} and {1$\bar{1}$0} imperfect.

Relief. Low, n always greater than balsam. (For indices of cleavage flakes see Figure 13-46.)

Birefringence. Weak, $n_\gamma - n_\alpha = 0.008$ so that the interference colors are gray or white of the first order.

Extinction. The maximum extinction angle in albite twins (twins according to the albite law) varies from 13° to 27½°. On (001) cleavage flakes the extinction angle varies from 0° to −7°; on (010) flakes, from 0° to −16°.

Twinning. As in albite. The angle of the rhombic section varies from +3° to −2° in andesine.

Interference Figure. The figure is biaxial, either positive or negative with a large axial angle, or neutral ($2V = 90°$) for An_{38}. Dispersion, $r < v$.

Distinguishing Features. Andesine is distinguished from other plagioclases by maximum extinction angles of twinned crystals and by the indices of refraction (extinction angles, Figure 13-26).

Occurrence. Andesine is a common and widely distributed mineral in igneous rocks especially in diorites and andesites. Andesine also occurs in metamorphic rocks. The composition An_{50} marks the boundary between silicic (or acidic) and calcic (or basic) igneous rock types.

LABRADORITE

An_{50-70} Triclinic

$$n_\alpha = 1.554 \text{ to } 1.564$$
$$n_\beta = 1.558 \text{ to } 1.569$$
$$n_\gamma = 1.562 \text{ to } 1.573$$
$$2V = 76° \text{ to } 90°; \text{ Opt. } (+)$$

Color. Colorless in thin sections, often with regularly arranged inclusions.

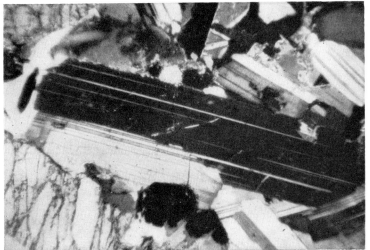

FIG. 13-53. ($\times 15$) Labradorite crystals showing albite twinning. ($\times$ nicols.)

Form. Labradorite occurs in euhedral to anhedral crystals. The anhedral crystals are often large as compared with those of other plagioclases.

Cleavage. {001} perfect, {010} less perfect, {110} and {1$\bar{1}$0} imperfect.

Relief. Fairly low, $n >$ balsam. (For indices of cleavage flakes see Figure 13-46.)

Birefringence. Weak, $n_\gamma - n_\alpha = 0.008$ to 0.009; interference colors are gray or white of the first order.

Extinction. The maximum extinction angle in albite twins (twinning according to the albite law) varies from $27\frac{1}{2}°$ to $39°$. The extinction angle on (001) cleavage flakes varies from $-7°$ to $-16°$; on (010) flakes, from $-16°$ to $-29°$.

Twinning. As in albite.

Interference Figure. The figure is usually biaxial positive with a large axial angle but is biaxial negative at times and neutral for An_{68}. Dispersion, $r < v$.

Distinguishing Features. Labradorite is distinguished from the other plagioclases by the maximum extinction angles of albite twins and by the indices of refraction (Figure 13-26, 13-45a).

Occurrence. Labradorite is a very common mineral in subsilicic igneous rocks such as auganites, basalts, gabbros, and olivine gabbros. It is the principal constituent of most anorthosites. Labradorite also occurs in metamorphic rocks.

BYTOWNITE

An_{70-90} Triclinic

$$n_\alpha = 1.564 \text{ to } 1.573$$
$$n_\beta = 1.569 \text{ to } 1.579$$
$$n_\gamma = 1.573 \text{ to } 1.585$$
$$2V = 79° \text{ to } 88°; \text{ Opt. } (-)$$

FIG. 13-54. ($\times$15) Bytownite showing albite twinning. ($\times$ nicols.)

Color. Colorless in thin sections.

Form. Bytownite occurs in subhedral to anhedral crystals.

Cleavage. {001} perfect, {010} less perfect, {110} and {1̄10} imperfect.

Relief. Moderate, $n >$ balsam. (For indices of cleavage flakes see Figure 13-46.)

Birefringence. Rather weak, $n_\gamma - n_\alpha = 0.009$ to 0.012. Interference colors are gray, white, or pale yellow of the first order.

Extinction. The maximum extinction angle in albite twins (twinning according to the albite law) varies from 39° to 51°. The extinction angle on (001) cleavage flakes varies from $-16°$ to $-32°$; on {010} flakes, from $-29°$ to $-36°$.

Twinning. As in albite.

Interference Figure. The figure is biaxial negative with a very large axial angle. Dispersion, $r > v$.

FIG. 13-55. ($\times 15$) Bytownite showing albite and Carlsbad twinning. ($\times$ nicols.)

Distinguishing Features. Bytownite is distinguished from other plagioclases by extinction angles and refractive indices (Figures 13-26, 13-45a).

Occurrence. Bytownite usually occurs in gabbros, anorthosites, or basalts, but it is a comparatively rare mineral.

ANORTHITE

An$_{90-100}$ Triclinic

$$n_\alpha = 1.573 \text{ to } 1.577$$
$$n_\beta = 1.579 \text{ to } 1.585$$
$$n_\gamma = 1.585 \text{ to } 1.590$$
$$2V = 77° \text{ to } 79°; \text{ Opt. } (-)$$

Color. Colorless.

Form. Anorthite occurs in anhedral to subhedral plates or laths.

Cleavage. {001} perfect, {010} less perfect, {110} and {1̄10} imperfect.

Relief. Fair, $n >$ balsam. (For indices of cleavage flakes see Figure 13-46.)

Birefringence. Rather weak, $n_\gamma - n_\alpha = 0.012$ to 0.013; interference colors are gray, white, or yellow of the first order.

Extinction. The maximum extinction angle in albite twins (twinning according to the albite law) varies from 51° to 70°. The extinction angle on (001) cleavage flakes varies from —32° to —40°; on (010) it is about —37°.

Twinning. As in albite.

Interference Figure. The figure is biaxial negative with a large axial angle. Dispersion, $r > v$.

Distinguishing Features. Anorthite is distinguished from other plagioclases by the extinction angles and refractive indices (Figures 13-26, 13-45a).

Occurrence. Anorthite is rare compared with the other plagioclases. It is found in a few contact-metamorphic deposits and in a few lavas.

THE FELDSPATHOIDS

The role of the feldspathoids in some igneous rocks is similar to the role of feldspars. They either occur in place of feldspars or may be found with them but are comparatively rare. Nepheline may be a prominent constituent as well as leucite.

THE FELDSPATHOIDS

Mineral	Chemical composition	Crystal system	Indices of refraction
Leucite	KAl	Pseudoisometric	$n_\alpha = 1.508$, $n_\gamma = 1.509$
Nepheline	NaAl	Hexagonal	$n_\epsilon = 1.527$–1.543, $n_\omega = 1.530$–1.547
Cancrinite	NaAl + CO$_3$	Hexagonal	$n_\epsilon = 1.496$–1.500, $n_\omega = 1.507$–1.524
Sodalite	NaAl + Cl	Isometric	$n = 1.483$–1.487
Haüyne	NaAl + S	Isometric	$n = 1.496$–1.510
Melilite	Ca,Mg,Al	Tetragonal	$n_\epsilon = 1.626$–1.629, $n_\omega = 1.632$–1.634.

LEUCITE

$KAl(SiO_3)_2$ Pseudoisometric

(Isometric above 600°C)

$$n_\alpha = 1.508$$
$$n_\gamma = 1.509$$

Color. Colorless in thin sections.

Form. Leucite practically always occurs in euhedral crystals. The crystal form is the trapezohedron {211}, which shows octagonal sections. It often contains inclusions, and these may be arranged in a regular manner, either radially or concentrically (Figure 8-12).

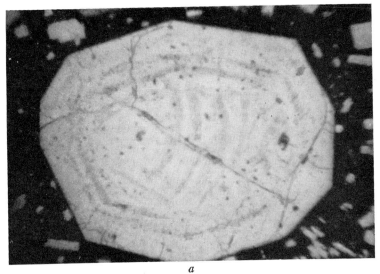

a

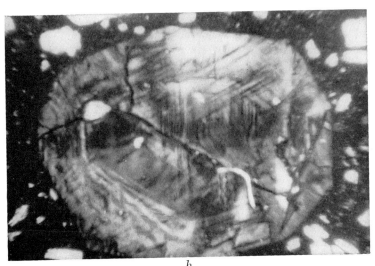

b

FIG. 13-56 *a,b.* (×15) (*a*) Leucite showing an unequally developed trapezohedral outline. (*b*) The same crystal showing twinning. (× nicols.)

Relief. Fair, $n <$ balsam.

Birefringence. Very weak, $n_\gamma - n_\alpha = 0.001$; it is best detected by using the sensitive-violet test plate. Minute crystals may not show any birefringence.

Extinction. Is often wavy.

Twinning. A characteristic feature of leucite is the complicated polysynthetic twinning in several directions, which often resembles that of microcline. When heated to about 600°C the twinning disappears, which proves that $KAl(SiO_3)_2$ is dimorphous.

Distinguishing Features. Leucite resembles analcime. The latter shows weak birefringence but does not have definite polysynthetic twinning. Microcline has greater birefringence and lower relief.

Occurrence. Leucite occurs almost exclusively as phenocrysts in lavas (leucite tephrite, leucitite, leucite basalt, leucite phonolite, etc.) and the corresponding tuffs. Leucite-bearing rocks are common in Italy but rare in most other parts of the world. A prominent American locality for leucite-bearing rocks is the Leucite Hills, Wyoming.

Fig. 13-57. (×12) Cross twinning in leucite. (× nicols.)

Leucite is exceedingly rare in grained igneous rocks (fergusite). In such rocks it usually has been altered to so-called *pseudoleucite* (ortho-clase-nepheline mixture).

NEPHELINE

$(Na,K)(Al,Si)_2O_4$	(Eleolite in part)	Hexagonal
(Essentially $NaAlSiO_4$ with an excess of SiO_2)		(Hexagonal subsystem)

$$n_\epsilon = 1.527 \text{ to } 1.543$$
$$n_\omega = 1.530 \text{ to } 1.547$$
$$\text{Opt. } (-)$$

Color. Colorless to turbid in thin sections. It may show rows of inclusions.

Form. Nepheline occurs in short prismatic hexagonal crystals (phenocrysts) in dense rocks and in anhedra in grained rocks. The crystals have

FIG. 13-58. (×12) Euhedral nepheline in thin section.

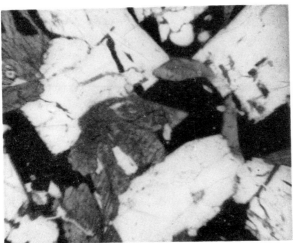

FIG. 13-59. (×12) Anhedral and euhedral nepheline crystals in thin section. (× nicols.)

rectangular and hexagonal sections and sometimes show zonal structure (Figure 8-27).

Cleavage. Imperfect parallel to $\{10\bar{1}0\}$, not always apparent.

Relief. Very low, n about the same as balsam but usually slightly higher.

Birefringence. Weak, $n_\omega - n_\varepsilon = 0.003$ to 0.004; interference colors are gray of the first order.

Extinction. Parallel for rectangular sections. Basal sections are dark between crossed nicols.

Orientation. The rectangular sections are length-fast.

Interference Figure. Basal sections give a negative uniaxial figure without any rings.

Distinguishing Features. The mineral most likely to be mistaken for nepheline is orthoclase, but the latter has better cleavage and is biaxial. It also resembles melilite and scapolite; the former has higher relief and the latter stronger birefringence.

Alteration. Nepheline alters very readily to zeolites, sodalite, muscovite (gieseckite), cancrinite, or hydronephelite (a variety of natrolite).

Occurrence. Nepheline is confined to soda-rich igneous rocks such as nepheline syenites, phonolites, and a few basaltic rocks. It is not associated with original quartz.

CANCRINITE

3NaAlSiO$_4$.CaCO$_3$.H$_2$O(?)   Hexagonal

$$n_\epsilon = 1.496 \text{ to } 1.500$$
$$n_\omega = 1.507 \text{ to } 1.524$$
$$\text{Opt. } (-)$$

Color. Colorless in thin sections to very pale yellow in sections a little thicker than normal.

Form. Crystals are usually anhedral with a tendency toward elongation parallel to the c-axis. Euhedral crystals are rare.

Cleavage. Good cleavage parallel to $\{10\bar{1}0\}$.

Relief. Fair, $n <$ balsam.

Birefringence. Variable from rather weak (0.007) to moderate (0.028); the interference colors vary from first-order pale yellow up to middle second order.

Extinction. Parallel to outlines and to the cleavage traces. Some sections are isotropic.

Orientation. Crystal outlines and cleavage traces are length-fast.

Interference Figure. Basal sections give a negative uniaxial interference figure with not more than one or two rings.

Distinguishing Features. Cancrinite is distinguished from similar minerals by its stronger birefringence.

Alteration. There is sometimes alteration along cleavage cracks and fractures.

Related Minerals. Hydronephelite, a zeolitic alteration of nepheline, is a closely related mineral.

Occurrence. Cancrinite is a rare, but widely distributed, mineral characteristic of nepheline syenites. It is probably a deuteric mineral since it often surrounds and apparently replaces feldspars. Its associates are plagioclase (especially albite), microcline, nepheline, and sodalite.

SODALITE

3NaAlSiO$_4$.NaCl   Isometric

$$n = 1.483 \text{ to } 1.487$$

Color. In thin sections colorless to gray, often with dark borders.

Form. Sodalite occurs in six-sided euhedral crystals (cross sections of dodecahedra) and in anhedra.

Cleavage. Imperfect parallel to {110}, more likely to show on edges of the slide.

Relief. Fair, $n <$ balsam.

Birefringence. Nil.

Extinction. Dark between crossed nicols.

Distinguishing Features. Sodalite resembles analcime, but the latter is usually secondary. It may be necessary to make microchemical tests to confirm the determination of sodalite.

Alteration. Sodalite is readily altered to zeolites.

Related Minerals. Nosean (sometimes called *noselite*) is a related mineral containing the sulfate radical in the place of chlorine.

Occurrence. Sodalite is practically confined to soda-rich igneous rocks such as syenites and trachytes. It is especially prominent in rocks called sodalite syenites. It is a common associate of nepheline.

HAÜYNE

m3NaAlSiO$_4$.CaSO$_4$.   (Lazurite in part)   Isometric
n3NaAlSiO$_4$.Na$_2$S

$$n = 1.496 \text{ to } 1.510$$

With haüyne, often given in the less euphonious variant haüynite, is included lazurite, here considered to be simply a sulfide-bearing haüyne. (The name *lazurite* is discarded because of its similarity to lazulite.)

Color. Colorless, gray, pale blue, bluish green to deep blue in thin sections. The color may vary within a single crystal. Transparent to translucent.

Form. Haüyne usually occurs in euhedral to anhedral crystals and in crystal aggregates. Both octahedrons and dodecahedrons are common crystal forms.

Cleavage. It may show imperfect cleavage (dodecahedral, as in sodalite).

Relief. Rather low, $n <$ balsam.

Birefringence. Haüyne is usually isotropic, but occasionally it may show very weak birefringence up to about 0.004.

Distinguishing Features. Haüyne resembles sodalite, but its refractive index is higher and its cleavage less prominent than that of sodalite. The presence of pyrite is characteristic of the sulfide-bearing haüyne of lapis lazuli.

Related Minerals. Nosean (or noselite), a mineral of the sodalite group, is similar to haüyne, but it contains little or no calcium.

Occurrence. Haüyne occurs in (1) soda-rich volcanic rocks such as phonolite and in (2) the contact-metamorphic limestones or muscovite-diopside gneisses known as lapis lazuli. Pyrite is an invariable constituent of lapis lazuli.

MELILITE

$m(Ca_2Al_2SiO_7)$.   Tetragonal
$n(Ca_2MgSi_2O_7)$

$$n_\epsilon = 1.626 \text{ to } 1.629$$
$$n_\omega = 1.632 \text{ to } 1.634$$
$$\text{Opt. } (-)$$

Fig. 13-60. (×190) Melilite (fair relief) in nephelinite.

Melilite, although complex in composition, is essentially an isomorphous mixture of the two end members gehlenite (CaAl) and åkermanite (CaMg), according to Buddington.

Color. Colorless to pale yellow in thin sections.

Form. The usual forms of melilite are euhedral crystals of tabular habit that show as rectangular sections. It often has "peg structure" due to lines normal to the length of the sections.

Cleavage. Indistinct parallel to {001}, which often appears as a single crack in the center of the section.

Relief. Fairly high, $n >$ balsam.

Birefringence. Weak, $n_\omega - n_\varepsilon = 0.005$ to 0.006; interference colors are first-order gray and often anomalous Berlin blue.

Extinction. Parallel.

Orientation. The rectangular sections are length-slow, since the mineral is tabular in habit and optically negative.

Interference Figure. Basal sections give a uniaxial negative figure without any rings.

Distinguishing Features. Elongated sections with weak birefringence and peg structure are characteristic. It somewhat resembles nepheline but the relief is fairly high instead of low.

Related Minerals. Other minerals of the melilite group are gehlenite, $Ca_2Al_4SiO_7$, found in metamorphic limestones and åkermanite, $Ca_2MgSi_2O_7$, found in furnace slags and as a laboratory product.

Alteration. Incipient alteration takes place along lines normal to the length of the crystal. This gives the so-called *peg structure*. It may also be altered to calcite and zeolites.

Occurrence. Melilite occurs in subsilicic igneous rocks such as nepheline- and leucite-bearing lavas and in melilite basalts (alnöites). Usual associates are augite, olivine, nepheline, leucite, and perovskite. It is also a prominent constituent of a coarse-grained alkaline igneous rock called uncompahgrite in the San Juan region, Colorado.

Melilite is also found in furnace and in Portland-cement clinker slags.

SCAPOLITE GROUP

(Wernerite)

$m[3NaAlSi_3O_8.NaCl] = Ma$ Tetragonal
$n[3CaAl_2Si_2O_8.Ca(O,CO_3,SO_4)] = Me$

$$n_\epsilon = 1.540 \text{ to } 1.571$$
$$n_\omega = 1.550 \text{ to } 1.607$$
$$\text{Opt. } (-)$$

Scapolite is an isomorphous mixture of the two end members given above. The sodium end member is called *marialite*, and the calcium end member, *meionite*. The name *wernerite* is applied to certain intermediate members.

It will be noted that the chemical composition is similar to that of the plagioclases but with added $NaCl, CaCO_3$, etc.

Color. Colorless in thin sections.

Form. Minerals of the scapolite group usually occur in columnar aggregates. Crystals are usually rather large.

Relief. Low to fair, $n >$ balsam.

Cleavage. Distinct parallel to {100}, less distinct parallel to {110}. In most sections the cleavage traces are parallel to the length; in cross sections the cleavage shows in two directions at right angles.

Birefringence. Rather weak to rather strong, $n_\omega - n_\varepsilon = 0.010$ to 0.036. The maximum interference color varies from yellow of the first order up to second-order violet, depending upon the chemical composition. The birefringence increases with calcium or meionite content.

Extinction. Parallel in most sections. Basal sections remain dark between crossed nicols.

Orientation. The cleavage traces and main crystal outlines are parallel to the faster ray.

Interference Figure. Basal sections give a uniaxial negative figure with a few rings. Longitudinal sections give a "flash figure."

Distinguishing Features. Scapolite is similar to plagioclase but lacks twinning, has parallel extinction, and usually has stronger birefringence. Varieties with weaker birefringence resemble cordierite, which is biaxial, or quartz, which is optically positive. Without chemical analyses it is difficult to determine the various kinds of scapolite, but the birefringence increases with the calcium content.

Alteration. Scapolite is often altered to muscovite and to ill-defined fibrous aggregates.

Occurrence. The characteristic occurrence of scapolite is contact-metamorphic limestones where it is often associated with idocrase, diopside, garnet, etc. It also occurs in certain gneisses and in some gabbros as a high-temperature alteration of plagioclase.

THE ZEOLITES

The zeolites are hydrous sodium calcium aluminum silicates that commonly occur as secondary minerals in cavities of subsilicic volcanic rocks,

ZEOLITES

Mineral	Chemical composition	Crystal system	n_α	n_β	n_γ
Analcime	Na	Isometric		$n = 1.487$	
Heulandite	Ca	Monoclinic	1.496–1.499	1.497–1.501	1.501–1.505
Stilbite	Ca,Na	Monoclinic	1.494–1.500	1.498–1.504	1.500–1.508
Chabazite	Ca,Na	Monoclinic	$n_\alpha = 1.478$–1.485, $n_\gamma = 1.480$–1.490		
Natrolite	Na	Orthorhombic	1.473–1.480	1.476–1.482	1.485–1.493
Mesolite	Na,Ca	Monoclinic	1.505	1.505	1.506
Thomsonite	Na,Ca	Orthorhombic	1.512–1.530	1.513–1.532	1.518–1.542
Scolecite	Ca	Monoclinic	1.512	1.519	1.519

especially basalts. Although variable in optical properties, they all have low indices of refraction and rather weak birefringence. The last four in the list are fibrous or columnar, but there are also other fibrous zeolites such as ptilolite, mordenite, and laumontite. A few rare zeolites such as harmotome and brewsterite contain barium.

ANALCIME

$NaAl(SiO_3)_2.H_2O$ (Analcite)   Isometric

$$n = 1.487$$

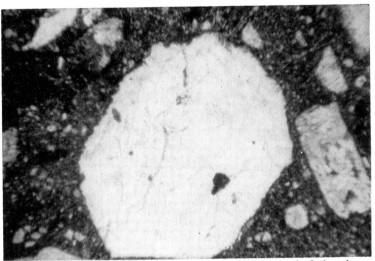

Fig. 13-61. ($\times 15$) Euhedral analcime with rough trapezohedral outline.

Color. Colorless in thin sections.

Form. Analcime occurs in equant crystals of trapezohedral habit that are octagonal to rounded in sections (Figure 8-25). It may also occur in the groundmass in irregular masses.

Cleavage. Imperfect cubic, which in sections often appears as two sets of lines at right angles.

Relief. Moderate, $n <$ balsam.

Birefringence. Analcime is either dark between crossed nicols or shows very weak birefringence (not over 0.002). Use the sensitive-violet plate to detect the double refraction.

Distinguishing Features. Leucite very much resembles analcime but has a slightly greater refractive index (1.508 as against 1.487).

Occurrence. Analcime is a secondary mineral in cavities and seams of igneous rocks, usually associated with other zeolites and calcite. In some igneous rocks, such as teschenites and analcime basalts, it occurs in the groundmass as a deuteric mineral. In several western localities it occurs in lake beds.

HEULANDITE

$H_4CaAl_2(SiO_3)_6.3H_2O$ Monoclinic
$\angle\beta = 88°34'$

$$n_\alpha = 1.496 \text{ to } 1.499$$
$$n_\beta = 1.497 \text{ to } 1.501$$
$$n_\gamma = 1.501 \text{ to } 1.505$$
$$2V = 0° \text{ to } 48°; \text{ Opt. } (+)$$
$$b = \gamma \text{ or } Z, c \wedge \beta \text{ or } Y = -6°$$

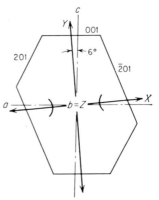

Fig. 13-62. Orientation diagram of heulandite. Section parallel to (010).

Color. Colorless in thin sections.

Form. Heulandite usually occurs in distinct crystals that are tabular parallel to {010}.

Cleavage. Perfect in one direction {010}.

Relief. Rather low, $n <$ balsam.

Birefringence. Weak, $n_\gamma - n_\alpha = 0.007$; the interference colors range up to white of the first order. Sections parallel to {010} that include cleavage flakes have very weak birefringence since $n_\beta - n_\alpha = 0.001$.

Extinction. Parallel to the cleavage traces.

Orientation. Cleavage traces are parallel to the faster ray.

Interference Figure. The figure is biaxial positive with a moderate axial angle. The axial plane is normal to {010}. Dispersion, $r < v$.

Distinguishing Features. Heulandite resembles stilbite but has better cleavage and is optically positive, whereas stilbite is optically negative. The side pinacoid {010} sections of heulandite are unsymmetrical and the corresponding sections of stilbite symmetrical on account of twinning.

Occurrence. Heulandite is a secondary mineral in the seams and cavities of igneous rocks, especially basalts. Stilbite is a common associate.

STILBITE

$H_4(Ca,Na_2)Al_2(SiO_3)_6.4H_2O$ Monoclinic
                                                  $\angle\beta = 51°$

$$n_\alpha = 1.494 \text{ to } 1.500$$
$$n_\beta = 1.498 \text{ to } 1.504$$
$$n_\gamma = 1.500 \text{ to } 1.508$$
$$2V = 33° \pm ; \text{ Opt. } (-)$$
$$b = \beta \text{ or } Y, a \wedge \alpha' \text{ or } X = +5°$$

FIG. 13-63. ($\times 12$) Tapered crystals of stilbite in radial arrangement. ($\times$ nicols.)

FIG. 13-64. ($\times 12$) Stilbite with euhedral outlines in a granular stilbite mass. ($\times$ nicols.)

Color. Colorless in thin sections.

Form. Stilbite usually occurs in sheaf-like aggregates.

Cleavage. Good in one direction {010}.

Relief. Rather low, $n <$ balsam.

Birefringence. Weak, $n_\gamma - n_\alpha = 0.006$ to 0.008; interference colors are gray and white of the first order.

Extinction. Extinction of sections showing the best cleavage is parallel. The extinction angle of sections with the highest interference colors is about 5°. The extinction is usually wavy and not uniform.

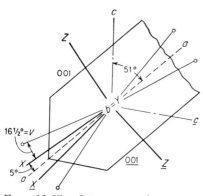

Orientation. The cleavage traces are parallel either to the slow ray or to the fast ray.

Twinning. Twins with {001} as twin-plane are common.

Interference Figure. The figure is biaxial negative with a moderate axial angle. The axial plane is {010}. Dispersion, $r < v$.

Distinguishing Features. Heulandite is similar to stilbite, but it has better cleavage and is optically positive instead of negative.

FIG. 13-65. Orientation diagram of twinned stilbite. Section parallel to (010); twin-plane = (001).

Occurrence. Stilbite is a secondary mineral in cavities and seams of igneous rocks. Usual associates are calcite, heulandite, and other zeolites. It has been found as a hot-spring mineral in the interstices of sandstone.

CHABAZITE

$(Ca,Na_2)Al_2(SiO_3)_6.6H_2O$ Monoclinic
                                           (Pseudorhombohedral)

$$n_\alpha = 1.478 \text{ to } 1.485$$
$$n_\gamma = 1.480 \text{ to } 1.490$$
$$2V = 0° \text{ to } 32°; \text{ Opt. } (+)$$

Color. Colorless in thin sections.

Form. Chabazite is usually found in euhedral rhombohedral crystals that approach the cube ($10\bar{1}1 : \bar{1}101 = 85°14'$).

Cleavage. Imperfect rhombohedral, hence almost rectangular.

Relief. Moderate, $n <$ balsam.

Birefringence. Very weak to weak, $n_\gamma - n_\alpha = 0.002$ to 0.010; interference colors are first-order gray.

Extinction. The extinction is symmetrical to crystal outlines and cleavage traces.

Interference Figure. The figure is either uniaxial or biaxial with a small axial angle. The optical character is positive.

Distinguishing Features. Chabazite may be mistaken for other zeolites, especially analcime. The birefringence of chabazite is a little higher than that of analcime.

Related Minerals. Gmelinite is a zeolite very similar to chabazite in properties, but with slightly lower indices of refraction.

Occurrence. Chabazite is a secondary mineral in cavities and seams of igneous rocks, especially basalts. It is often associated with calcite, prehnite, and other zeolites.

NATROLITE

$Na_2Al_2Si_3O_{10}.2H_2O$ Orthorhombic

$$n_\alpha = 1.473 \text{ to } 1.480$$
$$n_\beta = 1.476 \text{ to } 1.482$$
$$n_\gamma = 1.485 \text{ to } 1.493$$
$$2V = 60° \text{ to } 63°; \text{ Opt. } (+)$$
$$a = \alpha \text{ or } X, \, b = \beta \text{ or } Y, \, c = \gamma \text{ or } Z$$

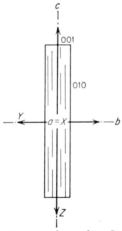

Fig. 13-66. Orientation diagram of natrolite. Section parallel to (100).

Color. Colorless in thin sections.

Form. Natrolite usually occurs in long prismatic crystals or fibrous aggregates that are often more or less radiating. Cross sections of crystals are nearly square ($110 \wedge 1\bar{1}0 = $ ca. $89°$).

Cleavage. Parallel to the length of the crystals $\{110\}$.

Relief. Moderate, $n <$ balsam.

Birefringence. Rather weak, $n_\gamma - n_\alpha = 0.012$ to 0.013; the maximum interference color is yellow or orange of the first order.

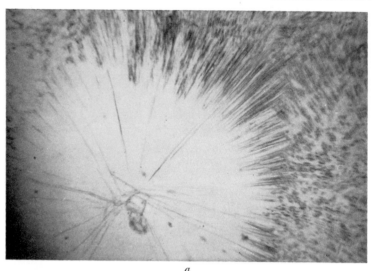

Fig. 13-67 *a,b.* (×15) (*a*) Natrolite showing a radial acicular group. (*b*) The same view between crossed nicols.

Extinction. Parallel in longitudinal sections, symmetrical in cross sections.

Orientation. The crystals are always length-slow.

Interference Figure. A good figure is difficult to obtain on account of the small size of most of the crystals.

Distinguishing Features. Scolecite resembles natrolite but is length-fast instead of length-slow and has oblique extinction. Thomsonite has parallel extinction but is length-slow in some sections and length-fast in others.

Occurrence. Natrolite is a secondary mineral found in cavities of igneous rocks, especially basalt. The associates are other zeolites and calcite.

Fig. 13-68. (×15) Clusters of natrolite crystals. (× nicols.)

MESOLITE

$Na_2Ca_2Al_6(Si_3O_{10})_3 \cdot 8H_2O$ Monoclinic

$$n_\alpha = 1.505$$
$$n_\beta = 1.505$$
$$n_\gamma = 1.506$$
$$2V = ca.\ 80°;\ Opt.\ (+)$$
$$c \wedge \beta \text{ or } Y = 2° \text{ to } 5°$$

Color. Colorless in thin sections.

Form. Mesolite usually occurs in fibrous aggregates.

Cleavage. Perfect in two directions (110) and (1$\bar{1}$0).

Relief. Moderate, $n <$ balsam.

Birefringence. Very weak, $n_\gamma - n_\alpha = 0.001$; the maximum interference color is first-order gray.

Extinction. The maximum extinction angle in longitudinal sections is very small, from 2° to 5°.

Orientation. The fibers are in part length-slow and in part length-fast.

Twinning. Twins with {100} as twin-plane are universal, but the twinning is not conspicuous.

Interference Figure. The figure is biaxial positive with a very large axial angle. The figure lies across the fibers. Dispersion, $r > v$ strong.

Distinguishing Features. Mesolite very much resembles the other fibrous zeolites. In common with thomsonite the fibers are in part length-slow and in part length-fast. From thomsonite it may be distinguished by the maximum extinction angle of 2° to 5° and by its larger axial angle.

Occurrence. The occurrence of mesolite is the same as that of other zeolites, in the cavities of basalts and related rocks.

THOMSONITE

$NaCa_2Al_5(SiO_4)_5.6H_2O$ Orthorhombic

$$n_\alpha = 1.512 \text{ to } 1.530$$
$$n_\beta = 1.513 \text{ to } 1.532$$
$$n_\gamma = 1.518 \text{ to } 1.542$$
$$2V = 44° \text{ to } 55°; \text{ Opt. } (+)$$
$$a = \alpha \text{ or } X, b = \gamma \text{ or } Z, c = \beta \text{ or } Y$$

Color. Colorless in thin sections.

Form. Thomsonite usually occurs in fibrous or columnar aggregates. Euhedral crystals are very rare.

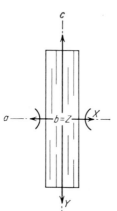

Cleavage. In one direction {010}.

Relief. Rather low, $n <$ balsam.

Birefringence. Rather weak, $n_\gamma - n_\alpha = 0.006$ to 0.012; maximum interference colors range from first-order white up to low second-order blue in different specimens. Cross sections of fibers show the highest interference color for a given thickness.

Extinction. Parallel.

Orientation. Some of the fibers are length-slow and some length-fast since $c = Y$.

Interference Figure. The figure is biaxial positive with rather large axial angle. The figure lies across the fibers since the axial plane is {001}. Dispersion, $r > v$ strong.

FIG. 13-69. Orientation diagram of thomsonite. Section parallel to (010).

Distinguishing Features. Thomsonite is much like the other fibrous zeolites in general appearance and optical properties. Natrolite is length-slow and scolecite length-fast, whereas some of the fibers of thomsonite are length-slow and some length-fast. The same is true of mesolite, but in mesolite the maximum extinction angle $c \wedge \beta$ or Y is about 3°. The axial angle of mesolite is much larger than that of thomsonite.

Occurrence. Thomsonite occurs as a cavity filling in subsilicic volcanic rocks such as amygdaloidal basalts.

FIG. 13-70. (×12) Radial thomsonite crystals forming a group. (× nicols.)

SCOLECITE

$CaAl_2Si_3O_{10}.3H_2O$ Monoclinic
$\angle\beta = 89°18'$

$$n_\alpha - 1.512$$
$$n_\beta = 1.519$$
$$n_\gamma = 1.519$$
$$2V = 36°; \text{ Opt. } (-)$$
$$b = \gamma \text{ or } Z, c \wedge \alpha \text{ or } X = -15° \text{ to } -18°$$

Color. Colorless in thin sections.

Form. Scolecite occurs in crystal aggregates with a columnar to fibrous structure.

Cleavage. Distinct in two directions {110} at angles of ca. 88°.

Relief. Low, $n <$ balsam.

Birefringence. Weak, $n\gamma - n_\alpha = 0.007$; so the interference colors are gray and white of the first order.

Extinction. The maximum extinction angle in longitudinal sections is $-15°$ to $-18°$.

Orientation. The crystals are always length-fast.

Twinning. Twinning is common. The c-axis [001] is the twin-axis and (100) the composition face.

Interference Figure. The figure is biaxial negative with a moderate axial angle. The axial plane is normal to {010}. Dispersion, $r < v$ strong.

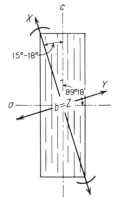

FIG. 13-71. Orientation diagram of scolecite. Section parallel to (010).

Distinguishing Features. Scolecite is much like natrolite and other rare fibrous zeolites. The oblique extinction of about 17° and twinning are the most distinctive features of scolecite.

Occurrence. Scolecite is a secondary mineral found in cavities of igneous rocks, especially basalts.

REFERENCES

Silica

Brown, C. S., et al.: The Growth and Properties of Large Crystals of Synthetic Quartz, *Mineral. Mag.*, vol. 29, pp. 858–874, 1952.

Coes, L. J., Jr.: A New Dense Crystalline Silica, *Science*, vol. 118, pp. 131–132, 1953.

Eitel, W.: "The Physical Chemistry of the Silicates," pp. 620–629, University of Chicago Press, Chicago, 1954.

Hale, D. R.: The Properties of Synthetic Quartz Crystals and Their Growing Technique, *Brush Strokes*, Brush Development Company, Cleveland, 1952.

————: The Laboratory Growing of Quartz, *Science*, no. 2781, pp. 393–394, 1948.

Kerr, P. F., and E. Armstrong: Recorded Experiments in the Production of Quartz, *Bull. Geol. Soc. Am.*, vol. 54, suppl. 1, pp. 1–34, 1943.

Ramsdell, L. S.: The Crystallography of "Coesite," *Am. Mineralogist*, vol. 40, pp. 975–982, 1955.

Tuttle, O. F.: The Variable Inversion Temperature of Quartz as a Possible Geologic Thermometer, *Am. Mineralogist*, vol. 34, pp. 723–730, 1949.

Feldspars

Baskin, Y.: A Study of Authigenic Feldspars, *J. Geol.*, vol. 64, pp. 132–155, 1956.

Bowen, N. L., and O. F. Tuttle: The System $NaAlSi_3O_8$-$KAlSi_3O_8$-H_2O, *J. Geol.*, vol. 58, pp. 489–511, 1950.

Bradley, O.: An Investigation of High-Temperature Optics in Some Naturally Occurring Plagioclases, *Mineral. Mag.*, vol. 30, pp. 227–245, 1953.

Calkins, F. C.: A Decimal Grouping of the Plagioclases, *J. Geol.*, vol. 25, pp. 157–159, 1917.

Chayes, F.: Relations between Composition and Indices of Refraction in Natural Plagioclase, *Am. J. Sci.*, Bowen Volume, pp. 85–105, 1952.

Chudoba, K.: "The Determination of the Feldspars in Thin Section" (trans. by W. Q. Kennedy), pp. 1–61, Thomas Murby & Co., London, 1933.

Day, A. L., E. T. Allen, and J. P. Iddings: The Isomorphism and Thermal Properties of the Feldspars, *Carnegie Inst. Wash. Publ. 31*, pp. 1–95, 1902.

Donnay, J. D. H.: Plagioclase Twinning, *Bull. Geol. Soc. Am.*, vol. 54, pp. 1645–1652, 1943.

Emmons, R. C., and R. M. Gates: Plagioclase Twinning, *Bull. Geol. Soc. Am.*, vol. 54, pp. 287–304, 1943.

Foster, W. R.: Simple Method for the Determination of the Plagioclase Feldspars, *Am. Mineralogist*, vol. 40, pp. 179–185, 1955.

Gay, P., and J. V. Smith: Phase Relations in the Plagioclase Feldspars: Composition Range An_0-An_{20}, *Acta Cryst.*, vol. 8, pp. 64–65, 1955.

Grunner, J. W., and G. A. Thiel: The Occurrence of Fine Grained Authigenic Feldspar in Shales and Silts, *Am. Mineralogist*, vol. 22, pp. 842–846, 1937.

Kennedy, G. C.: Charts for Correlation of Optical Properties with Chemical Composition of Some Common Rock-forming Minerals, *Am. Mineralogist*, vol. 32, pp. 561–574, 1947.

Köhler, A.: Recent Results of Investigations on the Feldspars, *J. Geol.*, vol. 57, pp. 592–599, 1949.

Laves, F.: Artificial Preparation of Microcline, *J. Geol.*, vol. 59, pp. 511–512, 1951.

————: Phase Relations of the Alkali Feldspars, *J. Geol.*, vol. 60, pp. 436–450, 1952.

Mackenzie, W. S.: The Effect of Temperature on the Symmetry of High-Temperature Soda-Rich Feldspars, *Am. J. Sci.*, Bowen Volume, pp. 319–342, 1952.

———— and J. V. Smith: Orthoclase Microperthites, *Am. Mineralogist*, vol. 40, pp. 707–732, 1955.

———— and ————: The Alkali Feldspars (3 papers), *Am. Mineralogist*, vol. 40, pp. 707–732, 733–747, 1955; and vol. 41, pp. 405–427, 1956.

Muir, I. D.: Transitional Optics of Some Andesines and Labradorites, *Mineral. Mag.*, vol. 30, pp. 545–568, 1955.

Reinhard, M.: "Universaldrehtischmethoden," Wepf & Cie., Basel, 1931.

Schmidt, E.: Die Winkel der kristallographischen Achsen der Plagioklase, *Chem. Erde*, vol. 1, pp. 351–406, 1919.

Smith, J. R., and H. S. Yoder: Variations in X-ray Powder Diffraction Patterns of Plagioclase Feldspars, *Am. Mineralogist*, vol. 41, pp. 632–647, 1956.

Smith, J. V., and W. S. Mackenzie: The Alkali Feldspars—A Simple X-ray Technique, *Am. Mineralogist*, vol. 40, pp. 733–747, 1955.

Tröger, W. E.: Optische Eigenschaften und Bestimmung der Wichtigsten Gesteinbildenden Minerale (Feldspäte) (H. Freund, ed.), "Handbuch der Mikroskopie in der Tecknik," 1st ed., vol. 4, pp. 79–119, Umschau Verlag, Frankfurt, 1955.

Turner, F. J.: Determination of Plagioclase with the Four-Axis Universal Stage, *Am. Mineralogist*, vol. 32, pp. 389–410, 1947.

Tuttle, O. F.: Optical Studies on Alkali Feldspars, *Am. J. Sci.*, Bowen Volume, pp. 553–567, 1952.

Yoder, H. S., D. B. Stewart, and J. R. Smith: Feldspars, Annual Report of the Director, Geophys. Lab., *Carnegie Inst. Wash.*, no. 1277, pp. 206–217, 1957.

CHAPTER 14

Silicates: Chain Structures (Inosilicates)

PYROXENE GROUP	AMPHIBOLE GROUP	EPIDOTE GROUP
Orthopyroxenes	Orthoamphiboles	Orthorhombic
Enstatite	Anthophyllite	Zoisite
Hypersthene	Clinoamphiboles	Monoclinic
Clinopyroxenes	Cummingtonite	Clinozoisite
Diopside	Grunerite	Epidote
Augite	Tremolite-	Piedmontite
Pigeonite	Actinolite	Allanite
Hedenbergite	Hornblende	
Aegirine-augite	Lamprobolite	
Aegirine	Riebeckite	
Jadeite	Glaucophane	
Spodumene		

The inosilicates contain a number of minerals important in igneous and metamorphic rocks. In this structural division SiO_4 groups may form a continuous chain $(SiO_3)_n$. After the tectosilicates, the inosilicates constitute one of the most important assemblages of rock-forming minerals.

PYROXENE GROUP

The pyroxenes are metasilicates which frequently form original rock constituents (Figure 14-1). A considerable range in chemical composition and corresponding optical properties prevails throughout the group. Crystals exhibit significant cross sections (Figures 8-30, 8-33). Cleavage is parallel to {110} and the angle (110:1$\bar{1}$0) is about 93°. At times parting occurs parallel to {001} or {100}. Twinning with {100} as twin-plane is rather common. The minerals are all biaxial with rather large axial angles. The axial plane of the optic axes is (010).

Individual members of the group are often identified by use of the maximum extinction angles in longitudinal sections (Figure 14-1 and 14-2).

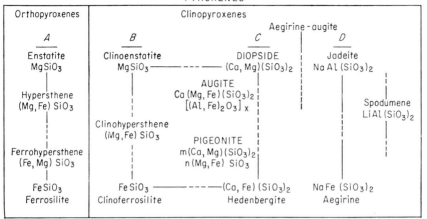

PYROXENES

Orthopyroxenes	Clinopyroxenes		
		Aegirine-augite	
A	B	C	D
Enstatite MgSiO₃	Clinoenstatite MgSiO₃ — — — — — (Ca, Mg)(SiO₃)₂	DIOPSIDE	Jadeite NaAl(SiO₃)₂
Hypersthene (Mg,Fe) SiO₃		AUGITE Ca(Mg,Fe)(SiO₃)₂ [(Al,Fe)₂O₃]ₓ	
	Clinohypersthene (Mg,Fe) SiO₃		Spodumene LiAl(SiO₃)₂
Ferrohypersthene (Fe, Mg) SiO₃		PIGEONITE m(Ca, Mg)(SiO₃)₂ n(Mg,Fe) SiO₃	
FeSiO₃ Ferrosilite	FeSiO₃ — — — — —(Ca, Fe) (SiO₃)₂ Clinoferrosilite	Hedenbergite	NaFe (SiO₃)₂ Aegirine

FIG. 14-1. A diagram showing the approximate chemical relations of the metasilicates that comprise the pyroxene group. A: Enstatite-Ferrosilite series; B: Clinoenstatite-Clinoferrosilite series; C: Diopside-Hedenbergite series; D: Jadeite-Aegirine series. Augite and pigeonite are intermediate in composition. Spodumene represents a species on the border of the pyroxene group. Aegirine-augite is intermediate.

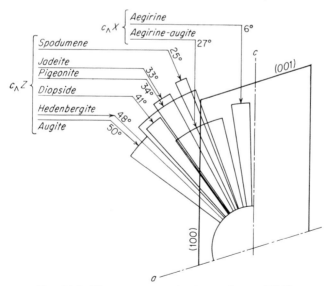

FIG. 14-2. Clinopyroxene extinction angles on (010).

Augite and pigeonite are by far the most common minerals of the group. Jadeite and aegirine are known as *soda pyroxenes*.

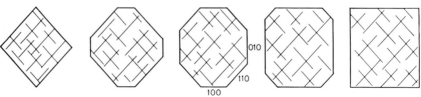

FIG. 14-3. Cross sections of minerals of the pyroxene group showing cleavage.

The Orthopyroxenes

ENSTATITE

MgSiO₃   (inc. Bronzite)   Orthorhombic

$$n_\alpha = 1.650 \text{ to } 1.665$$
$$n_\beta = 1.653 \text{ to } 1.670$$
$$n_\gamma = 1.658 \text{ to } 1.674$$
$$2V = 58° \text{ to } 80°; \text{ Opt. } (+)$$
$$a = \alpha \text{ or } X, \ b = \beta \text{ or } Y; \ c = \gamma \text{ or } Z$$

Color. Colorless to neutral in thin sections. Bronzite has faint pleochroism.

Form. Enstatite is found in prismatic crystals with the characteristic pyroxene cross section. Inclusions are common and produce what is known as *schiller* structure in the ferroan variety known as *bronzite*.

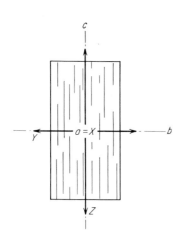

FIG. 14-4. Orientation diagram of enstatite. Section parallel to (100).

Cleavage. {110} in two directions at nearly right angles (88° and 92°). Cleavage or parting parallel to {010} is also sometimes present. In longitudinal sections the cleavage traces are in one direction parallel to the outlines.

Relief. High, $n >$ balsam.

Birefringence. Rather weak, $n_\gamma - n_\alpha = 0.008$ to 0.009; the maximum interference color is pale yellow of the first order.

Extinction. Parallel in most sections.

Twinning. Rarely present.

Orientation. The crystals and cleavage traces are length-slow.

Interference Figure. The figure is biaxial positive with a moderate to very large axial angle. The axial plane is {010}. Dispersion, $r < v$ weak.

Intergrowth. The intergrowth of enstatite with a monoclinic pyroxene is rather common. They have their *c*-axes in common and at first glance resemble polysynthetic twins.

Distinguishing Features. Enstatite is distinguished from hypersthene by lack of pleochroism and from the monoclinic pyroxenes by parallel extinction.

Alteration. It is common to find enstatite more or less altered to antigorite. Pseudomorphs of antigorite after enstatite are known as *bastite*.

Occurrence. Enstatite is a characteristic mineral of subsilicic igneous rocks and derived serpentites. It is also found in meteorites.

HYPERSTHENE

$(Mg,Fe)SiO_3$ Orthorhombic

$$n_\alpha = 1.673 \text{ to } 1.715$$
$$n_\beta = 1.678 \text{ to } 1.728$$
$$n_\gamma = 1.683 \text{ to } 1.731$$
$$2V = 63° \text{ to } 90°; \text{ Opt. } (-)$$
$$a = \alpha \text{ or } X, b = \beta \text{ or } Y, c = \gamma \text{ or } Z$$

Color. Neutral to pale green or pale red in thin sections. Pleochroic from greenish to pale reddish. Inclusions are common and produce schiller structure (Figure 8-15).

Form. Hypersthene usually occurs in subhedral crystals of prismatic habit. The cross sections are nearly square.

Cleavage. Parallel to {110}; sometimes parallel to {010} and {100}.

Relief. High, $n >$ balsam.

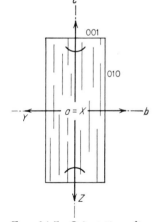

FIG. 14-5. Orientation diagram of hypersthene. Section parallel to (100).

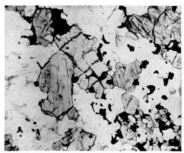

FIG. 14-6. (×9) Hypersthene (gray) in norite. The light mineral is plagioclase and the black one magnetite.

Birefringence. Rather weak, $n_\gamma - n_\alpha = 0.010$ to 0.016; the maximum interference color is yellow to red of the first order.

Extinction. Parallel in most sections.

Orientation. The cleavage traces are length-slow.

Interference Figure. The figure is biaxial negative with a large axial angle. The axial plane is {010}. Dispersion, $r > v$ weak.

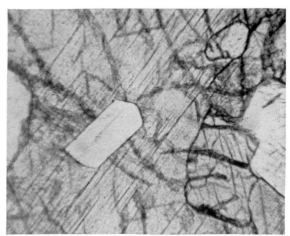

Fig. 14-7. (×80) Hypersthene showing cleavage. An included crystal of feldspar is shown.

Distinguishing Features. The pleochroism is the most distinctive feature of hypersthene. It resembles some varieties of andalusite, but the latter mineral is length-fast, whereas hypersthene is length-slow.

Occurrence. Hypersthene is found in a number of igneous rocks but is especially characteristic of norite, hypersthene gabbro, some andesite, and a peculiar hypersthene granite known as charnockite.

The Clinopyroxenes

DIOPSIDE

$Ca(Mg,Fe)(SiO_3)_2$ Monoclinic
$\angle\beta = 74°10'$

$$n_\alpha = 1.650 \text{ to } 1.698$$
$$n_\beta = 1.657 \text{ to } 1.706$$
$$n_\gamma = 1.681 \text{ to } 1.727$$
$$2V = 58° \text{ to } 60°; \text{ Opt. } (+)$$
$$b = \beta \text{ or } Y, c \wedge \gamma \text{ or } Z = -37° \text{ to } -44°$$

Color. Colorless, neutral, pale green to bright green in thin sections.

Form. Diopside usually occurs in subhedral crystals of short prismatic habit. Cross sections are four- or eight-sided.

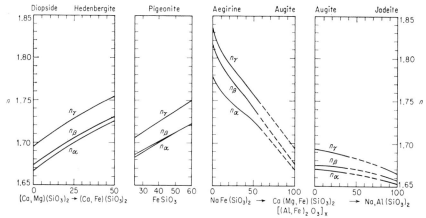

FIG. 14-8. Indices of refraction of common clinopyroxenes. Molecular constituents are shown in per cent from left to right. (*See Hess and Poldervaat.*)

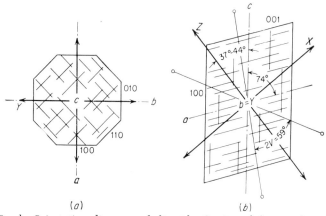

(*a*)   (*b*)

FIG. 14-9 *a,b*. Orientation diagrams of diopside. Sections (*a*) normal to the *c*-axis and (*b*) parallel to (010).

Cleavage. Parallel to {110} and so in two directions at angles of 87° and 93°. Parting parallel to {001} is sometimes developed.

Relief. Fairly high, $n >$ balsam.

Birefringence. Rather strong, $n_\gamma - n_\alpha = 0.029$ to 0.031; the maximum interference color is about upper second order.

Extinction. The maximum extinction angle in sections cut parallel to the *c*-axis varies from $-37°$ to $-44°$. In cross sections the extinction is symmetrical to the cleavage traces.

Orientation. The extinction direction that makes the smaller angle with the cleavage traces in longitudinal sections is the slower ray.

Twinning. Twins with {100} as twin-plane are rather common. Polysynthetic twinning with {001} as twin-plane is common as secondary twinning.

Interference Figure. Diopside gives a biaxial positive figure with a rather large axial angle. The axial plane is {010}. Dispersion, $r < v$ weak.

FIG. 14-10. (×36) Diopside from contact metamorphic zone.

Flakes parallel to the {001} parting give a good optic-axis figure.

Distinguishing Features. Diopside is distinguished from hedenbergite by lower refractive indices. From tremolite it is distinguished by larger extinction angle. Augite has a little higher extinction angle ($c \wedge \gamma$ or Z) and is usually a darker color. Pigeonite has a smaller axial angle.

Alteration. Diopside is sometimes more or less altered to tremolite-actinolite.

Related Minerals. Chrome diopside and omphacite are similar to diopside.

Occurrence. Diopside is especially characteristic of contact-metamorphic zones. It occurs with garnet, wollastonite, idocrase, and other

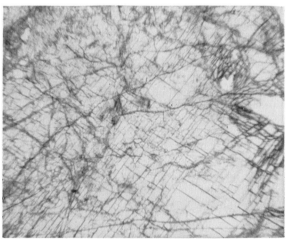

FIG. 14-11. (×20) Diopside showing cleavage parallel to (110). The two directions are almost at right angles.

silicates. It is found in some gneisses and schists and in some igneous rocks.

Diallage. This name is used for a variety of ferroan diopside with prominent parting parallel to {100}. It is scratched by a knife blade and has a pearly, more or less metalloidal luster. Parting flakes have parallel extinction, but sections cut parallel to {010} give the large extinction angles characteristic of diopside. The parting flakes give an uncentered optic-axis interference figure that serves to distinguish it from the ortho-pyroxenes. Diallage is especially characteristic of coarse-grained gabbros.

AUGITE

$Ca(Mg,Fe)(SiO_3)_2[(Al,Fe)_2O_3]_x$
Monoclinic
$\angle\beta = 74°10'$

$$n_\alpha = 1.688 \text{ to } 1.712$$
$$n_\beta = 1.701 \text{ to } 1.717$$
$$n_\gamma = 1.713 \text{ to } 1.737$$
$$2V = 58° \text{ to } 62°; \text{ Opt. } (+)$$
$$b = \beta \text{ or } y, \ c \wedge \gamma \text{ or } Z = -45° \text{ to } -54°$$

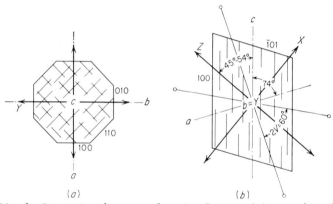

(a)   (b)

Fig. 14-12 a,b. Orientation diagrams of augite. Sections (a) normal to the c-axis and (b) parallel to (010).

Color. Almost colorless, neutral, pale greenish, or pale purplish brown in thin sections. Zonal structure is sometimes present. Pleochroism absent to weak; it is best shown in (100) sections.

Form. Augite usually occurs in short prismatic crystals with four- or eight-sided cross sections.

Cleavage. {110} in two directions at angles of 87° and 93°. Cleavage traces are in one direction in longitudinal sections. Diallage has prominent parting parallel to {100}.

Relief. High, $n >$ balsam.

Birefringence. Moderate, $n_\gamma - n_\alpha = 0.021$ to 0.025. The maximum interference color is about middle second order. Sections parallel to {100} have low first-order colors.

Extinction. The maximum extinction angle of longitudinal sections varies from 36° to 45°. These sections have the maximum interference colors for the slide. Some varieties have a peculiar concentric wavy extinction known as the *hourglass* structure. Cross sections have parallel or symmetrical extinction depending upon whether {100} and {010} or {110} predominates.

Orientation. The extinction direction that makes the smaller angle with the cleavage traces is the faster ray.

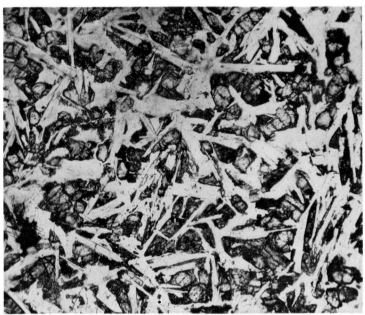

Fig. 14-13. (×24) Augite (high relief) with plagioclase in basalt.

Twinning. Twins with {100} as twin-plane are common; these often appear as twin seams. Polysynthetic twins with {001} as twin-plane are occasionally found. Combined {100} twins with {001} polysynthetic twins give what is known as *herringbone* structure.

Interference Figure. The figure is biaxial positive with a rather large axial angle. The axial plane is {010}. Dispersion, $r > v$.

Distinguishing Features. Augite is often difficult to distinguish from diopside. The extinction angle $c \wedge \gamma$ or Z is a little smaller and the color lighter in diopside.

Alteration. There are two common alteration products of augite: (1) hornblende formed at a late magmatic stage and in parallel position on the augite; (2) uralite or secondary tremolite-actinolite formed by hydrothermal alteration.

Occurrence. Augite is a very common mineral in subsilicic igneous rocks such as auganites, gabbros, basalts, olivine gabbros, limburgites, and peridotites. Locally it is found in gneisses and granulites.

Augite is also a common detrital mineral.

PIGEONITE

$m\mathrm{CaMg(SiO_3)_2}$.   (Enstatite-augite)   Monoclinic
$n\mathrm{(Mg,Fe)SiO_3}$ $\angle\beta = (?)$

$$n_\alpha = 1.680 \text{ to } 1.718$$
$$n_\beta = 1.698 \text{ to } 1.725$$
$$n_\gamma = 1.719 \text{ to } 1.744$$
$$2V = 0° \text{ to } 40°; \text{ Opt. } (+)$$
$$b = \beta,\ c \wedge \gamma \text{ or } Z = -22° \text{ to } -45°$$

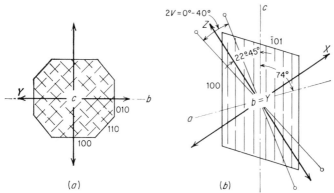

FIG. 14-14 *a,b*. Orientation diagrams of pigeonite. Sections (*a*) normal to the *c*-axis and (*b*) parallel to (010).

Pigeonite (named by A. N. Winchell from Pigeon Point, Minn.) is an isomorphous mixture of diopside and clinoenstatite, a monoclinic pyroxene found in meteorites and also produced in the laboratory.

Color. Colorless or neutral in thin sections. It may show faint pleochroism.

Form. Pigeonite usually occurs in anhedral crystals.

Cleavage. In two directions {110} at angles of about 87° and 93°.

Relief. Fairly high, $n >$ balsam.

Birefringence. Moderate, $n_\gamma - n_\alpha = 0.021$ to 0.033; so the maximum interference color varies from lower to upper second order.

Extinction. The maximum extinction angle varies from about 22° to 45°. It increases with increase of the clinoenstatite content.

Orientation. The extinction direction that makes the smaller angle with the cleavage traces in longitudinal sections is the slower ray.

Twinning. Polysynthetic twinning with (100) as the twin-plane is characteristic of pigeonite.

Interference Figure. The interference figure of pigeonite is biaxial positive with a rather small to very small axial angle. The axial plane is usually (010), but in varieties with very low calcium content the axial plane is normal to (010). For a certain composition pigeonite should have $2V = 0°$; a uniaxial pigeonite from Mull has been described by Hallimond.

Distinguishing Features. The only mineral that is likely to be mistaken for pigeonite is augite, from which it may be distinguished by its small axial angle.

Related Minerals. Clinoenstatite, the calcium-free end member of the pigeonite series, is a well-known laboratory product (the Geophysical Laboratory), but as a mineral it is known only in meteorites.

Occurrence. According to Barth, pigeonite is the most abundant member of the pyroxene group in volcanic rocks. It occurs in basalts, dolerites, and diabases. It is largely confined to the groundmass and is rarely found in phenocrysts.

HEDENBERGITE

$Ca(Fe,Mg)(SiO_3)_2$ Monoclinic

$\angle\beta = 74°30'$

$$n_\alpha = 1.732 \text{ to } 1.739$$
$$n_\beta = 1.737 \text{ to } 1.745$$
$$n_\gamma = 1.751 \text{ to } 1.757$$
$$2V = 60°; \text{ Opt. } (+)$$
$$b = \beta \text{ or } Y, c \wedge \gamma \text{ or } Z = -48°$$

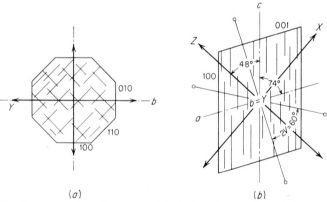

(*a*)   (*b*)

Fig. 14-15 *a,b*. Orientation diagrams of hedenbergite. Sections (*a*) normal to the *c*-axis and (*b*) parallel to (010).

Color. Neutral to greenish in thin sections.

Form. Hedenbergite usually occurs in columnar aggregates.

Cleavage. {110} in two directions at angles of 87° and 93° (like the other pyroxenes).

Relief. Very high, $n >$ balsam.

Birefringence. Moderate, $n_\gamma - n_\alpha = 0.018$ to 0.019; the maximum interference color is about first-order violet.

Extinction. The maximum extinction angle in longitudinal sections is about 42° ($c \wedge \alpha$ or X).

Orientation. The extinction direction that makes the smaller angle with the cleavage traces is the faster ray.

Interference Figure. The figure is biaxial positive with a rather large axial angle. The axial plane is {010}. Dispersion, $r > v$ weak.

Distinguishing Features. Hedenbergite is distinguished from diopside and augite by higher indices of refraction.

Occurrence. The characteristic occurrence of hedenbergite is in contact-metamorphic zones. It is often associated with iron ores as a skarn mineral.

AEGIRINE-AUGITE

Intermediate between   Monoclinic
aegirine and augite
in chemical composition

$$n_\alpha = 1.680 \text{ to } 1.745$$
$$n_\beta = 1.687 \text{ to } 1.770$$
$$n_\gamma = 1.709 \text{ to } 1.782$$
$$2V = \text{ca. } 60°; \text{ Opt. } (+) \text{ or } (-)$$
$$b = \beta \text{ or } Y, c \wedge \alpha \text{ or } X = -15° \text{ to } -38°$$

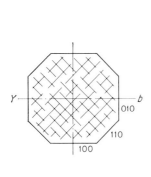
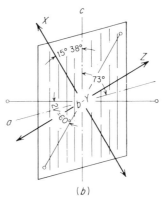

(a)   (b)

FIG. 14-16 a,b. Orientation diagrams of aegirine-augite. Sections (a) normal to the c-axis and (b) parallel to (010).

Color. Green in thin sections. Pleochroic from yellow-green (β or Y) to greenish (α or X, γ or Z).

Form. Aegirine-augite usually occurs in euhedral crystals of short prismatic habit with {100} as the dominant form.

Cleavage. In two directions {110} at angles of 87° and 93°.

Relief. High, $n >$ balsam.

Birefringence. Rather strong, $n_\gamma - n_\alpha = 0.029$ to 0.037; interference colors range up to the middle of the second order.

Extinction. The maximum extinction in longitudinal sections varies from −15° to −38°.

Orientation. In sections with the maximum extinction angle the extinction direction nearest the *c*-axis is the faster ray.

Twinning. Twins with {100} as twin-plane are common.

Interference Figure. Is biaxial positive with a rather large axial angle. The axial plane is {010}. Dispersion, $r > v$.

Distinguishing Features. Aegirine-augite resembles aegirine but may be distinguished by the larger extinction angles. It is most easily distinguished from the green varieties of hornblende by pyroxene cross sections and cleavage.

Occurrence. Aegirine-augite occurs in soda-rich igneous rocks such as syenites, trachytes, nepheline, syenites, phonolites, etc.

AEGIRINE

$NaFe(SiO_3)_2$ Monoclinic

$\angle\beta = 73°9'$

$n_\alpha = 1.745$ to 1.777

$n_\beta = 1.770$ to 1.823

$n_\gamma = 1.782$ to 1.836

$2V = 60°$ to $66°$; Opt. $(-)$

$b = \beta$ or Y, $c \wedge \alpha$ or $X = -2$ to $-10°$

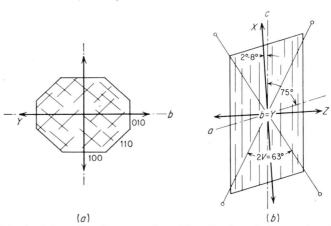

(*a*)   (*b*)

FIG. 14-17 *a,b*. Orientation diagrams of aegirine. Sections (*a*) normal to the *c*-axis and (*b*) parallel to (010).

Color. Green in thin sections. Strongly pleochroic. Axial colors: α or *X*, dark green; β or *Y*, light green; γ or *Z*, yellow.

Form. Aegirine is usually found in long prismatic crystals, often bladed, with the typical four- to eight-sided cross section of the pyroxenes but with {100} frequently better developed than {010}.

Cleavage. {110} in two directions at angles of 87° and 93°.

Relief. High, $n >$ balsam.

Birefringence. Strong to very strong, $n_\gamma - n_\alpha = 0.037$ to 0.059; the interference colors should be third or fourth order but may be difficult to determine because the color of the mineral may mask the interference colors.

Extinction. The maximum extinction angle in longitudinal sections is very small (from 2° to 10°).

Orientation. The crystals are always length-fast.

Interference Figure. The figure is biaxial negative with a rather large axial angle. The axial plane is {010}. Dispersion, $r > v$.

Distinguishing Features. Aegirine resembles some of the amphiboles but is distinguished by the small maximum extinction angle and length-fast character. All the other monoclinic pyroxenes have larger extinction angles.

Related Minerals. Acmite is a pyroxene closely related to aegirine. It differs from the latter in its brown color.

Occurrence. Aegirine, although a rather rare mineral, is characteristic of soda-rich igneous rocks such as nepheline syenite, phonolite, syenite, trachyte, soda granite, soda aplite, etc. In these rocks it often occurs as an overgrowth on aegirine-augite crystals.

JADEITE

$NaAl(SiO_3)_2$ (Jade in part) Monoclinic

$$\angle\beta = 72°44\tfrac{1}{2}'$$

$$n_\alpha = 1.655 \text{ to } 1.666$$
$$n_\beta = 1.659 \text{ to } 1.674$$
$$n_\gamma = 1.667 \text{ to } 1.688$$
$$2V = 70° \text{ to } 75°; \text{ Opt. } (+)$$
$$b = \beta \text{ or } Y, c \wedge \gamma \text{ or } Z = -30° \text{ to } -36°$$

Color. Colorless to green in thin sections. Some of the deeply colored varieties are pleochroic.

Form. Jadeite usually appears in granular to columnar or somewhat fibrous aggregates. The texture varies from fine-grained to coarse-grained. Euhedral crystals are exceedingly rare.

Cleavage. {110} in two directions at angles of about 87° and 93°.

Relief. Rather high, $n >$ balsam.

Birefringence. Moderate, $n_\gamma - n_\alpha = 0.012$ to 0.023; the maximum interference colors are second order.

Extinction. The maximum extinction angle in longitudinal sections varies from 30° to 44°.

Orientation. The extinction direction nearest the *c*-axis is the slower ray.

Twinning. Twins with {100} as twin-plane are occasionally found.

Interference Figure. The figure is biaxial positive with a large axial angle. The axial plane is {010}. Dispersion, $r < v$.

Distinguishing Features. Jadeite is distinguished from nephrite (variety of tremolite-actinolite) by larger extinction angle and higher refractive indices. From diopside it is distinguished by smaller maximum extinction angles and columnar habit.

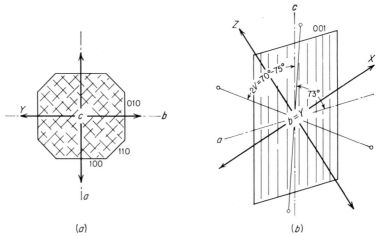

(*a*)   (*b*)

Fig. 14-18 *a,b*. Orientation diagrams of jadeite. Sections (*a*) normal to the *c*-axis and (*b*) parallel to (010).

Related Minerals. Chloromelanite is an iron-bearing greenish black jadeite that is strongly pleochroic in thin sections.

Alteration. Jadeite is sometimes found more or less altered to tremolite-actinolite.

Occurrence. Jadeite occurs exclusively in jadeite rock (jadeitite), a monomineralic metamorphic rock formed according to Grubenmann in the deep zone of metamorphism. Albite is mentioned as one of the characteristic associates. The origin of jadeitite is obscure; it is found in only a few localities in Upper Burma, eastern Turkestan, northern Italy, and Guatemala.

Jade. The name *jade* (Chinese, Yü) is a general term for two distinct minerals: (1) nephrite, a tough, compact variety of tremolite-actinolite and (2) jadeite, an independent member of the pyroxene group, including its iron-bearing variety, chloromelanite.

The jadelike minerals or *pseudojades* include bowenite, a hard tough serpentine; californite, a compact variety of idocrase; "South African jade," a massive green grossularite; "Oregon jade," also a variety of grossularite; "Styrian jade," a kind of pseudophite, a compact chlorite; as well as sillimanite, pectolite, and wollastonite.

SPODUMENE

$LiAl(SiO_3)_2$

Monoclinic

$\angle\beta = 69°40'$

$$n_\alpha = 1.651 \text{ to } 1.668$$
$$n_\beta = 1.665 \text{ to } 1.675$$
$$n_\gamma = 1.677 \text{ to } 1.681$$
$$2V = 54° \text{ to } 69°; \text{ Opt. } (+)$$
$$b = \beta \text{ or } Y, c \wedge \gamma \text{ or } Z = -23° \text{ to } -27°$$

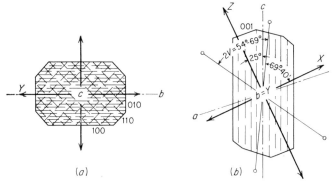

(a) (b)

FIG. 14-19 a,b. Orientation diagram of spodumene. Sections (a) normal to the c-axis and (b) parallel to (010).

Color. Colorless in thin sections. Some varieties show color (amethystine for kunzite, greenish for hiddenite) in thick sections and are pleochroic.

Form. Spodumene usually occurs in euhedral crystals tabular parallel to {100} and elongated in the direction of [001]. Crystals as a rule are inclined to be large but are sometimes on the order of several millimeters.

Cleavage. Perfect parallel to {110} (110 $\wedge$ $\bar{1}$10) = 93°. Parting parallel to {100}, which is often more prominent than the cleavage.

Relief. Fairly high, $n >$ balsam.

Birefringence. Moderate, $n_\gamma - n_\alpha = 0.013$ to 0.027; the maximum interference color varies from upper first order to middle second order.

Extinction. The maximum extinction angle in longitudinal sections varies from 23° to 27°. In cross sections the extinction is parallel or symmetrical. Oriented sections cut parallel to the (100) parting have parallel extinction.

Orientation. The extinction direction that makes the smaller angle with the cleavage traces is the slower ray.

Twinning. Twins with {100} as twin-plane are known.

Interference Figure. Spodumene gives a positive biaxial interference figure with a rather large axial angle. The axial plane is (010). Dispersion, $r < v$.

Distinguishing Features. Spondumene resembles diopside in general appearance, from which it may be distinguished by smaller extinction angle ($c \wedge \gamma$ = ca. 25°) and frequently by very conspicuous (100) parting.

Alteration. Spodumene is sometimes altered to a mixture of albite and muscovite known as *cymatolite*. The muscovite here is an alteration of eucryptite (hexagonal $LiAlSiO_4$).

Kunzite is known to be altered to cookeite, a lithium aluminum silicate related to lepidolite.

Occurrence. The typical occurrence of spodumene is the lithium granite pegmatites where it is associated with albite, lepidolite, elbaite, and rare lithium minerals.

The Pyroxenoids. Berman has suggested the term *pyroxenoid* for a number of pyroxene-like metasilicates that are not isomorphous with any of the pyroxenes. Pyroxenoids include rhodonite, bustamite, pectolite, and wollastonite. Of these, only wollastonite is important as a rock-forming mineral.

AMPHIBOLE GROUP

The amphiboles may be considered in terms of five series (1) anthophyllite, (2) cummingtonite-grunerite, (3) tremolite-actinolite, (4) aluminous amphibole, and (5) soda amphibole.

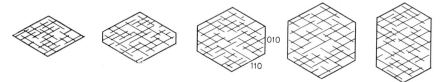

FIG. 14-20. Cross sections of minerals of the amphibole group showing cleavage.

The anthophyllite series is orthorhombic while the others are monoclinic. The composition $RSiO_3$ is fundamental to the group with R=Ca,Mg,Fe. The anthophyllite, cummingtonite-grunerite and tremolite-actinolite series consist essentially of a range in $RSiO_3$ compositions, while the aluminous and soda amphiboles contain Al and Na in addition to the fundamental composition. The general chemical relationships are outlined below.

The amphiboles have rhombic to pseudohexagonal cross sections and perfect cleavage parallel to {110} at angles of about 56° and 124°, as shown in Figure 14-20. Twinning parallel to {100} is fairly common.

With the exception of crossite, in all the amphiboles the plane of the optic axes is {010}.

AMPHIBOLE GROUP

Mineral		Chemical composition	n_α	n_β	n_γ	2V	$c:\gamma$ or Z
Ortho-rhombic	Anthophyllite........	MgFe	1.598 1.652	1.615 1.662	1.623 1.676	70–90°	0°
Monoclinic	Cummingtonite......	FeMg	1.639 1.657	1.645 1.669	1.664 1.686	68–87°	15–20°
	Grunerite...........	Fe	1.657 1.663	1.684 1.697	1.699 1.717	79–86°	10–14°
	Tremolite-actinolite (inc. nephrite).....	CaMgFe	1.600 1.628	1.613 1.644	1.625 1.655	79–85°	10–20°
	Hornblende.........	CaMgFeAl	1.614 1.675	1.618 1.691	1.633 1.701	52–85°	12–30°
	Lamprobolite........	CaMgFeAl	1.670 1.692	1.683 1.730	1.693 1.760	64–80°	0–10°
	Riebeckite..........	NaFe	1.693	1.695	1.697	Large	85°
	Glaucophane........	NaAlFe	1.621 1.655	1.638 1.664	1.639 1.668	45°	4– 6°

The amphibole group is more or less parallel to the pyroxene group. Corresponding members of the two groups, however, are not dimorphous. Hornblende is by far the most common mineral of the group. Cummingtonite is a pale brown monoclinic amphibole with the composition of anthophyllite. It is rare. Basaltic hornblende is considered a distinctive mineral under the name lamprobolite. Riebeckite, glaucophane, and a few rarer minerals are known as *soda amphiboles*.

The amphibole group is one of the most complex of all mineral groups. There are many amphiboles that cannot be placed under any of the minerals listed here.

Orthoamphiboles

ANTHOPHYLLITE

$(Mg,Fe)_7(OH)_2(Si_4O_{11})_2$ Orthorhombic

$$n_\alpha = 1.598 \text{ to } 1.652$$
$$n_\beta = 1.615 \text{ to } 1.662$$
$$n_\gamma = 1.623 \text{ to } 1.676$$
$$2V = 70° \text{ to } 90°; \text{ Opt. } (+)$$
$$a = \alpha \text{ or } X, \ b = \beta \text{ or } Y, \ c = \gamma \text{ or } Z$$

Color. Colorless or pale colored in thin sections. Some of the colored varieties show pleochroism.

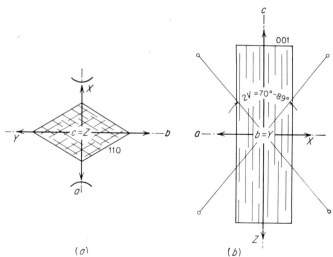

FIG. 14-21 *a,b*. Orientation diagrams of anthophyllite. Sections (*a*) normal to the *c*-axis and (*b*) parallel to (010).

Form. Long prismatic crystals and columnar to fibrous aggregates are characteristic of anthophyllite. It is sometimes asbestiform.

Cleavage. In two directions {110} at angles of 54° and 126°. Cross fractures are common.

Relief. High, $n >$ balsam.

Birefringence. Moderate, $n_\gamma - n_\alpha = 0.016$ to 0.025; interference colors range up to low second order.

Extinction. Parallel in longitudinal sections, in cross sections symmetrical to outline or cleavage.

Orientation. Length-slow.

Twinning. Absent.

Interference Figure. The figure is biaxial positive with a large axial angle, or neutral ($2V = 90°$). The axial plane is {010}. Dispersion, $r > v$ or $r < v$.

Distinguishing Features. Anthophyllite resembles tremolite-actinolite and also cummingtonite but may be distinguished from these minerals by its parallel extinction.

Related Minerals. Gedrite is an aluminous variety of anthophyllite. It is optically negative instead of positive.

Alteration. Anthophyllite is often altered to talc. The partially altered mineral was formerly called *hydrous anthophyllite*.

Occurrence. Anthophyllite is characteristic of metamorphic rocks. It is the main constituent of anthophyllite schist and is also a secondary mineral in peridotites and dunites.

Anthophyllite is the principal constituent of mass-fiber asbestos.

Clinoamphiboles

MONOCLINIC AMPHIBOLES

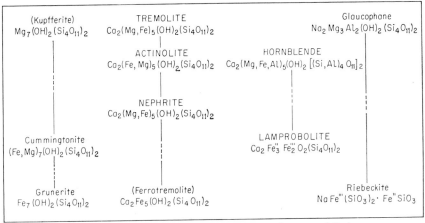

| (Kupfferite)
$Mg_7(OH)_2(Si_4O_{11})_2$ | TREMOLITE
$Ca_2(Mg,Fe)_5(OH)_2(Si_4O_{11})_2$ | Glaucophane
$Na_2Mg_3Al_2(OH)_2(Si_4O_{11})_2$ |

| | ACTINOLITE
$Ca_2(Fe,Mg)_5(OH)_2(Si_4O_{11})_2$ | HORNBLENDE
$Ca_2(Mg,Fe,Al)_5(OH)_2[(Si,Al)_4O_{11}]_2$ |

| | NEPHRITE
$Ca_2(Mg,Fe)_5(OH)_2(Si_4O_{11})_2$ | |

| Cummingtonite
$(Fe,Mg)_7(OH)_2(Si_4O_{11})_2$ | | LAMPROBOLITE
$Ca_2Fe_3''Fe_2'''O_2(Si_4O_{11})_2$ |

| Grunerite
$Fe_7(OH)_2(Si_4O_{11})_2$ | (Ferrotremolite)
$Ca_2Fe_5(OH)_2(Si_4O_{11})_2$ | Riebeckite
$NaFe'''(SiO_3)_2 \cdot Fe''SiO_3$ |

Fig. 14-22. Major groups among the monoclinic amphiboles.

CUMMINGTONITE

$(Fe,Mg)_7(OH)_2(Si_4O_{11})_2$ Monoclinic

$$n_\alpha = 1.639 \text{ to } 1.657$$
$$n_\beta = 1.645 \text{ to } 1.669$$
$$n_\gamma = 1.664 \text{ to } 1.686$$
$$2V = 68° \text{ to } 87°; \text{ Opt. } (+)$$
$$b = \beta \text{ or } Y, c \wedge \gamma \text{ or } Z = -15° \text{ to } -20°$$

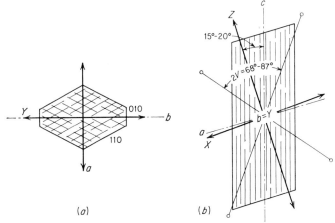

(a)   (b)

Fig. 14-23 a,b. Orientation diagrams of cummingtonite. Sections (a) normal to the c-axis and (b) parallel to (010).

Color. Colorless to neutral in thin sections. It may show slight pleochroism.

Form. Cummingtonite usually occurs in parallel to subradiating aggregates of prismatic crystals. The crystals are sometimes curved.

Cleavage. Cleavage in two directions at angles of about 56° and 124° as in the other amphiboles.

Relief. Moderately high, $n >$ balsam.

Birefringence. Rather strong, $n_\gamma - n_\alpha = 0.025$ to 0.029.

Extinction. The maximum extinction angle in longitudinal sections varies from about 15° to 20°; the angle increases with increase of magnesium content.

Orientation. Elongate sections are length-slow.

Twinning. Twins with {100} as a twin-plane are highly characteristic of cummingtonite. The twinning is polysynthetic, and the twin-lamellae are usually very narrow.

Interference Figures. The figure is biaxial positive with a large axial angle. The axial plane is (010). Dispersion, $r < v$.

Distinguishing Features. Cummingtonite has a larger extinction angle and lower indices of refraction than grunerite. Cummingtonite is optically positive, and grunerite is negative. From tremolite, cummingtonite is distinguished by higher indices of refraction. Anthophyllite is very similar to cummingtonite but may be distinguished by its parallel extinction and absence of twinning.

Occurrence. Cummingtonite, as far as known, is confined to metamorphic rocks. It is a characteristic mineral in schists at the Homestake Mine in South Dakota. It is a characteristic mineral of hornfels at several localities in California.

GRUNERITE

$Fe_7(OH)_2(Si_4O_{11})_2$ Monoclinic

$$n_\alpha = 1.657 \text{ to } 1.663$$
$$n_\beta = 1.684 \text{ to } 1.697$$
$$n_\gamma = 1.699 \text{ to } 1.717$$
$$2V = 79° \text{ to } 86°; \text{ Opt. } (-)$$
$$b = \beta \text{ or } Y, c \wedge \gamma \text{ or } Z = -10° \text{ to } -14°$$

Grunerite (not grünerite) is the name used for the minerals of the cummingtonite-grunerite series in which iron greatly predominates over magnesium.

Color. Neutral in thin sections.

Form. Grunerite usually occurs in fibrous to columnar aggregates. It is sometimes asbestiform. Cross sections are rhombic as in other amphiboles.

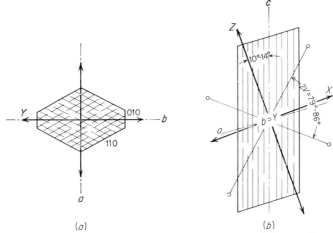

Fig. 14-24 *a,b*. Orientation diagrams of grunerite. Sections (*a*) normal to the *c*-axis and (*b*) parallel to (010).

Cleavage. Cleavage is in two directions at angles of about 56° and 124° as in the other amphiboles. Cross fractures are common.

Relief. Fairly high, $n >$ balsam.

Birefringence. Strong, $n_\gamma - n_\alpha = 0.042$ to 0.054; the interference colors range up to upper second order or low third order. Sections with parallel extinction show low first-order colors.

Extinction. The maximum extinction angle in longitudinal sections varies from 10° up to about 15°. The variation in maximum extinction angle is due to variation in chemical composition. The replacement of some of the iron by magnesium brings about an increase in the extinction angle.

Orientation. Elongate sections are length-slow.

Twinning. A characteristic feature of grunerite is the polysynthetic twinning with (100) as the twin-plane. The twin-lamellae are often very narrow.

Interference Figure. Interference figures are often difficult to obtain, but when found they are biaxial negative with a large axial angle. The axial plane is (010). Dispersion, $r > v$, weak.

Distinguishing Features. Grunerite has a smaller maximum extinction angle and higher indices of refraction than cummingtonite. It is optically negative and cummingtonite positive. The indices of refraction of grunerite are also higher than those of tremolite-actinolite. Anthophyllite, similar in many ways, has parallel extinction and never shows any twinning.

Occurrence. Grunerite is a product of metamorphism. It occurs in metamorphic rocks like the mica schists at Collobrières, Department of

Var, France (the original locality), also as an alteration product in the eulysite of Tunaberg, Sweden, and is very prominent in some of the iron ores of the Lake Superior region, notably the magnetite ores of the Upper Peninsula of Michigan.

TREMOLITE-ACTINOLITE

$Ca_2(Mg,Fe)_5(OH)_2(Si_4O_{11})_2$ 　　　　　　　　　　　Monoclinic
$\angle\beta = 74°48'$

$$n_\alpha = 1.600 \text{ to } 1.628$$
$$n_\beta = 1.613 \text{ to } 1.644$$
$$n_\gamma = 1.625 \text{ to } 1.655$$
$$2V = 79° \text{ to } 85°; \text{ Opt. } (-)$$
$$b = \beta \text{ or } Y, \ c \wedge \gamma \text{ or } Z = -10° \text{ to } -20°$$

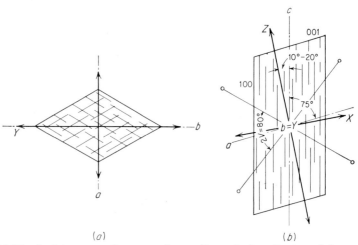

(a)   (b)

Fig. 14-25 a,b. Orientation diagrams of tremolite-actinolite. Sections (a) normal to the c-axis and (b) parallel to (010).

Color. Colorless to pale green in thin sections. The green varieties show faint pleochroism. Green ferriferous tremolite is known as *actinolite*.

Form. Tremolite-actinolite occurs in long prismatic crystals and columnar to fibrous aggregates. Asbestiform varieties are common. The typical cross section is rhombic with $(110 \wedge 110) = 56°$.

Cleavage. {110} in two directions at angles of about 56° and 124°. Longitudinal sections show cleavage traces parallel to the length. There may be parting parallel to (100).

Relief. Fairly high, $n >$ balsam.

Birefringence. Moderate to rather strong, $n_\gamma - n_\alpha = 0.022$ to 0.027; so the interference colors range up to low or middle second order. Narrow longitudinal sections show the highest colors. Cross sections have white to yellow interference colors.

Extinction. The maximum extinction in longitudinal sections varies from $10°$ to $20°$. A few longitudinal sections have parallel or nearly parallel extinction. Cross sections have symmetrical extinction.

Orientation. Elongate sections are length-slow. In cross sections the long diagonal is the slower ray.

Twinning. Twins with {100} as twin-plane are frequent. Fine polysynthetic twinning with {001} as twin-plane is occasionally encountered.

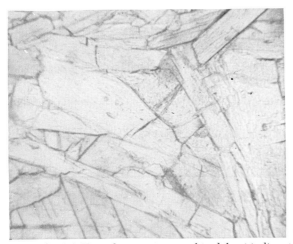

FIG. 14-26. ($\times 50$) Tremolite in metamorphic dolomitic limestone.

Interference Figure. Tremolite-actinolite gives a biaxial negative figure with very large axial angle. The axial plane is {010}. Dispersion, $r < v$ weak. Broad elongate sections with low interference colors give the best figure.

Distinguishing Features. The extinction angle and amphibole cross sections are characteristic. Wollastonite has the same general appearance as tremolite, but the trace of the optic axial plane is normal to the cleavage instead of parallel to it as in tremolite.

Related Minerals. A colorless amphibole, edenite, greatly resembles tremolite but has larger extinction angles.

Alteration. Tremolite-actinolite is sometimes found altered to talc.

Occurrence. Tremolite-actinolite occurs in contact-metamorphic deposits, in schists and gneisses, and in metamorphic limestones. It is also found as a replacement of pyroxene in igneous rocks.

NEPHRITE

(Jade in part)

$Ca_2(Mg,Fe)_5(OH)_2(Si_4O_{11})_2$ Monoclinic

$$n_\alpha = 1.600 \text{ to } 1.628$$
$$n_\beta = 1.613 \text{ to } 1.644$$
$$n_\gamma = 1.625 \text{ to } 1.655$$
$$2V = 79° \text{ to } 85°; \text{ Opt. } (-)$$
$$b = \beta \text{ or } Y; c \wedge \gamma \text{ or } Z = -10° \text{ to } -20°$$

Nephrite is really a tough compact variety of tremolite-actinolite, but for emphasis it is treated separately.

Color. Colorless to gray in thin sections.

Form. Nephrite usually occurs in fibrous to fibro-lamellar aggregates of imperfect prismatic crystals.

Cleavage. Is like that of tremolite-actinolite but is rarely distinct on account of interfelted fibers.

Relief. Fairly high, $n >$ balsam.

Birefringence. Moderate, $n_\gamma - n_\alpha = 0.022$ to 0.027; so the interference colors range from first-order gray up to bright colors of the middle second order.

Extinction. Varies from parallel to a maximum of about 10° to 20°. A few of the broader longitudinal sections may have parallel extinction. The extinction of nephrite is often wavy and indistinct.

Orientation. Most sections are length-slow.

Twinning. With {100} as twin-plane is occasionally found but does not seem to be common.

Interference Figure. Nephrite does not usually give a good interference figure on account of the aggregate structure. The figure when obtained is biaxial negative with a large axial angle. The axial plane is {010} as in the other amphiboles.

Related Minerals. There is no very sharp distinction between nephrite and other varieties of tremolite-actinolite. The term *seminephrite* has been used by F. J. Turner for an amphibole intermediate between nephrite and less compact, more coarsely crystalline tremolite-actinolite.

Distinguishing Features. Nephrite is distinguished from jadeite, the other jade mineral, by its smaller maximum extinction angle and its lower indices of refraction and also by its lower specific gravity. From other varieties of tremolite-actinolite it is distinguished by its greater compactness, which is due to interfelted crystalline aggregates.

Alteration. Nephrite is sometimes altered to talc.

Occurrence. Nephrite usually occurs in association with serpentine as "kidneys" with more or less schistose structure and in derived water-worn pebbles and boulders. It is doubtless a product of metamorphism, but its origin is not well understood.

Nephrite is a widely distributed mineral much valued by the natives of many countries as material for both weapons and ornaments.

HORNBLENDE

$Ca_2(Mg,Fe,Al)_5(OH)_2[(Si,Al)_4O_{11}]_2$ Monoclinic
$\angle \beta = 75°2'$

$$n_\alpha = 1.614 \text{ to } 1.675$$
$$n_\beta = 1.618 \text{ to } 1.691$$
$$n_\gamma = 1.633 \text{ to } 1.701$$
$$2V = 52° \text{ to } 85°; \text{ Opt. } (-)$$
$$b = \beta \text{ or } Y, c \wedge \gamma \text{ or } Z = -12° \text{ to } -30°$$

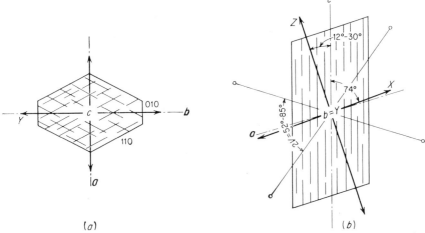

(a)   (b)

FIG. 14-27 a,b. Orientation diagrams of hornblende. Sections (a) normal to the c-axis and (b) parallel to (010).

Color. Green or brown of various tones in thin sections. Pleochroism as follows:

α or X	β or Y	γ or Z
Yellow green	Olive green	Dark green
Pale green	Green	Dark green
Pale brown	Greenish	Dark green
Yellow green	Yellow	Brown
Greenish brown	Reddish brown	Red brown

Absorption scheme: γ or $Z > \beta$ or $Y > \alpha$ or X.

Form. Crystals are prismatic in habit with pseudohexagonal cross sections ($110 \wedge 1\bar{1}0 = 55°49'$). Crystals are rarely well terminated (Figure 8-21).

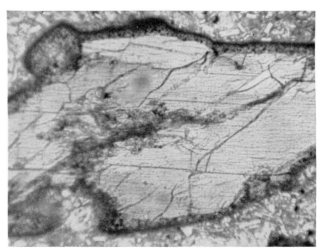

FIG. 14-28. (×60) Hornblende in a rounded crystal showing faint cleavage.

FIG. 14-29. (×22) Late magmatic hornblende (dark) formed at the expense of pyroxene.

Cleavage. {110} in two directions at angles of about 56° and 124°.

Relief. Rather high, $n >$ balsam.

Birefringence. Moderate, $n_\gamma - n_\alpha = 0.019$ to 0.026. The maximum interference colors are about middle second order, but in many varieties the color of the mineral modifies or even masks the interference colors.

Extinction. The maximum extinction angle in longitudinal sections varies from about 12° to about 30°. In cross sections the extinction is symmetrical to the outlines or to cleavage traces.

Twinning. Twins with {100} as the twin-plane are rather common. Twinning is often manifest as twin seams.

Interference Figure. The figure is biaxial negative with a large axial angle. The axial plane is {010}. Dispersion, $r < v$ weak.

Distinguishing Features. Hornblende differs from augite in cleavage, pleochroism, and maximum extinction angle. Brown hornblende resembles biotite, but the latter has better cleavage (in one direction only) and parallel or almost parallel extinction. Lamprobolite has a smaller extinction angle, higher indices of refraction, and stronger birefringence.

Occurrence. Hornblende is a very common and widely distributed mineral in many types of igneous rocks. It also occurs in schists, gneisses, and amphibolites.

It is a prominent constituent of many detrital sediments.

LAMPROBOLITE[1]

(Basaltic Hornblende)

Ca,Mg,Fe,Al silicate   Monoclinic

$\angle\beta = 73°58'$

$n_\alpha = 1.670$ to 1.692

$n_\beta = 1.683$ to 1.730

$n_\gamma = 1.693$ to 1.760

$2V = 64$ to $80°$; Opt. $(-)$

$b = \beta$ or Y, $c \wedge \gamma$ or $Z = 0$ to $-12°$

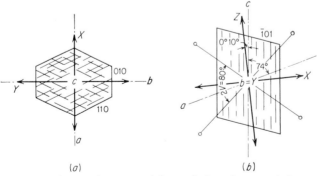

(a)   (b)

FIG. 14-30 *a,b*. Orientation diagrams of lamprobolite. Sections (*a*) normal to the *c*-axis and (*b*) parallel to (010).

---

[1] The name *lamprobolite* was proposed by A. F. Rogers [*Am. Mineralogist,* **25**: 826–828 (1940)] for the mineral usually called *basaltic hornblende*.

Color. Yellow to brown, often with opaque borders. Pleochroism rather strong: α or X, light yellow; β or Y, brown; γ or Z, dark red-brown.

Form. Lamprobolite occurs almost invariably in euhedral crystals with the pseudohexagonal cross section of the amphiboles. The habit is usually short prismatic.

Cleavage. {110} in two directions at angles of 56° and 124° as in the other amphiboles.

Relief. High, $n >$ balsam.

Birefringence. Rather strong to very strong, $n_\gamma - n_\alpha = 0.026$ to 0.072. The interference colors should be high order, but they are usually masked by the color of the mineral.

Extinction. The maximum extinction angle is very small, from zero up to as much as 12° in some varieties.

Orientation. The crystals are length-slow. Cross sections have symmetrical extinction.

Twinning. Twins with {100} as twin-plane are found but are not conspicuous on account of the small size of the extinction angle.

Interference Figure. The figure is biaxial negative with a large axial angle. The axial plane is {010}. Dispersion, $r < v$.

Distinguishing Features. Lamprobolite is distinguished from ordinary brown hornblende by the smaller extinction angle and the stronger birefringence. Biotite shows no cleavage in six-sided sections.

Related Minerals. Kaersutite is a titanian amphibole related to lamprobolite.

Occurrence. Lamprobolite occurs in volcanic rocks such as andesites, auganites, basalts, basanites, tephrites, and the corresponding tuffs. It is also fairly common as a detrital mineral.

It seems likely that lamprobolite has been produced from ordinary hornblende by the oxidation of the iron, probably by hot gases at the end of the magmatic stage.

RIEBECKITE

(inc. Crocidolite)

$NaFe^{III}(SiO_3)_2 . Fe^{II}SiO_3$ Monoclinic

$\angle\beta = 76°10'$

$$n_\alpha = 1.693$$
$$n_\beta = 1.695$$
$$n_\gamma = 1.697$$
$$2V \text{ large; Opt. } (-)$$
$$b = \beta \text{ or } Y, c \wedge \alpha \text{ or } X = +5°$$

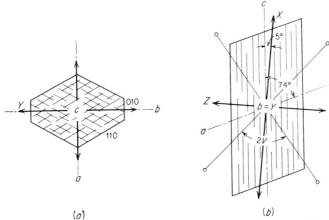

(a)   (b)

FIG. 14-31 a,b. Orientation diagram of riebeckite. Sections (a) normal to the c-axis and (b) parallel to (010).

Color. Dark blue in thin sections. Pleochroism strong: α or X, deep blue; β or Y, lighter blue; γ or Z, greenish. Absorption: α or $X > \beta$ or $Y > \gamma$ or Z.

Form. Riebeckite occurs in subhedral prismatic crystals and in fibrous and asbestiform aggregates. According to recent investigations, crocidolite is a fibrous variety of riebeckite.

Cleavage. {110} in two directions at angles of about 56° and 124°.

Relief. High, $n >$ balsam.

Birefringence. Very weak, $n_\gamma - n_\alpha = 0.004$; the interference colors are masked by the deep color of the mineral.

Extinction. The maximum extinction angle in elongate sections is about 5°, but the fibrous variety, crocidolite, has parallel extinction.

Orientation. The crystals are length-fast.

Interference Figure. The figure is biaxial negative with a large axial angle. The axial plane is {010}. Dispersion, $r > v$ strong.

Distinguishing Features. The color, pleochroism, and small extinction angle are distinctive.

Alteration. Crocidolite is often altered to an iron-stained fibrous quartz known as "tiger's eye."

Occurrence. Riebeckite is characteristic of soda-rich granites, microgranites, granite aplites, granite pegmatites, syenites, nepheline syenites, and trachytes. In these rocks it is often associated with aegirine. Crocidolite is found in certain highly siliceous metamorphic rocks such as the "ironstones" of Griqualand West, South Africa.

GLAUCOPHANE

$Na_2Mg_3Al_2(OH)_2(Si_4O_{11})_2$ Monoclinic
                                                                    $\angle\beta = 77°$

$$n_\alpha = 1.621 \text{ to } 1.655$$
$$n_\beta = 1.638 \text{ to } 1.664$$
$$n_\gamma = 1.639 \text{ to } 1.668$$
$$2V = 0° \text{ to } 68°; \text{ Opt. } (-)$$
$$b = \beta \text{ or } Y; c \wedge \gamma \text{ or } Z = -4° \text{ to } -6°$$

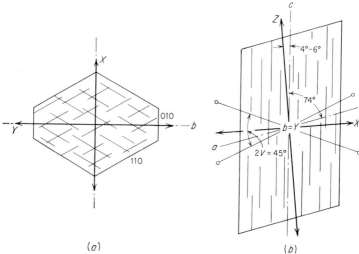

(a)   (b)

FIG. 14-32 a,b. Orientation diagrams of glaucophane. Sections (a) normal to the c-axis and (b) parallel to (010).

Color. Blue to violet in thin sections. Pleochroism: α or X, neutral; β or Y, violet; γ or Z, blue.

Form. Glaucophane occurs in prismatic crystals or columnar aggregates. The cross sections are pseudohexagonal or rhombic.

Cleavage. {110} in two directions at angles of 56° and 124°.

Relief. Fairly high, $n >$ balsam.

Birefringence. Moderate, $n_\gamma - n_\alpha = 0.013$ to 0.018; the maximum interference color is about sensitive violet, but the color of the mineral may modify or even mask the interference colors.

Extinction. The maximum extinction angle in longitudinal sections is very small (4° to 6°). Cross sections have symmetrical extinction.

Orientation. The crystals are length-slow.

Interference Figure. The figure is biaxial negative with a small to moderate axial angle. The axial plane is {010}. Dispersion, $r < v$ strong.

Distinguishing Features. The axial colors, together with the small extinction angle and amphibole cross section and cleavage, distinguish glaucophane from all other minerals except crossite and glastaldite.

Related Minerals. Crossite is a soda amphibole intermediate between glaucophane and riebeckite, but the axial plane of crossite is normal to (010). Gastaldite is a soda amphibole related to glaucophane but paler blue in color because of lower iron content.

Occurrence. Glaucophane is found in certain schists and gneisses. The usual associates are muscovite, quartz, garnet, sphene, lawsonite,

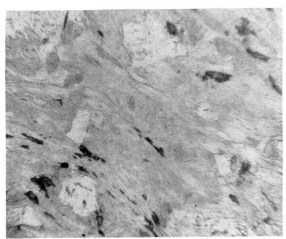

FIG. 14-33. (×50) Glaucophane forming a felted crystalline mass in schist.

and clinozoisite. Glaucophane schists are abundant in the Coast Ranges of California and are also found in Syra (Greece), Italy, and Japan, but are rare, taken the world over.

EPIDOTE GROUP

The epidote group consists of silicates of calcium and aluminum with occasional addition or substitution of iron, manganese, or cerium. Calcium aluminum silicate may occur as zoisite (orthorhombic) or clinozoisite (monoclinic). Other members of the group are monoclinic.

Orthorhombic

ZOISITE

$Ca_2(Al,Fe)_3(OH)(SiO_4)_3$ Orthorhombic

$$n_\alpha = 1.696 \text{ to } 1.700$$
$$n_\beta = 1.696 \text{ to } 1.703$$
$$n_\gamma = 1.702 \text{ to } 1.718$$
$$2V = 30° \text{ to } 60°; \text{ Opt. } (+)$$

Two orientations:

(1) $a = \gamma$ or Z, $b = \beta$ or Y, $c = \alpha$ or X
(2) $a = \gamma$ or Z, $b = \alpha$ or X, $c = \beta$ or Y

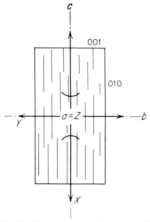

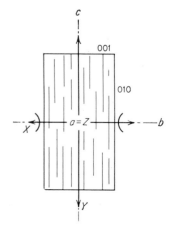

Fig. 14-34. Orientation diagrams of zois-   Fig. 14-35. Orientation (2).
ite. Sections parallel to (100). Orienta-
tion (1).

There are two varieties of zoisite: a non-ferrian variety with orientation (1) and anomalous interference colors, and a ferrian variety with orientation (2) and normal interference colors.

Color. Usually colorless in thin sections, but manganian zoisite (thulite) is pink and pleochroic.

Form. Zoisite usually occurs in columnar aggregates, but euhedral crystals are not uncommon.

Cleavage. Perfect in one direction {010}.

Relief. High, $n >$ balsam.

Birefringence. Weak to moderate, $n_\gamma - n_\alpha = 0.006$ to 0.018; the interference colors in one variety (2) are normal; in the other variety (1) they are anomalous (deep blue).

Extinction. Parallel in most sections.

Orientation. In some specimens (1) the crystals are length-fast; in others (2) either length-fast or length-slow.

Twinning. Polysynthetic twinning may be present.

Interference Figure. The interference figure is biaxial positive with a moderate axial angle. The axial plane is either (1) {010} or (2) {001}. Dispersion, (1) $r < v$ distinct or (2) $r > v$ distinct.

Distinguishing Features. Ferrian zoisite (orientation 2) is distinguished from clinozoisite by normal interference colors. Non-ferrian zoisite (orientation 1) is distinguished from clinozoisite by a smaller axial angle and by deep blue anomalous interference color.

Occurrence. Zoisite is a rather rare mineral found in some metamorphic rocks. Clinozoisite is much more common than zoisite.

a

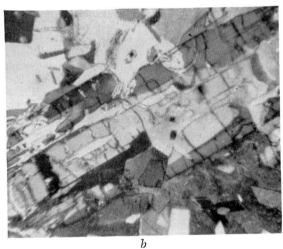

b

FIG. 14-36 *a,b.* (×20) Bladed zoisite crystals in a quartz matrix. (*a*) Ordinary illumination and (*b*) × nicols.

Monoclinic

CLINOZOISITE

$Ca_2Al_3(OH)(SiO_4)_3$ (Iron-free Epidote)   Monoclinic
                                                              $\angle\beta = 64°30'$

$$n_\alpha = 1.710 \text{ to } 1.723$$
$$n_\beta = 1.715 \text{ to } 1.729$$
$$n_\gamma = 1.719 \text{ to } 1.734$$
$$2V = 66° \text{ to } 90°; \text{ Opt. } (+)$$
$$b = \beta \text{ or } Y, c \wedge \alpha \text{ or } X = 0° \text{ to } +12°$$

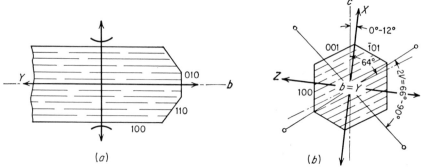

Fig. 14-37 *a,b*. Orientation diagrams of clinozoisite. Sections (*a*) normal to the *c*-axis and (*b*) parallel to (010).

Color. Colorless and non-pleochroic in thin sections.

Form. Clinozoisite, an iron-free or iron-poor epidote, usually occurs in elongated crystals or columnar aggregates. Cross sections are six-sided, with $(100 \wedge 001) = 64\frac{1}{2}°$.

Cleavage. Perfect in one direction {001}.

Relief. High, $n >$ balsam.

Birefringence. Weak to rather weak, $n_\gamma - n_\alpha = 0.005$ to 0.011; interference colors are middle first order but anomalous. The gray is somewhat blue, white is absent, and the yellow is greenish yellow. Upper first-order colors of thicker sections are normal.

Extinction. In most sections the extinction is parallel since the crystals are nearly always elongated in the direction of the *b*-axis.

Orientation. Some sections are length-slow and some length-fast since $b = \beta$ or *Y*.

Twinning. Polysynthetic twinning with {100} as twin-plane may be found in some specimens.

Interference Figure. The interference figure is biaxial positive with large to very large axial angle. The axial plane is {010}. Dispersion, $r < v$ strong.

Distinguishing Features. Clinozoisite is distinguished from epidote by weaker birefringence, lack of pleochroism, and optically positive sign; from zoisite by the distinctive yellow-green interference color of the first order and larger axial angle.

Occurrence. The occurrence of clinozoisite is practically the same as that of epidote. It is a rather common and widely distributed mineral and has often been identified as zoisite. It is usually a deuteric mineral in igneous rocks. Clinozoisite is also found as a product of dynamic metamorphism in such rocks as amphibolites, hornblende schists, and glaucophane schists.

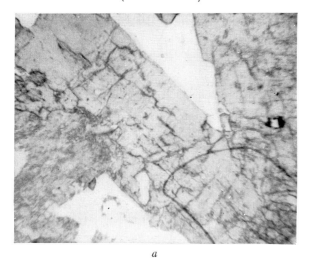

a

b

FIG. 14-38 *a,b*. (×20) Elongated crystals of clinozoisite set in quartz. (*a*) Ordinary illumination and (*b*) × nicols.

EPIDOTE

(Pistacite)

$Ca_2(Al,Fe)_3(OH)(SiO_4)_3$ Monoclinic

$\angle\beta = 64°37'$

$$n_\alpha = 1.720 \text{ to } 1.734$$
$$n_\beta = 1.724 \text{ to } 1.763$$
$$n_\gamma = 1.734 \text{ to } 1.779$$
$$2V = 69° \text{ to } 89°; \text{ Opt. } (-)$$
$$b = \beta \text{ or } Y, c \wedge \alpha \text{ or } X = +1° \text{ to } +5°$$

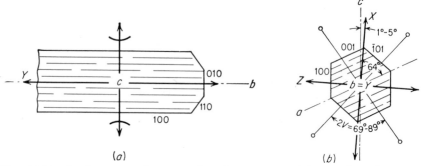

F<small>IG.</small> 14-39 *a,b.* Orientation diagrams of epidote. Sections (*a*) normal to the *c*-axis and (*b*) parallel to (010).

Color. In thin sections it is colorless to yellowish green, not usually uniform. The mineral is somewhat pleochroic.

Form. Epidote occurs in granular to columnar aggregates and in more or less distinct crystals that are elongated in the direction of the *b*-axis and have a pseudohexagonal cross section with the forms {001}, {100}, and {$\bar{1}$01}. (100 $\wedge$ 001) = 64°37'.

Cleavage. Perfect in one direction {001}.

Relief. High, $n >$ balsam.

Birefringence. Moderate to strong, $n_\gamma - n_\alpha = 0.014$ to 0.045, increasing with increase in iron content. The maximum interference colors range from low second-order to upper third-order colors. The middle first-order colors are anomalous like those of clinozoisite.

Extinction. Parallel in elongate sections since epidote, unlike most monoclinic crystals, is elongated in the direction of the *b*-axis.

Orientation. Since $b = \beta$ or *Y*, some longitudinal sections are length-slow and some length-fast.

Twinning. Twins with {100} as twin-plane are not uncommon.

Interference Figure. The interference figure is biaxial negative with a large axial angle. Cleavage flakes give an optic-axis figure since one of the optic axes is almost normal to {001}. The axial plane is {010}. Dispersion, $r > v$.

Distinguishing Features. Epidote is distinguished from clinozoisite and zoisite by stronger birefringence and from diopside and augite by parallel extinction.

Occurrence. Epidote is a commmon and widely distributed mineral in many types of igneous and metamorphic rocks. In igneous rocks it is usually a deuteric or late magmatic mineral. It is the dominant mineral in epidosite, a metamorphic epidote-quartz rock.

Epidote is rather common as a detrital mineral.

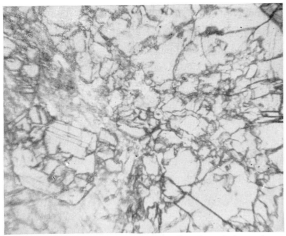

FIG. 14-40. (×20) Crystals of epidote distributed through quartz.

PIEDMONTITE

(Manganese Epidote)

$Ca_2(Al,Fe,Mn)_3(OH)(SiO_4)_3$

Monoclinic
$\angle\beta = 64°39'$

$n_\alpha = 1.745$ to 1.758
$n_\beta = 1.764$ to 1.789
$n_\gamma = 1.806$ to 1.832
$2V = 56°$ to $86°$; Opt. (+)
$b = \beta$ or Y, $c \wedge \alpha$ or $X = -5°$ to $-7°$

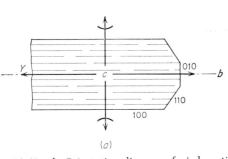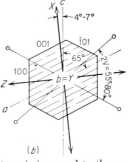

(a)   (b)

FIG. 14-41 a,b. Orientation diagram of piedmontite. Sections (a) normal to the c-axis and (b) parallel to (010).

Color. Vivid characteristic axial colors: yellow, orange, red, violet. Pleochroic: α or X, yellow to orange; β or Y, amethyst to violet; γ or Z, carmine to deep red.

Form. In form piedmontite is very much like epidote.

Cleavage. In one direction {001}.

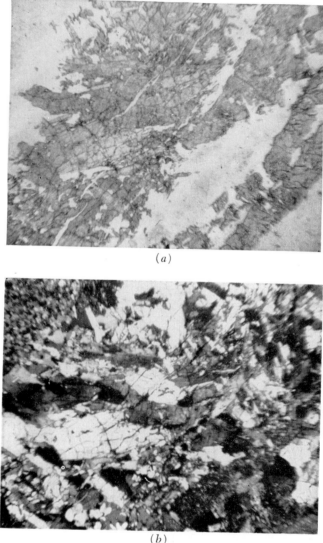

(a)

(b)

Fig. 14-42 *a,b.* (×20) Piedmontite associated with quartz. (*a*) Ordinary illumination and (*b*) × nicols.

Relief. High, $n >$ balsam.

Birefringence. Very strong, $n_\gamma - n_\alpha = 0.061$ to 0.082. The interference colors are high order but are more or less masked by the color of the mineral.

Extinction. Parallel in elongate sections since the crystals, like those of epidote, are elongated in the direction of the b-axis.

Orientation. The direction of the faster or slower ray is difficult to determine.

Interference Figure. The figure is biaxial positive with a large axial angle. The axial plane is {010}. Dispersion, $r > v$ strong.

Distinguishing Features. The color and pleochroism of piedmontite are so distinctive that there is little chance of mistaking it for any other mineral.

Occurrence. Piedmontite occurs for the most part in schists and gneisses, also in altered quartz porphyries, as at South Mountain, Pa.

ALLANITE

(Orthite)

$(Ca,Fe^{II})_2(Al,Ce,Fe^{III})_3(OH)(SiO_4)_3$ Monoclinic
$\angle \beta = 65°$

$n_\alpha = 1.64$ to 1.77
$n_\beta = 1.65$ to 1.77
$n_\gamma = 1.66$ to 1.80
$2V = $ large; Opt. $(-)$
$b = \beta$ or Y, $c \wedge \alpha$ or $X = +36°$

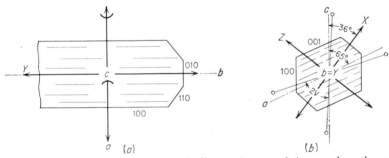

FIG. 14-43 *a,b*. Orientation diagrams of allanite. Sections (*a*) normal to the *c*-axis and (*b*) parallel to (010).

Color. Brown and pleochroic from pale brown to dark brown in thin sections.

Form. In form allanite is similar to epidote, of which it is a cerium-bearing variety. It often occurs in parallel position as an overgrowth on epidote.

Relief. High, $n > $ balsam.

Cleavage. Imperfect parallel to {001}.

Birefringence. Rather strong, $n_\gamma - n_\alpha = 0.01$ to 0.03; the interference colors are usually masked by the brown color of the mineral.

Extinction. Usually parallel, like other members of the epidote group.

Orientation. Difficult to obtain.

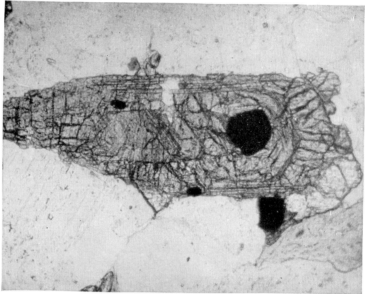

FIG. 14-44. (×40) Allanite in granite.

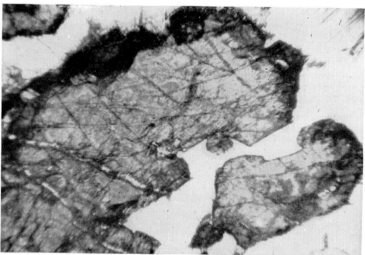

FIG. 14-45. (×20) Allanite crystals in a quartz matrix.

Twinning. It is like that of epidote.

Distinguishing Features. Allanite is distinguished from brown horn-blende by parallel extinction and cleavage in one direction instead of two.

Related Minerals. Magnesium orthite is a rare magnesium variety of allanite.

Alteration. Allanite is often altered or inverted to an amorphous substance with about the same chemical composition as allanite. This metamict mineraloid is produced by the breakdown of the space lattice by radioactive emanations.

Occurrence. Allanite is found in granites, syenites, granite pegmatites, and gneisses.

REFERENCES

Pyroxenes

Hess, H. H.: Pyroxenes of Common Mafic Magmas, *Am. Mineralogist*, vol. 26, pp. 515–535, 1941.
————: Chemical Composition and Optical Properties of Common Clinopyroxenes, Part I, *Am. Mineralogist*, vol. 34, pp. 621–666, 1949.
————, R. J. Smith, and G. Dengo: Antigorite from the Vicinity of Caracas, Venezuela, *Am. Mineralogist*, vol. 37, pp. 68–75, 1952.
Poldervaart, A.: Correlation of Physical Properties and Chemical Composition in the Plagioclase, Olivine, and Orthopyroxene Series, *Am. Mineralogist*, vol. 35, pp. 1067–1079, 1950.
————: The Relationship of Orthopyroxene to Pigeonite, *Mineral. Mag.*, vol. 28, pp. 164–172, 1947.
———— and H. H. Hess: Pyroxenes in the Crystallization of Basaltic Magma, *J. Geol.*, vol. 59, pp. 472–489, 1951.
Tröger, E.: Über den Fassait und über die Einteilung der Klinopyroxene, *Neues Jahrb. Mineral. Monatschefte*, no. 6, pp. 132–139, 1951.
————: "Tabellen zur optischen Bistimmung der gesteinbilden Minerale," p. 149, Verlag Schweizerbart, Stuttgart, 1952.
Winchell, A. N.: Mineralogical and Petrographic Study of the Gabbroid Rocks of Minnesota, and More Particularly, of the Plagioclasytes, *Am. Geologist*, vol. 26, pp. 197–245, 1900.

Silicates: Single, Multiple, and Ring SiO₄ Structures

SINGLE SiO₄ STRUCTURES (NESOSILICATES)

Olivine Group	Garnet Group	Sillimanite Family
Forsterite	Staurolite	Andalusite
Olivine	Sphene	Sillimanite
Fayalite	Idocrase	Kyanite
Monticellite	Zircon	Mullite
Humite Group	Axinite	Dumortierite
Chondrodite	Iddingsite	Topaz

MULTIPLE SiO₄ STRUCTURES (SOROSILICATES)

Lawsonite

6-UNIT RING STRUCTURES (CYCLOSILICATES)

Beryl
Tourmaline
Cordierite
Wollastonite

The minerals of Chapter 15 represent three divisions of silicate structure, nesosilicates, sorosilicates, and cyclosilicates. Minerals with single tetrahedral groups are more numerous and include a number of important species. Only one multiple group silicate is included (lawsonite) and four ring-group silicates (beryl, tourmaline, cordierite, and wollastonite).

SINGLE SiO₄ STRUCTURES

The Olivine Group

The olivine group consists of the two end members, forsterite and fayalite, and the intermediate isomorphous mixture, olivine. The rare mineral tephroite, Mn_2SiO_4, also belongs to the olivine group. The double salt, monticellite, ($CaMgSiO_4$), is closely related to olivine and is often

344

considered to be a member of the group. Its crystal system is orthorhombic. Larnite, with the composition Ca_2SiO_4, is not a member of the olivine group since it is monoclinic.

THE OLIVINE GROUP

Mineral	Chemical composition	n_α	n_β	n_γ	$2V$
Forsterite (Fo)...........	Mg_2SiO_4	1.635 1.640	1.651 1.660	1.670 1.680	85–90°
Olivine (Fo_mFa_n)........	$(Mg,Fe)_2SiO_4$	1.651 1.681	1.670 1.706	1.689 1.718	70–90°
Fayalite (Fa)............	Fe_2SiO_4	1.805 1.835	1.838 1.877	1.847 1.886	47–54°
Monticellite.............	$CaMgSiO_4$	1.641 1.651	1.646 1.662	1.655 1.669	75–80°

Minerals of the olivine group are characterized by rather high refractive indices and strong birefringence. The axial plane is (001), and the axial angle is usually very large.

Olivine is exceedingly abundant as a rock-forming mineral in subsilicic igneous rocks. Forsterite is practically limited to metamorphic limestones or contact metamorphic zones. Fayalite is found in granite pegmatites, in lithophysae of rhyolitic obsidians, and in some ores, but it is rather rare.

FORSTERITE

Mg_2SiO_4 Orthorhombic

$$n_\alpha = 1.635 \text{ to } 1.640$$
$$n_\beta = 1.651 \text{ to } 1.660$$
$$n_\gamma = 1.670 \text{ to } 1.680$$
$$2V = 85° \text{ to } 90°; \text{ Opt. } (+)$$
$$a = \gamma \text{ or } Z, b = \alpha \text{ or } X, c = \beta \text{ or } Y$$

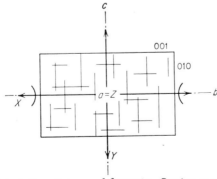

FIG. 15-1. Orientation diagram of forsterite. Section parallel to (100).

Color. Colorless in thin sections.

Form. Forsterite usually occurs in euhedral to subhedral crystals.

Relief. Fairly high, $n >$ balsam. The indices increase with increasing iron content.

Cleavage. {010} imperfect. Irregular fractures common.

Birefringence. Strong, $n_\gamma - n_\alpha = 0.035$ to 0.040. The maximum interference color is upper second order.

Extinction. Parallel to crystal outlines and cleavage traces.

Orientation. Crystals showing cleavage are length-slow.

Interference Figure. The interference figure is biaxial positive with a very large axial angle. The axial plane is {001}. Dispersion, $r < v$.

Distinguishing Features. Forsterite is an iron-free olivine and so resembles ordinary olivine but has somewhat lower indices of refraction.

Alteration. Forsterite is often altered to antigorite, but the secondary magnetite so common with altered olivine is absent.

Occurrence. Forsterite occurs for the most part in metamorphic limestones as a product of dedolomitization. Phlogopite is a common associate. Forsterite also occurs in contact-metamorphic zones, where it is often associated with magnetite.

OLIVINE

(Mg,Fe)$_2$SiO$_4$ (Chrysolite)   Orthorhombic

$n_\alpha = 1.651$ to 1.681

$n_\beta = 1.670$ to 1.706

$n_\gamma = 1.689$ to 1.718

$2V = 70°$ to $90°$; Opt. $(+)$, also $(-)$

$a = \gamma$ or Z, $b = \alpha$ or X, $c = \beta$ or Y

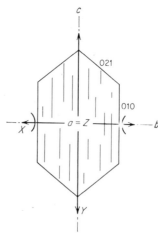

FIG. 15-2. Orientation diagram of olivine. Section parallel to (100).

Color. Colorless in thin sections.

Form. Olivine occurs in anhedra with polygonal outlines and in phenocrysts with the characteristic outline of Figure 8-28, which is a section parallel to {100}.

Cleavage. Imperfect parallel to {010}, irregular fractures common.

Relief. Fairly high, n > balsam.

Birefringence. Strong, $n_\gamma - n_\alpha = 0.037$ to 0.041; the maximum interference color is upper second order.

Extinction. Parallel to crystal outlines and cleavage traces.

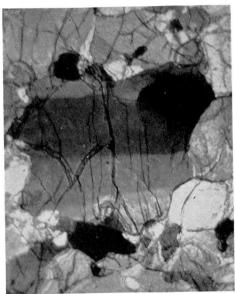

Fig. 15-3. ($\times 12$) Twinned olivine in dunite. ($\times$ nicols.)

Orientation. Crystals showing cleavage are length-slow.

Twinning. Sometimes found, but the lamellae are broad and not well defined. The twinning is probably vicinal.

Interference Figure. The interference figure is usually biaxial positive with a large axial angle, but olivine high in iron is optically negative. Olivine often shows a variation in the size of the axial angle within a single crystal, the angle decreasing toward the exterior of the crystal. According to Tomkeieff, this is evidence of zoning, the outer zones being richer in fayalite. The axial plane is {001}. Dispersion, $r < v$.

Distinguishing Features. The mineral most apt to be mistaken for olivine is diopside, but diopside has better cleavage, oblique extinction, and somewhat weaker birefringence.

(a)

(b)

Fig. 15-4 a,b. (×20) Interlocking anhedral crystals of olivine in dunite. (a) Ordinary illumination and (b) × nicols.

Related Minerals. Olivine fairly rich in iron with about 50 per cent of Fe_2SiO_4 is known as *hyalosiderite*. The indices of refraction and the birefringence are higher than those of olivine proper.

Alteration. Olivine commonly shows alteration to antigorite and secondary magnetite along irregular fractures (see Figure 16-38, page 417). In basaltic rocks the alteration of the outer iron-rich rims of olivine to brownish-red iddingsite is fairly common.

Occurrence. Olivine is an exceedingly common mineral in subsilicic igneous rocks such as basalts, olivine gabbros, and peridotites. In the monomineralic rock dunite it is the dominant mineral. It is a relict mineral in many serpentines.

Locally, olivine may be important as a detrital mineral.

FAYALITE

(Fe,Mg)$_2$SiO$_4$ (Iron Olivine)   Orthorhombic

$$n_\alpha = 1.805 \text{ to } 1.835$$
$$n_\beta = 1.838 \text{ to } 1.877$$
$$n_\gamma = 1.847 \text{ to } 1.886$$
$$2V = 47° \text{ to } 54°; \text{ Opt. } (-)$$
$$a = \gamma \text{ or } Z, \ b = \alpha \text{ or } X, \ c = \beta \text{ or } Y$$

Color. Colorless to yellowish or neutral in thin sections; it may show faint pleochroism.

Form. In cavities fayalite is euhedral, but as a rule it occurs in anhedral crystals.

Cleavage. Imperfect in one direction {010}.

Relief. Very high, $n >$ balsam.

Birefringence. Strong, $n_\gamma - n_\alpha =$ 0.042 to 0.051.

Extinction. Parallel to cleavage traces.

Orientation. Cleavage traces and crystals showing cleavage are length-slow.

Twinning. Vicinal twinning with broad lamellae seems to be characteristic of fayalite as well as of olivine.

Interference Figure. The interference figure is biaxial negative with a moderate axial angle. The axial plane is {001} as in olivine. Dispersion, $r > v$.

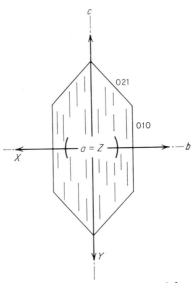

Fig. 15-5. Orientation diagram of fayalite. Section parallel to (100).

Distinguishing Features. Fayalite resembles olivine in its properties but may be distinguished by smaller axial angle, higher indices of refraction, and optically negative character.

Alteration. Fayalite is sometimes found with grunerite as an alteration product.

Related Minerals. Knebelite, a manganian fayalite, and hortonolite (Fe,Mg,Mn)$_2$SiO$_4$ are intermediate members of the olivine group and are similar to fayalite in optical properties.

Tephroite, Mn$_2$SiO$_4$, a characteristic mineral of the Franklin Furnace and Långban ore deposits, is also similar to fayalite.

Occurrence. Fayalite is a rather rare mineral. It is an associate of iron ores. Manganian fayalite, a low-grade iron ore in Tunaberg, Sweden, occurs in a rock called eulysite, the origin of which is in doubt. It is also found in abundance in high-temperature deposits in Santa Eulalia, Chihuahua, Mexico, according to Basil Prescott.

It is a widely distributed mineral in lithophysae of rhyolitic obsidian accompanying cristobalite.

Fayalite is one of the most characteristic constituents of furnace slags.

MONTICELLITE

CaMgSiO₄   Orthorhombic

$$n_\alpha = 1.641 \text{ to } 1.651$$
$$n_\beta = 1.646 \text{ to } 1.662$$
$$n_\gamma = 1.655 \text{ to } 1.669$$
$$2V = 75° \text{ to } 80°; \text{ Opt. } (-)$$
$$a = \gamma \text{ or } Z, b = \alpha \text{ or } X, c = \beta \text{ or } Y$$

Monticellite is usually considered to be a member of the olivine group, but, strictly speaking, it is a double salt.

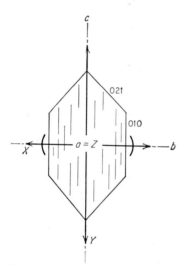

FIG. 15-6. Orientation diagram of monticellite. Section parallel to (100).

Color. Colorless in thin sections.

Form. Usually in granular aggregates of anhedral to subhedral crystals, but it may also occur in euhedral prismatic crystals. In some igneous rocks it is found in rims around olivine crystals.

Cleavage. Imperfect parallel to {010}.

Relief. Rather high, $n >$ balsam.

Birefringence. Moderate, $n_\gamma - n_\alpha = 0.014$ to 0.018; so the maximum interference color is first-order red.

Extinction. Parallel to cleavage traces and to the main crystal outlines.

Orientation. Crystals showing cleavage are length-slow.

Interference Figure. The interference figure is biaxial with a large axial angle. The axial plane is (001) as in olivine. Dispersion, $r > v$.

Distinguishing Features. Monticellite is a rather difficult mineral to recognize since it has no very distinctive properties. It resembles forsterite and olivine but has weaker birefringence than either of these. It may also be distinguished from forsterite and from most olivines by its negative optical sign.

Alteration. Some of the Crestmore monticellite is replaced by idocrase.

Occurrence. Monticellite is a contact-metamorphic mineral usually found in limestones and dolomites. Large masses of monticellite constituting a veritable monticellite rock occur at Crestmore, the famous mineral locality in Riverside County, California.

Monticellite is occasionally found in igneous rocks such as alnöite (Bowen), polzenite (Scheumann), and nepheline basalt. In these rocks it occurs as overgrowths or rims in parallel position on olivine.

Humite Group

Representatives of this group include humite, chondrodite, clinohumite, ilvaite, ardennite, and langbanite.

CHONDRODITE

$2Mg_2SiO_4 \cdot Mg(OH,F)_2$ Monoclinic
$\angle \beta = 90°$

$$n_\alpha = 1.592 \text{ to } 1.643$$
$$n_\beta = 1.602 \text{ to } 1.655$$
$$n_\gamma = 1.621 \text{ to } 1.670$$
$$2V = 70° \text{ to } 90°; \text{ Opt. } (+)$$
$$b = \gamma \text{ or } Z, a \wedge \alpha \text{ or } X = -26 \text{ to } -31°$$

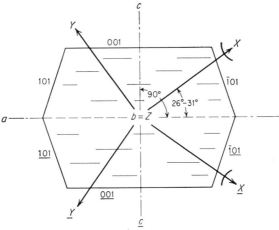

Fig. 15-7. Orientation diagram of chondrodite. Twin crystal with (001) as twin-plane. Section parallel to (010).

Color. Colorless to yellowish or brownish. The deeper colored varieties are pleochroic from neutral to brown or pale brown to red-brown, etc.

Form. Chondrodite is commonly found in subhedral crystals, which are often more or less rounded and in large anhedra. Although the mineral is monoclinic, the $\angle \beta$ between the a- and c-axes is 90° (orthorhombic syngony).

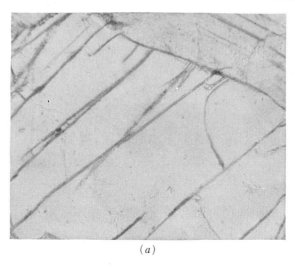

(a)

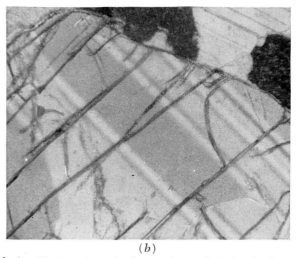

(b)

FIGS. 15-8 *a,b*. (×60) A portion of a fractured crystal of chondrodite. (*a*) Ordinary illumination and (*b*) × nicols showing twinning.

Cleavage. There is often parting parallel to (001) which is due to twinning.

Relief. Fairly high, $n >$ balsam.

Birefringence. Rather strong, $n_\gamma - n_\alpha = 0.027$ to 0.035; the maximum interference color varies from green to red of the second order for different varieties.

Extinction. The maximum extinction angle measured from the trace of the twin-plane {001} varies from $-26°$ to $-31°$.

Orientation. The extinction direction nearest the trace of the twin-plane is the faster ray.

Twinning. Twinning, which may appear as simple twins, twin seams, or polysynthetic twins, is rather common. The twin-plane is {001}. Without twinning it is very difficult to orient chondrodite. There may also be twinning parallel to {105} and {305}.

Interference Figure. The figure is biaxial positive with a large axial angle. The axial plane is normal to {010}. Dispersion, $r > v$ weak.

Distinguishing Features. The pleochroism usually distinguishes chondrodite from olivine.

Related Minerals. Three other minerals of the chondrodite group, *viz.*, norbergite, humite, and clinohumite, are similar to chondrodite. The distinction is based upon extinction angles and refractive indices.

Alleghanyite, the manganese analogue of chondrodite, is much like chondrodite, but it is optically negative.

Occurrence. Chondrodite is one of the characteristic minerals of metamorphic limestone. It is often associated with phlogopite and spinel.

Garnet Group

$$\begin{cases} \text{Pyrope} & \text{Mg}_3\text{Al}_2(\text{SiO}_4)_3 & n = 1.741 \text{ to } 1.760 \\ \text{Almandite} & \text{Fe}_3\text{Al}_2(\text{SiO}_4)_3 & n = 1.778 \text{ to } 1.815 \\ \text{Spessartite} & \text{Mn}_3\text{Al}_2(\text{SiO}_4)_3 & n = 1.792 \text{ to } 1.820 \end{cases}$$

$$\begin{cases} \text{Uvarovite} & \text{Ca}_3\text{Cr}_2(\text{SiO}_4)_3 & n = 1.838 \text{ to } 1.870 \\ \text{Grossularite} & \text{Ca}_3\text{Al}_2(\text{SiO}_4)_3 & n = 1.736 \text{ to } 1.763 \\ \text{Andradite} & \text{Ca}_3\text{Fe}_2(\text{SiO}_4)_3 & n = 1.857 \text{ to } 1.887 \end{cases}$$

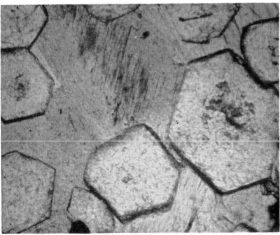

FIG. 15-9. (×25) Dodecahedral crystals of garnet.

The six minerals of the garnet group here listed may be classified in two subgroups: the pyrope-almandite-spessartite series (called *pyralspite*

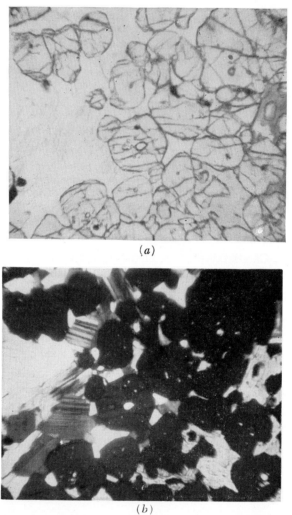

(a)

(b)

FIG. 15-10. (×20) Anhedral garnet crystals in a quartz-plagioclase matrix. (a) Ordinary illumination and (b) × nicols showing isotropic character.

by Winchell) and the uvarovite-grossularite-andradite series (called *ugrandite* by Winchell). It is rare to find a garnet that corresponds to any one of the formulae given. They are isomorphous mixtures of these end members in varying amount. The name is assigned according to the dominant end member present.

Color. Colorless, pale reddish, pale to dark brown, greenish gray, etc., in thin sections. Crystals are often zoned.

Form. Euhedral dodecahedral crystals in six-sided sections and trapezohedral crystals in eight-sided sections are common. Garnet also occurs

in polygonal grains, aggregates, and masses. Inclusions are frequent.
Cleavage. Absent, but it may have parting parallel to {110}. Irregular fractures are characteristic.

Relief. Very high, surface rough; n > balsam.

Birefringence. Most varieties are dark between crossed nicols but some have weak or very weak birefringence. The birefringent areas are often arranged in zones or sectors (see Figure 8-26).

Fɪɢ. 15-11. (×20) Anomalous garnet crystals from a contact metamorphic zone, Darwin, California. (*Courtesy of Prof. Vincent Kelley.*)

Distinguishing Features. Garnet resembles spinel, but the latter occurs in octahedra. The different kinds of garnet may be determined by indices of refraction combined with the determination of the specific gravity.

Alteration. The most common alteration product of garnet is chlorite.

Occurrence. Garnet is especially characteristic of metamorphic rocks. It is also a very common detrital mineral. Almandite is the common garnet of schists and gneisses. Pyrope is practically confined to peridotites and derived serpentines. Grossularite and andradite are common in contact-metamorphic zones. Melanite, a deep brown variety of andradite, occurs in soda-rich igneous rocks such as nepheline syenites, phonolites, etc.

Spessartite is found in pegmatites, schists, and quartzites.

Uvarovite, the rarest of the garnets, is found as a secondary mineral in chromite and also in some contact-metamorphic zones.

Garnet is common as a detrital mineral. The grains are often grooved or pitted.

STAUROLITE

$2Al_2SiO_5.Fe(OH)_2$ Orthorhombic

$$n_\alpha = 1.736 \text{ to } 1.747$$
$$n_\beta = 1.741 \text{ to } 1.754$$
$$n_\gamma = 1.746 \text{ to } 1.762$$
$$2V = 80° \text{ to } 88°; \text{ Opt. } (+)$$
$$a = \beta \text{ or } Y, b = \alpha \text{ or } X, c = \gamma \text{ or } Z$$

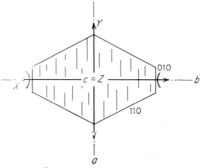

Fig. 15-12. Orientation diagram of staurolite. Section parallel to (001).

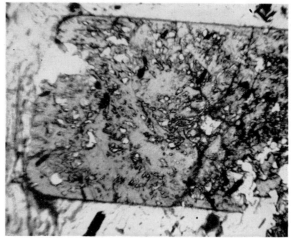

Fig. 15-13. (×20) A crystal of staurolite showing quartz inclusions.

Color. Pale yellow in thin sections. Pleochroism distinct from nearly colorless to yellow-brown. Absorption: γ or $Z > \beta$ or $Y > \alpha$ or X.

Form. Staurolite usually occurs in euhedral crystals of short prismatic habit and six-sided cross section with the form {110} and {010}.

$$(110 \wedge 1\bar{1}0) = 51°.$$

The crystals are usually a centimeter or more long.

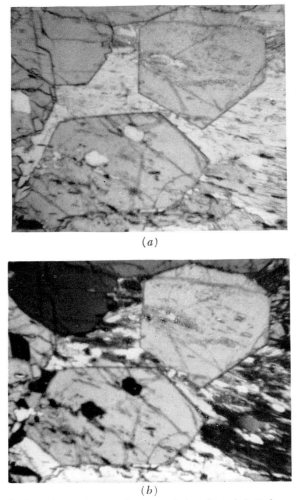

(a)

(b)

FIGS. 15-14 a,b. (×20) Coarse staurolite crystals in schist. (a) Ordinary illumination and (b) × nicols showing lineation in quartz grains of the matrix.

Relief. High, n > balsam.

Cleavage. Inconspicuous parallel to (010).

Inclusions. Irregularly arranged inclusions of quartz are nearly always prominent (Figure 8-29).

Birefringence. Rather weak, $n_\gamma - n_\alpha = 0.010$ to 0.015; the maximum interference color is first-order yellow to red.

Extinction. Parallel in most sections, symmetrical in cross sections.

Orientation. The crystals are length-slow.

Twinning. Penetration twins with {023} or {232} as twin-planes are common, but polysynthetic twins are unknown. Twinning is rarely noted in thin sections.

Interference Figure. The interference figure is biaxial positive with a very large axial angle. The axial plane is {100}. Dispersion, $r > v$ weak.

Distinguishing Features. The color, pleochroism, and quartz inclusions are distinctive.

Occurrence. Staurolite is found as metacrysts in metamorphic rocks such as schists, phyllites, and gneisses. Common associates are garnet, kyanite, and sillimanite in addition to quartz.

The presence of staurolite proves that the original rock was a sedimentary one.

It is also a common detrital mineral.

SPHENE

CaTiSiO₅   (Titanite)   Monoclinic
                                                                       $\angle\beta = 60°17'$

$$n_\alpha = 1.887 \text{ to } 1.913$$
$$n_\beta = 1.894 \text{ to } 1.921$$
$$n_\gamma = 1.979 \text{ to } 2.054$$
$$2V = 23° \text{ to } 50°; \text{ Opt. } (+)$$
$$b = \beta \text{ or } Y, c \wedge \alpha \text{ or } X = +33° \text{ to } 43°$$

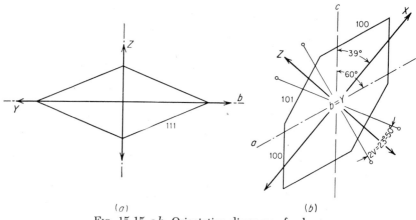

(a)   (b)

Fɪɢ. 15-15 a,b. Orientation diagrams of sphene.

Color. Almost colorless to neutral in thin sections. Some varieties are pleochroic in thick sections. Axial colors: α or X, nearly colorless; β or Y, pale yellow to pale greenish; γ or Z, yellow to red-brown.

Form. Sphene usually occurs in euhedral crystals that have an acute rhombic cross section or in irregular grains.

Cleavage. Sphene often has prominent parting (parallel to 221). These parting directions are not parallel to the crystal outlines.

Relief. Very high, $n >$ balsam.

Birefringence. Extreme, $n_\gamma - n_\alpha = 0.092$ to 0.141; the interference colors are high-order white but are usually obscured by total reflection.

Extinction. On account of strong dispersion sphene does not always show complete extinction. Rhombic sections have symmetrical extinction.

Twinning. Twins with {100} as twin-plane are sometimes present (Figure 8-18). Polysynthetic twinning parallel to (221) may also be present.

Interference Figure. The figure is biaxial positive with a moderate axial angle. The axial plane is {010}. The acute bisectrix is almost normal to (102). Dispersion, $r > v$ strong.

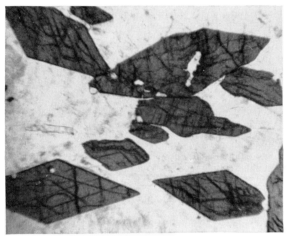

FIG. 15-16. (×20) Euhedral sphene crystals showing high relief, angular rhombic sections, and prominent parting.

Distinguishing Features. Monazite is somewhat like sphene but has lower birefringence and weaker dispersion. The acute rhombic cross sections of sphene are very characteristic.

Occurrence. Sphene is a widely distributed accessory (probably deuteric) mineral in grained rocks and in such metamorphic rocks as gneisses and schists. It has probably formed at a late stage in igneous rocks.

It is not very common as a detrital mineral except locally, as on the southern shore of Lake Tahoe, where it is derived from granodiorites.

IDOCRASE

$Ca_2Al_2(OH,F)Si_2O_7$ (Vesuvianite)   Tetragonal

$n_\epsilon = 1.701$ to 1.726
$n_\omega = 1.705$ to 1.732
Opt. $(-)$

Color. Colorless to neutral in thin sections. It may be pleochroic in thick sections.

Form. Idocrase occurs in euhedral crystals, in columnar aggregates, in anhedra with polygonal outlines, and in fine aggregates.

Cleavage. Imperfect parallel to {110}.

Relief. High, $n >$ balsam.

Birefringence. Very weak to weak, $n_\omega - n_\varepsilon = 0.004$ to 0.006; interference colors are low first-order gray, sometimes normal, sometimes anomalous gray-green, purple, or deep blue.

Extinction. Parallel.

Orientation. Length-fast in columnar aggregates.

Interference Figure. The figure is usually uniaxial negative but may be biaxial with a small axial angle.

Distinguishing Features. Anomalous idocrase resembles zoisite and clinozoisite and is often difficult to distinguish from them.

Alteration. Rarely observed.

Occurrence. The principal occurrence of idocrase is in contact-metamorphic zones. Associated minerals are garnet, diopside, wollastonite, epidote, and calcite. Idocrase is also found in association with serpentine as a kind of pseudojade (californite).

ZIRCON

ZrSiO$_4$ Tetragonal

$$n_\omega = 1.925 \text{ to } 1.931$$
$$n_\epsilon = 1.985 \text{ to } 1.993$$
$$\text{Opt. } (+)$$

Color. Colorless to pale colors in thin sections.

Form. Zircon usually occurs in minute crystals of short prismatic habit. They are often found as inclusions and may be surrounded by pleochroic haloes.

Cleavage. Absent.

Relief. Very high, $n >$ balsam.

Birefringence. Very strong, $n_\varepsilon - n_\omega = 0.060$ to 0.062; the maximum interference colors are usually pale tints of the fourth order, but minute crystals show lower interference colors.

Extinction. Parallel.

Orientation. Crystals are length-slow.

Interference Figure. The interference figure is uniaxial but may be difficult to obtain on account of the small size of the crystals.

Distinguishing Features. Zircon is distinguished from apatite by stronger birefringence and higher relief. It may be separated from crushed rocks with bromoform or other heavy liquids.

Related Minerals. Malacon is the metamict alteration product of zircon. It is an amorphous mineraloid.

Occurrence. Zircon is a widely distributed mineral in granite and other grained igneous rocks. In some syenites it is prominent enough to furnish the name zircon syenite. Zircon also occurs in certain metamorphic rocks.

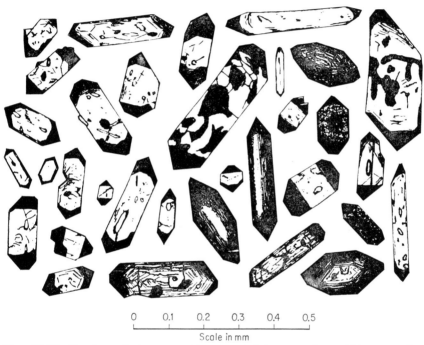

0 $\quad$ 0.1 $\quad$ 0.2 $\quad$ 0.3 $\quad$ 0.4 $\quad$ 0.5

Scale in mm

FIG. 15-17. Sketches of zircon crystals separated from southern African granites (*Courtesy of Prof. Arie Poldervaart*).

It is one of the most widespread and abundant detrital minerals being unusually resistant to destruction during erosion and deposition. The forms of zircon crystals observed in sandstones have been summarized by Poldervaart (1955).

Zircon ($ZrSiO_4$) and thorite ($ThSiO_4$) appear to form a structural series. Zircon also alters chemically with the addition of U, Th, Pb, and H_2O accompanied by a loss in silica. Altered zircon may consist of microcrystalline aggregates which become isotropic and opaque. Minute zircon crystals included in biotite are often surrounded by pleochroic halos.

AXINITE

$H(Fe,Mn)Ca_2Al_2B(SiO_4)_4$ Triclinic

$$n_\alpha = 1.678 \text{ to } 1.684$$
$$n_\beta = 1.685 \text{ to } 1.692$$
$$n_\gamma = 1.688 \text{ to } 1.696$$
$$2V = 70° \text{ to } 75°; \text{ Opt. } (-)$$
$$\alpha \text{ or } X \text{ almost } \perp \text{ to } (011)$$

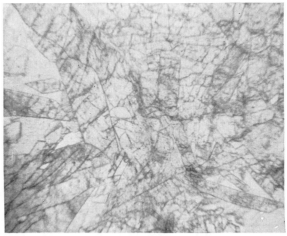

Fig. 15-18. (×20) Crystals of axinite forming a cluster in a matrix of calcite.

Color. Colorless to pale violet in thin sections. It may show pleochroism in thick sections.

Form. Axinite usually occurs in anhedral crystals with acute-angled sections. Inclusions are frequent.

Cleavage. Imperfect in several directions.

Relief. Fairly high, $n >$ balsam.

Birefringence. Rather weak, $n_\gamma - n_\alpha = 0.010$ to 0.012, a little higher than that of quartz.

Extinction. Oblique to outlines and to cleavage traces.

Interference Figure. The figure is biaxial negative with a large axial angle. Dispersion, $r < v$ or $r > v$.

Distinguishing Features. Axinite has no very distinctive features and is rather difficult to recognize in thin sections. Its birefringence is like that of quartz, but its refractive indices are considerably higher. It is biaxial, whereas quartz is uniaxial.

Occurrence. Axinite occurs in the calcareous rocks of contact-metamorphic zones. The more common associates are in addition to quartz and calcite, garnet and hedenbergite. Axinite is also found in granites and granite pegmatites. It is a comparatively rare mineral, but in a contact-metamorphic rock known as limurite it forms more than 50 per cent of the rock.

IDDINGSITE

$MgO.Fe_2O_3.3SiO_2.4H_2O$ Orthorhombic

$$n_\alpha = 1.674 \text{ to } 1.730$$
$$n_\beta = 1.715 \text{ to } 1.763$$
$$n_\gamma = 1.718 \text{ to } 1.768$$
$$2V = 25° \text{ to } 60°; \text{ Opt. } (+) \text{ or } (-)$$
$$a = \alpha \text{ or } X, b = \beta \text{ or } Y, c = \gamma \text{ or } Z$$

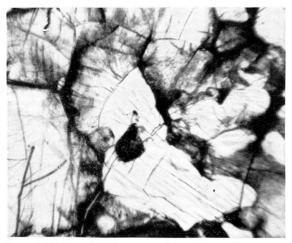

FIG. 15-19. (×20) Iddingsite under ordinary illumination.

Color. Brown in thin sections. Pleochroism slight to distinct. Absorption: γ or $Z > \beta$ or $Y > \alpha$ or X.

Form. Iddingsite, as far as known, always occurs as partial or complete pseudomorphs after olivine. It shows a lamellar structure.

Cleavage. In three directions {100}, {001}, {010} at right angles. Of these {100} has the most perfect cleavage.

Relief. High, $n >$ balsam.

Birefringence. Strong, $n_\gamma - n_\alpha = 0.038$ to 0.044; the maximum interference color should be in the third order, but the color of the mineral modifies or masks the interference color.

Extinction. Parallel to the cleavage traces.

Interference Figure. The figure is biaxial, either positive or negative, with a moderate axial angle. The axial plane is {010}. Dispersion, $r > v$ or $r < v$ strong.

Distinguishing Features. The reddish brown color and lamellar structure together with the mode of occurrence are distinctive for iddingsite.

Alteration. Iddingsite is sometimes found more or less altered to limonite or indefinite hydrous iron oxides.

Occurrence. Iddingsite is found in basalts and basalt porphyries as an alteration product of olivine. According to Ross and Shannon, it is a deuteric or hydrothermal mineral and is not formed by weathering.

Sillimanite Family

It is useful to consider certain anhydrous aluminum silicates and similar compounds containing fluorine or boron in a group. These are essentially anhydrous minerals which invert to mullite, $3Al_2O_3.2SiO_2$ at high temperatures. Sillimanite, andalusite, and kyanite are polymorphous forms of $Al_2O_3.SiO_2$ with an alumina:silica ratio of 1:1. Sillimanite is one of the most widely distributed minerals of the group although kyanite, andalusite, and topaz are common.

ANDALUSITE

Al_2SiO_5 (inc. Chiastolite)   Orthorhombic
$(Al_2O_3.SiO_2)$

$$n_\alpha = 1.629 \text{ to } 1.640$$
$$n_\beta = 1.633 \text{ to } 1.644$$
$$n_\gamma = 1.639 \text{ to } 1.647$$
$$2V = \text{ca. } 84°; \text{ Opt. } (-)$$
$$a = \gamma \text{ or } Z, b = \beta \text{ or } Y, c = \alpha \text{ or } X$$

Color. Usually colorless, more rarely reddish. The colored variety is pleochroic from rose-red (α or X) to pale green (β or Y) and (γ or Z).

Form. Andalusite usually occurs in euhedral crystals or coarse columnar aggregates. Cross sections are nearly square ($110:1\bar{1}0 = 89°12'$). Dark inclusions of carbonaceous matter are often present and arranged symmetrically to form a kind of cross. This variety is known as *chiastolite* (Figure 8-24).

Cleavage. Distinct parallel to {110}. In cross sections the cleavage traces are in two directions at approximately right angles.

Relief. Fairly high, $n >$ balsam.

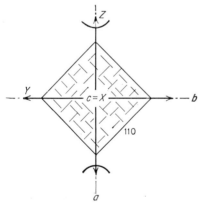

FIG. 15-20. Orientation diagram of andalusite. Section parallel to (001).

Birefringence. Rather weak, $n_\gamma - n_\alpha = 0.007$ to 0.011, near that of quartz. Interference colors range up to first-order yellow.

Extinction. Parallel in most sections. Cross sections have symmetrical extinction.

Orientation. Crystals of columnar aggregates are length-fast.

Interference Figure. Cross sections of crystals give a negative biaxial figure with a very large axial angle. The axial plane is {010}. Dispersion, $r > v$, weak.

Distinguishing Features. Andalusite is distinguished from sillimanite by its length-fast character, weaker birefringence, and large axial angle. The colored pleochroic variety resembles hypersthene, but the latter is length-slow instead of length-fast.

Related Minerals. Viridine is a manganian andalusite with higher indices of refraction and stronger birefringence than those recorded here.

Alteration. Andalusite is often found altered to sillimanite. The variety chiastolite is usually more or less altered to sericite along the lines of included carbonaceous matter.

Occurrence. Andalusite occurs in granite pegmatites and in high-temperature veins. In the form of chiastolite it is a characteristic contact-metamorphic mineral in schists, phyllites, and slates. It is a rather common and widely distributed mineral.

SILLIMANITE

Al_2SiO_5 Orthorhombic

$(Al_2O_3.SiO_2)$

$n_\alpha = 1.657$ to 1.661

$n_\beta = 1.658$ to 1.670

$n_\gamma = 1.677$ to 1.684

$2V = 20°$ to $30°$; Opt. $(+)$

$a = \alpha$ or $X, b = \beta$ or $Y, c = \gamma$ or Z

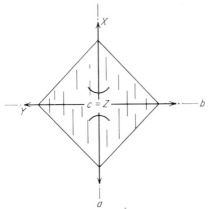

Fig. 15-21. Orientation diagram of sillimanite. Section parallel to (001).

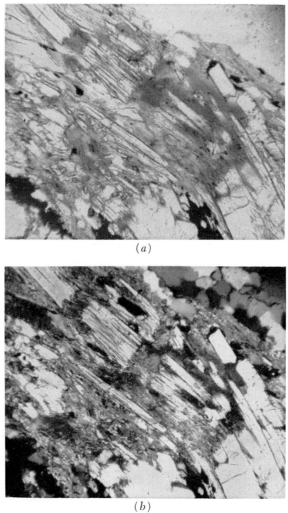

(a)

(b)

Fig. 15-22 a,b. (×60) Sillimanite in elongated crystals in schist. (a) Ordinary illumination showing dark patches of biotite and (b) × nicols.

Color. Colorless in thin sections.

Form. Sillimanite usually occurs in small, often minute, slender prismatic crystals and in a felted mass of fibers (Figure 8-6). The crystals are often more or less bent.

The crystals are nearly square in cross section with $(110 \wedge 1\bar{1}0) = 88°15'$.

Cleavage. Parallel to $\{010\}$ but not always noticed in sections. Transverse fractures are common.

Relief. Fairly high, $n >$ balsam.

Birefringence. Moderate, $n_\gamma - n_\alpha = 0.020$ to 0.023; so the interference colors range up to second-order blue. Cross sections show very low first-order colors since $n_\beta - n_\alpha = 0.001$ to 0.009.

Extinction. Parallel in longitudinal sections and symmetrical in cross sections.

Orientation. The crystals or fibers are length-slow.

Interference Figure. On account of the small size of the crystals, good figures are rarely obtained. The axial plane is {010}. Dispersion, $r > v$ strong.

Distinguishing Features. Sillimanite is distinguished from andalusite by its length-slow character, stronger birefringence, and smaller axial angle. It is even more like mullite, but the latter has higher dispersion of birefringence. At times it resembles apatite, but the latter is length-fast and has weaker birefringence.

Occurrence. Sillimanite is found in gneisses, schists, slates, hornfelses, and other metamorphic rocks. The more common associates are corundum, andalusite, kyanite, dumortierite, and cordierite.

KYANITE

Al₂SiO₅   Triclinic
(Al₂O₃.SiO₂) $\angle\alpha = 90°5\tfrac{1}{2}'$
                                      $\angle\beta = 101°2'$
                                      $\angle\gamma = 105°44\tfrac{1}{2}'$

$n_\alpha = 1.712$
$n_\beta = 1.720$
$n_\gamma = 1.728$
$2V = $ ca. $82°$; Opt. $(-)$
Ax. pl. almost $\perp$ {100}; $c \wedge \gamma$ or Z $-30° \pm$

Color. Colorless to pale blue. It may be pleochroic in thick sections.

Form. The characteristic sections of kyanite (Figure 8-17) are broad elongate plates tabular parallel to (100) and narrow sections parallel to (010). Crystals are often bent.

Cleavage. Perfect parallel to {100}, less perfect parallel to {010}, also cross parting {001} at angles of 85° with the length of the crystals.

Relief. High, $n >$ balsam.

Birefringence. Moderate, $n_\gamma - n_\alpha = 0.016$; hence interference colors range up to first-order red.

Extinction. Angle on {100} is about 30° with the length of the crystals. In other sections parallel

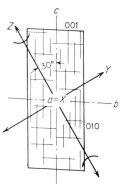

Fig. 15-23. Orientation diagram of kyanite. Section parallel to (100).

FIG. 15-24. (×20) A portion of a bladed crystal of kyanite.

FIG. 15-25. (×60) Kyanite in a matrix of quartz and muscovite. (× nicols.)

to the c-axis the extinction angle is small, sometimes practically zero. In cross sections the extinction is parallel or almost parallel.

Orientation. The extinction direction nearest the c-axis is the slow ray.

Twinning. Twinning is frequent; there are two common twin-laws: (1) {100} = twin-plane, (2) {001} = twin-plane.

Interference Figure. Sections cut parallel to {100} or cleavage flakes give a negative biaxial figure with a large axial angle. The axial plane makes an angle of 30° with the trace of the c-axis. Dispersion, $r > v$, weak.

Distinguishing Features. The extinction angle of 30° together with the biaxial interference figure obtained from the broad sections is distinctive for kyanite.

Occurrence. Kyanite occurs in schists and gneisses associated with quartz, muscovite, garnet, staurolite, and rutile. It never occurs in igneous rocks. It is also found as a detrital mineral.

MULLITE

$3Al_2O_3.2SiO_2$ Orthorhombic

$$n_\alpha = 1.642$$
$$n_\beta = 1.644$$
$$n_\gamma = 1.654$$
$$2V = 20°; \text{ Opt. } (+)$$
$$a = \alpha \text{ or } X, b = \beta \text{ or } Y, c = \gamma \text{ or } Z$$

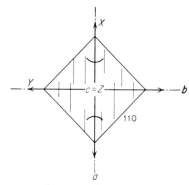

FIG. 15-26. Orientation diagram of mullite. Section parallel to (001).

The optical constants here given are for the artificial mineral; the indices, birefringence, and optic angle are all a little higher for the natural mineral.

Color. Colorless in thin sections.

Form. Mullite occurs in crystals of long prismatic habit with nearly square cross section. $110 \wedge 1\bar{1}0 = 89°13'$.

Cleavage. {010}, distinct.

Relief. Rather high, $n >$ balsam.

Birefringence. Rather weak, $n_\gamma - n_\alpha = 0.012$; the maximum interference color is about first-order yellow. Cross sections have dark gray interference colors since $n_\beta - n_\alpha = 0.002$.

Extinction. Parallel in longitudinal sections and symmetrical in cross sections.

Orientation. The crystals are length-slow.

Interference Figure. The figure is biaxial positive with a moderate axial angle. The axial plane is {010}. Dispersion, $r > v$.

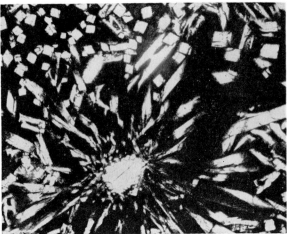

FIG. 15-27. (×25) A radiating cluster of mullite crystals (artificial).

FIG. 15-28. (×20) Bladed crystals of mullite (artificial × nicols).

Distinguishing Features. Mullite is so much like sillimanite in its properties that it was not recognized as a distinct mineral until about two decades ago. The refractive indices of sillimanite are a little higher than those of mullite.

Occurrence. Mullite occurs in fused argillaceous sediments found as inclusions (xenoliths) in igneous intrusions. Mullite is a very rare mineral found on the island of Mull off the west coast of Scotland.

Artificial Mullite. Artificial mullite is the substance formed by heating sillimanite, andalusite, or kyanite to a high temperature. It is used in the manufacture of high-grade porcelains such as those used in spark plugs for automobiles. Mullite is also found in ordinary porcelain as minute prismatic crystals.

DUMORTIERITE

HBAl$_8$Si$_3$O$_{20}$ Orthorhombic

$$n_\alpha = 1.659 \text{ to } 1.678$$
$$n_\beta = 1.684 \text{ to } 1.691$$
$$n_\gamma = 1.686 \text{ to } 1.692$$
$$2V = 20° \text{ to } 40°; \text{ Opt. } (-)$$
$$a = \gamma \text{ or } Z, b = \beta \text{ or } Y, c = \alpha \text{ or } X$$

Color. Colorless to blue, lavender, pink, or reddish. Pleochroic from colorless to blue or colorless to reddish with the greatest absorption when the length of the crystal is parallel to the vibration plane of the lower nicol. Minute crystals may not show pleochroism.

Form. Dumortierite occurs in prismatic to acicular crystals, which often form a felt of fibers. Cross sections are pseudohexagonal on account of twinning.

Cleavage. Imperfect parallel to the length. There are also cross fractures.

Relief. High, $n >$ balsam.

Birefringence. Rather weak to moderate, $n_\gamma - n_\alpha = 0.011$ to 0.020; so the maximum interference color varies from orange of the first order up to blue of the second order.

Extinction. Parallel in most sections.

Orientation. The crystals are length-fast.

Twinning. Cross sections are sometimes penetration trillings with {110} as the twin-plane.

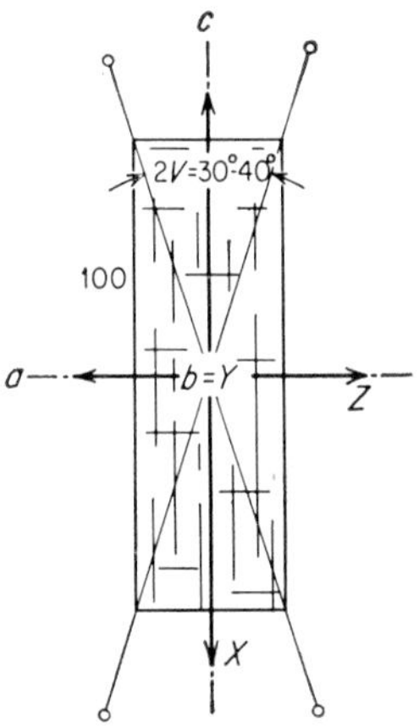

Fig. 15-29. Orientation diagram of dumortierite. Section parallel to (010).

Interference Figure. The interference figure is biaxial negative with a moderate axial angle, but on account of the small size of the crystals it may be difficult to obtain. The axial plane is {010}. Dispersion, $r < v$ or $r > v$.

Distinguishing Features. Dumortierite resembles some varieties of tourmaline, but the greater absorption is manifest when the crystals are parallel to the vibration plane of the lower nicol instead of normal to that direction. Non-pleochroic dumortierite resembles sillimanite, but the latter is length-slow.

Alteration. Dumortierite is sometimes more or less altered to sericite.

Occurrence. Dumortierite occurs in granite pegmatites, schists, gneisses, and other metamorphic rocks. The common associates are

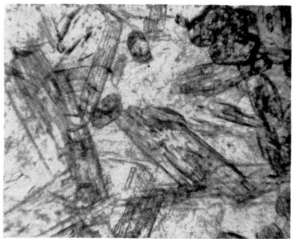

FIG. 15-30. (×50) Crystals of dumortierite in a matrix of sericite.

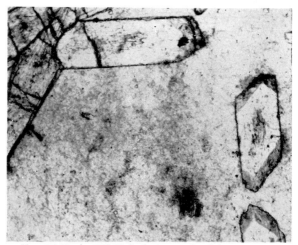

FIG. 15-31. (×25) Euhedral crystals of dumortierite.

quartz, muscovite, tourmaline, andalusite, sillimanite, topaz, and rutile.

TOPAZ

$Al_2(F,OH)_2SiO_4$ Orthorhombic

$$n_\alpha = 1.607 \text{ to } 1.629$$
$$n_\beta = 1.610 \text{ to } 1.631$$
$$n_\gamma = 1.617 \text{ to } 1.638$$
$$2V = 48° \text{ to } 65°; \text{ Opt. } (+)$$
$$a = \alpha \text{ or } X, \ b = \beta \text{ or } Y, \ c = \gamma \text{ or } Z$$

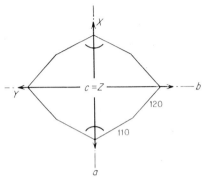

FIG. 15-32. Orientation diagram of topaz. Section parallel to (001).

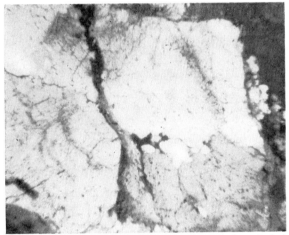

FIG. 15-33. (×20) Anhedral crystals of topaz. (× nicols.)

Color. Colorless in thin sections.

Form. Topaz appears in euhedral crystals of short prismatic habit, in anhedral grains, and in columnar aggregates. Negative crystals with fluid inclusions and gas bubbles are not uncommon.

Cleavage. Perfect in one direction parallel to {001}.

Relief. Fairly high, $n >$ balsam.

Birefringence. Rather weak, $n_\gamma - n_\alpha = 0.009$ to 0.010, about the same as that of quartz. Interference colors are gray, white, or straw yellow of the first order. Cleavage flakes show very weak birefringence since $n_\beta - n_\alpha = 0.003$.

Extinction. Parallel in longitudinal sections and symmetrical in basal sections.

Orientation. Cleavage traces are parallel to the faster ray.

Interference Figure. Cleavage flakes and basal sections give a biaxial positive figure with a rather large axial angle. The axial plane is {010}. Dispersion, $r > v$ distinct.

Distinguishing Features. Topaz resembles quartz but has higher relief, is biaxial, and has perfect cleavage.

Alteration. To muscovite or sericite is not uncommon.

Occurrence. Topaz occurs in high-temperature veins, in granite pegmatites, and occasionally in rhyolites. Associated minerals are tourmaline, fluorite, cassiterite (wood tin in the rhyolite occurrences), and muscovite.

MULTIPLE SiO₄ STRUCTURES—SOROSILICATES

LAWSONITE

H₄CaAl₂Si₂O₁₀   Orthorhombic

$$n_\alpha = 1.665$$
$$n_\beta = 1.674$$
$$n_\gamma = 1.684$$
$$2V = 84°; \text{Opt. } (+)$$
$$a = \alpha \text{ or } X, b = \beta \text{ or } Y, c = \gamma \text{ or } Z$$

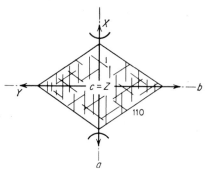

FIG. 15-34. Orientation diagram of lawsonite. Section parallel to (001).

Color. Colorless in thin sections. It may be pleochroic in very thick sections.

Form. Lawsonite occurs in euhedral crystals of varying habit. Sections are usually rhombic (110 ∧ 1Ī0 = 67°) or rectangular.

Cleavage. Good parallel to {010} and {001}, fair parallel to {110}.

Relief. Rather high, $n >$ balsam.

Birefringence. Moderate, $n_\gamma - n_\alpha = 0.019$; so the interference colors range up to second-order blue.

Extinction. Parallel or symmetrical.

Orientation. The long diagonal of rhombic sections is parallel to the slower ray.

Twinning. Polysynthetic twinning with {110} as twin-plane is rather common. The lamellae are usually thin, may be in either one or two directions, and are sometimes curved.

Interference Figure. The figure is biaxial positive with a very large axial angle. The axial plane is {010}. Dispersion, $r > v$ strong.

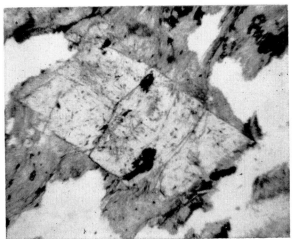

FIG. 15-35. (×20) A metacryst or porphyroblast of lawsonite in chlorite.

Distinguishing Features. Clinozoisite somewhat resembles lawsonite, but the anomalous interference colors distinguish it. Prehnite may also be mistaken for lawsonite, but its birefringence is higher.

Occurrence. The characteristic occurrence of lawsonite is in metamorphic rocks such as glaucophane schists. It is also found in gabbros and diorites as the result of incipient metamorphism. The type locality is Tiburon Peninsula on San Francisco Bay, California, but it has also been found in Italy, Corsica, and New Caledonia. The usual associates of lawsonite are muscovite, glaucophane, garnet, and sphene.

6-UNIT RING STRUCTURES—CYCLOSILICATES

BERYL

$Be_3Al_2(SiO_3)_6$ Hexagonal
                                                   (Hexagonal subsystem)

$$n_\epsilon = 1.564 \text{ to } 1.590$$
$$n_\omega = 1.568 \text{ to } 1.598$$
$$\text{Opt. } (-)$$

Color. Colorless in thin sections. In thick oriented sections colored varieties such as emerald are somewhat pleochroic.

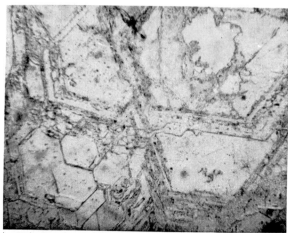

FIG. 15-36. (×20) Beryl crystals showing hexagonal outlines accentuated by inclusions.

FIG. 15-37. (×20) A granular aggregate of beryl and topaz. (× nicols.)

Form. Beryl usually occurs in rather large crystals of prismatic habit, occasionally in small, slender prisms, and also in massive form. Liquid inclusions with gas bubbles in six-sided negative crystals are common in oriented sections.

Cleavage. Imperfect parallel to (0001), not usually seen in thin sections.

Relief. Moderate, $n >$ balsam.

Birefringence. Weak, $n_\omega - n_\varepsilon = 0.004$ to 0.008; interference colors are gray, white, or straw yellow of the first order.

Extinction. Longitudinal sections have parallel extinction. Basal sections are dark in all positions.

Orientation. Crystal sections are length-fast.

Interference Figure. Basal sections give a negative uniaxial figure without any rings. The cross may show a slight opening in certain areas.

Distinguishing Features. Beryl resembles apatite, but the latter has higher indices of refraction. From quartz it is distinguished by its length-fast character and optical sign.

Alteration. It is sometimes altered to kaolin.

Occurrence. The principal occurrence of beryl is in granite pegmatites. It is also found in mica schists and in veins in limestone associated with albite.

Tourmaline Group

Three minerals are prominent in the tourmaline group:

Schorlite (Iron Tourmaline)
$NaFe_3B_3Al_3(OH)_4(Al_3Si_6O_{27})$ Hexagonal
Dravite (Magnesium Tourmaline)   (Rhombohedral subsystem)
$NaMg_3B_3Al_3(OH)_4(Al_3Si_6O_{27})$
Elbaite (Alkali Tourmaline)
$Na_2Li_3B_6Al_9(OH)_8(Al_3Si_6O_{27})_2$

Schorlite	Dravite	Elbaite
$n_\epsilon = 1.628$ to 1.658	$n_\epsilon = 1.613$ to 1.628	$n_\epsilon = 1.615$ to 1.629
$n_\omega = 1.652$ to 1.698	$n_\omega = 1.632$ to 1.655	$n_\omega = 1.635$ to 1.655
Opt. $(-)$	Opt. $(-)$	Opt. $(-)$

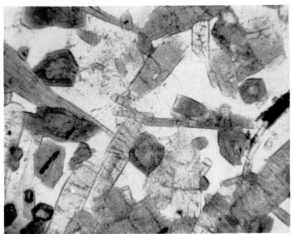

Fig. 15-38. ($\times 50$) Sections across and lengthwise cut through elongate tourmaline crystals in a quartz matrix.

Color. Schorlite is neutral gray, slate blue, buff, olive, etc. Pleochroism is usually marked $\omega > \epsilon$. Zonal structure is common in cross sections. Dravite is colorless to pale yellow in thin sections and somewhat pleochroic with absorption: $\omega > \epsilon$. Elbaite is colorless, but thick sections may show pleochroism: ϵ, colorless; ω, pink, pale green, or pale blue.

Form. Schorlite occurs in prismatic crystals and may form columnar or fibrous radiating aggregates. Spherulitic aggregates of elbaite known as *tourmaline suns* characterize luxullianite, a tourmalinized granite from Cornwall (Figure 8-14). Cross sections of tourmaline crystals may be triangular with curved convex sides, or hexagonal. Dravite crystals are generally large.

Cleavage. Absent but irregular fractures are common.

FIG. 15-39. ($\times$20) A section of a single tourmaline crystal in a matrix of quartz and feldspar. ($\times$ nicols.)

Relief. High, $n >$ balsam.

Birefringence. Moderate to strong (schorlite) or moderate (dravite and elbaite). Cross sections show no birefringence. Schorlite $n_\omega - n_\varepsilon = 0.022$ to 0.040, usually about 0.025. Dravite $n_\omega - n_\varepsilon = 0.019$ to 0.025. Elbaite $n_\omega - n_\varepsilon = 0.015$ to 0.023.

Extinction. Parallel in most sections. Cross sections remain dark on rotation.

Orientation. Crystals are length-fast. Interference colors in schorlite may be masked by natural color.

Interference Figure. Basal sections give a negative uniaxial figure with one or two rings.

Distinguishing Features. Among the members of the tourmaline group schorlite shows the strongest absorption normal to the plane of the polarizer. Dravite is ordinarily colorless to pale yellow. Elbaite may be colorless, pink, pale green, or pale blue.

Of the more common minerals schorlite resembles biotite and hornblende. Both of these have perfect cleavage, which is lacking in tourmaline. Elongate habit, parallel extinction, strong absorption, and triangular or hexagonal cross sections are significant.

Occurrence. Schorlite reaches its maximum development in granite pegmatites. It is also found in tourmalinized granites, in greisen, and in high-temperature veins, where it is often associated with cassiterite. It is also characteristic of certain schists and gneisses and is frequently found in hornfelses. It is a widely distributed detrital mineral, both in fragmentary prisms and well-rounded grains.

Dravite usually occurs in metamorphic limestones. It is also found in some schists.

Elbaite occurs in granite pegmatites. The usual associates are lepidolite, albite, and quartz.

CORDIERITE

Mg$_2$Al$_4$Si$_5$O$_{18}$ (Iolite)   Orthorhombic
                                                              (Pseudohexagonal)

$$n_\alpha = 1.532 \text{ to } 1.552$$
$$n_\beta = 1.536 \text{ to } 1.562$$
$$n_\gamma = 1.539 \text{ to } 1.570$$
$$2V = 40° \text{ to } 80°; \text{ Opt. } (-) \text{ or } (+)$$
$$a = \beta \text{ or } Y, b = \gamma \text{ or } Z, c = \alpha \text{ or } X$$

Color. Colorless in thin sections. Very thick sections are pleochroic. α or X, yellow; β or Y, dark violet or blue; γ or Z, pale blue or violet. Absorption: β or $Y > \gamma$ or $Z > \alpha$ or X.

Form. The characteristic form of cordierite is in pseudohexagonal crystals of short prismatic habit. These crystals are penetration twins. Cordierite also occurs in anhedra and anhedral aggregates.

Inclusions. Common; these are often surrounded by pleochroic halos.

Cleavage. Imperfect parallel to (010), but it may not show in sections. Parting parallel to {001} that is due to alteration.

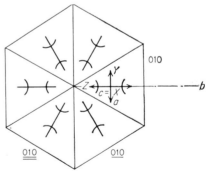

FIG. 15-40. Orientation diagram of cordierite. Section of twin-crystal parallel to (001). The twin-plane is {100}.

Relief. Low, n either a little less or a little greater than balsam.

Birefringence. Rather weak, $n_\gamma - n_\alpha = 0.007$ to 0.011, about the same as that of quartz; hence maximum interference colors are usually about straw yellow of the first order.

Extinction. Parallel to crystal outlines.

Twinning. The pseudohexagonal crystals are penetration twins with {110} as twin-plane. Twin-lamellae are also often present.

Interference Figure. The figure is usually biaxial negative with a variable axial angle. Optically positive cordierite has been described from several localities. The axial plane is {100}. Dispersion, $r < v$ weak.

Distinguishing Features. Cordierite is one of the few minerals that is easily mistaken for quartz. It is biaxial with a moderate to large axial angle and often shows twinning (either penetration or polysynthetic).

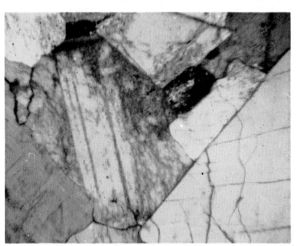

FIG. 15-41. (×20) Cordierite showing twinning. (× nicols.)

Alteration. Cordierite is usually more or less altered to sericite (pinite), chlorite, talc, or indefinite silicates.

Occurrence. Cordierite is a typical metamorphic mineral. It is found in gneisses and schists, often at the contact with persilicic igneous rocks. Sillimanite is a common associate. It is a characteristic mineral of hornfels. Rarely is it found in igneous rocks as an endomorphic mineral.

WOLLASTONITE

CaSiO$_3$ Triclinic

$$\angle\alpha = 90°0'$$
$$\angle\beta = 95°16'$$
$$\angle\gamma = 103°22'$$

$$n_\alpha = 1.620$$
$$n_\beta = 1.632$$
$$n_\gamma = 1.634$$
$$2V = \text{ca. } 39°; \text{ Opt. } (-)$$

b almost $\parallel$ to β or Y, $c \wedge \alpha$ or $X = +32°$

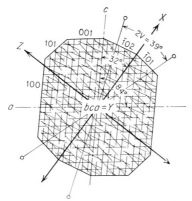

Fɪɢ. 15-42. Orientation diagram of wollastonite. Section parallel to (010).

Color. Colorless in thin sections.

Form. Wollastonite usually appears in columnar or fibrous aggregates. The cross sections are nearly rectangular.

Cleavage. In several directions in the zone [010]; perfect parallel to (100), less perfect (001) and ($\bar{1}$02) and imperfect (101) and ($\bar{1}$01).

Relief. Fairly high, $n >$ balsam.

Birefringence. Rather weak, $n_\gamma - n_\alpha = 0.014$; the maximum interference color is about orange of the first order. Longitudinal sections show gray or white interference colors.

Extinction. Parallel or almost parallel in longitudinal sections, oblique in cross sections.

Orientation. Longitudinal sections are either length-slow or length-fast since the elongation is in the direction of the b-axis and $b = \beta$ or Y.

Twinning. Twins with {100} as twin-plane are known.

Interference Figure. The figure is biaxial negative with a moderate axial angle. Since the axial plane is almost parallel to {010}, the figure lies normal to the length of the crystals. Dispersion, $r > v$ weak.

Distinguishing Features. Tremolite greatly resembles wollastonite not only in hand specimens but in thin sections as well. Tremolite, however, has oblique extinction and the typical amphibole cross section and cleavage. In tremolite the interference figure lies along the length of the crystal; in wollastonite it lies almost normal to the length.

Related Minerals. CaSiO₃ is trimorphous. In addition to triclinic wollastonite, there are also *parawollastonite* (Peacock), which is monoclinic, and the high-temperature modification called pseudowollastonite (Rankin and Wright). The uniaxial pseudowollastonite has been described as a natural mineral in Persia (McLintock).

Pectolite [HNaCa₂(SiO₃)₃] is much like wollastonite in some of its properties.

F<small>IG</small>. 15-43. (×20) Wollastonite showing elongated crystals in a radial aggregate. (× nicols.)

Occurrence. Wollastonite occurs in contact-metamorphic zones, in some schists and gneisses, and in limestone inclusions in volcanic rocks (parawollastonite).

REFERENCES

Olivine Group

Bowen, N. L., and J. F. Schairer: The System, MgO-FeO-SiO₂, Am. J. Sci., vol. 29, p. 197, 1935.
Deer, W. A., and L. R. Wager: Olivines from the Skaergaard Intrusion. Kangerdlugssuak, East Greenland, Am. Mineralogist, vol. 24, pp. 18–25, 1939.

Zircon

Frondel, C.: Hydroxyl Substitution in Thorite and Zircon, Am. Mineralogist, vol. 38, pp. 1007–1018, 1953.
Poldervaart, A.: Zircons in rocks, Am. J. Sci., vol. 253, pp. 433–461, 1955.

CHAPTER 16

Silicates: Sheet Structures and Mineraloids

SHEET STRUCTURES (PHYLLOSILICATES)

Minerals with sheet structures range from the large cleavable sheets of muscovite to the fine flaky crystals of clay minerals frequently revealed only with the electron microscope. Several minerals that show tubular structure with the electron microscope and are not found in single crystals suitable for X-ray measurement may not belong in a group of phyllosilicates. On the other hand, such minerals as palygorskite and sepiolite show an association with clay minerals and for this reason are included in this group.

Two examples of mineraloids are given at the end of Chapter 16, volcanic glass and palagonite. Both are somewhat indefinite in composition and show a range in properties.

383

The Mica Group

The micas constitute a well-defined group of silicates of aluminum together with the alkalies, magnesium, and ferrous iron. They are characterized by perfect cleavage in one direction {001} and by strong birefringence. The extinction angles of sections cut normal to the cleavage are small or practically zero. They may be divided into two classes depending upon whether the optic axial plane is (1) normal to or (2) parallel to {010} (see Figures 16-1 and 16-2). Muscovite and lepidolite belong to the first class, and phlogopite and biotite to the second. All the micas are optically negative.

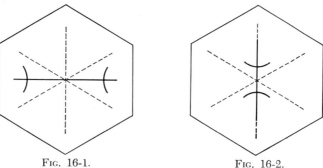

FIG. 16-1.   FIG. 16-2.

FIG. 16-1. Mica of the first class. The dotted lines represent the "percussion figure."
FIG. 16-2. Mica of the second class.

The micas are pseudohexagonal monoclinic. Structural studies show that the sheetlike arrangement of the atoms in mica permits intervals of rotation of 60° in the basal plane. This allows stacking of adjacent $(AlSi_3O_{10})$ tetrahedral sheets in a fixed series of alternative positions, summarized by Smith and Yoder (1956) as follows:

MICA POLYMORPHS

Structural nomenclature*	Rotation on basal plane	Space group
$1M$	0°	$C_{2/m}$
$2O$	180°	$Ccm2_1$
$3T$	120° or 240° (Mirror images)	$P3_112$ or $P3_212$
$2M_1$	120° or 240° (Alternating)	$C_{2/c}$
$6H$	60° or 300° (Mirror images)	$P6_122$ or $P6_522$
$2M_2$	60° or 300°	$C_{2/c}$

* M, O, T, and H represent, respectively, monoclinic, orthorhombic, trigonal, and hexagonal.

The 20 and $6H$ polymorphs have not been found in nature, but others have been identified as constituents of clay aggregates or zones of argillic alteration.

Through mineral synthesis and X-ray study it has been shown (Yoder and Eugster, 1955) that muscovite is restricted in conditions of formation below a range of 625° to 715°C and 5,000 to 30,000 pounds per square inch pressure. Thus the mineral is absent in rocks formed at higher temperatures.

Lepidomelane is the name given to iron-rich biotite. Fuchsite and mariposite are green chromium-bearing varieties of muscovite. Sericite is a secondary muscovite found in minute shreds and aggregates and formed by hydrothermal alteration.

THE MICA GROUP

Mineral	Chemical composition	n_α	n_β	n_γ	$2V$
Muscovite............	KAl	$\begin{cases}1.556\\1.570\end{cases}$	1.587 1.607	$\begin{cases}1.593\\1.611\end{cases}$	30°–40°
Hydromuscovite.........	KAl	$\begin{cases}1.535\\1.570\end{cases}$	....	$\begin{cases}1.565\\1.605\end{cases}$	small
Lepidolite..............	KLiAl	1.560	1.598	1.605	40°
Phlogopite.............	KMgAl	$\begin{cases}1.551\\1.562\end{cases}$	1.598 1.606	1.598 1.606	0°–10°
Biotite................	KMg,FeAl	$\begin{cases}1.541\\1.579\end{cases}$	1.574 1.638	$\begin{cases}1.574\\1.638\end{cases}$	0°–25°

MUSCOVITE

$KAl_2(OH)_2(AlSi_3O_{10})$ (inc. Sericite) Monoclinic
$\angle\beta = 89°54$

$$n_\alpha = 1.556 \text{ to } 1.570$$
$$n_\beta = 1.587 \text{ to } 1.607$$
$$n_\gamma = 1.593 \text{ to } 1.611$$
$$2V = 30° \text{ to } 40°; \text{ Opt. } (-)$$
$$b = \gamma \text{ or } Z, a \wedge \beta \text{ or } Y, = +1° \text{ to } +3°$$

Color. Colorless to pale green in thin sections. Some varieties are pleochroic.

Form. Muscovite usually occurs in thin tabular crystals or in scaly aggregates or shreds. The minutely crystalline variety is called *sericite*.

Cleavage. In one direction {001} very perfect.

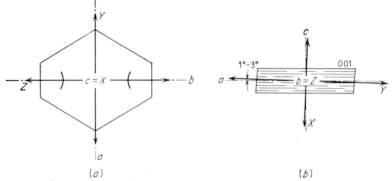

Fig. 16-3 *a,b*. Orientation diagrams of muscovite. Sections (*a*) parallel to (00$\bar{1}$) and (*b*) parallel to (010).

Fig. 16-4. (×30) A portion of a muscovite crystal. The crystal is slightly distorted as shown by the curved cleavage. (× nicols.)

Relief. Not marked, $n >$ balsam. On rotation there is some change of relief, fair when the cleavage traces are parallel to the vibration plane of the lower nicol and low in a position at right angles to this.

Birefringence. Strong, $n_\gamma - n_\alpha = 0.037$ to 0.041; hence the highest interference colors are upper second order. Sections parallel to the cleavage give first-order colors since $n_\gamma - n_\beta = 0.004$ to 0.006.

Extinction. The extinction is as a rule practically parallel to the cleavage traces, but it is often possible to find angles as high as $2°$ or $3°$.

Orientation. The direction of the cleavage traces is always the slower ray.

Twinning. Twinning according to the mica law [twin-plane = {110} and composition face = (001)] is fairly common. It may be detected by slight differences in interference colors as well as by extinction angles.

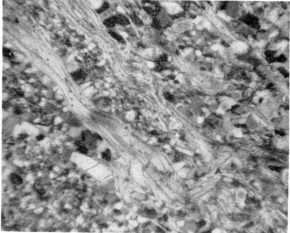

FIG. 16-5. (×30) Muscovite crystals showing alignment in a quartz-mica schist. (× nicols.)

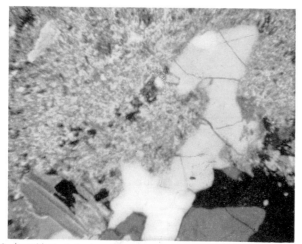

FIG. 16-6. (×10) Sericite in a fine aggregate surrounding quartz. (× nicols.)

Interference Figure. Sections parallel to {001} or cleavage flakes give a biaxial negative figure with a moderate axial angle. Dispersion, $r > v$ weak. The axial plane is normal to {010}.

Distinguishing Features. Talc is so similar to muscovite and pyrophyllite in its optical properties that it is distinguished with difficulty. The axial angle of talc is smaller. It may be necessary to make a microchemical test for magnesium (use Na_2CO_3 fusion) in order to differentiate them.

Related Minerals. Hydromuscovite is very similar to the sericite variety of muscovite.

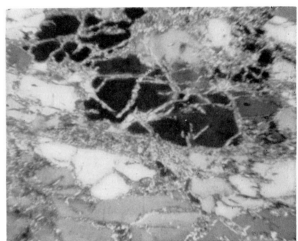

FIG. 16-7. (×10) A network of sericite veinlets cutting quartz. (× nicols.)

Occurrence. Muscovite is very common in metamorphic rocks such as phyllites, schists, and gneisses. It is found in some granites and reaches its maximum development in granite pegmatites. It is common as a detrital mineral, especially in arkoses.

Sericite. Sericite occurs in minute shreds and is a secondary mineral formed by hydrothermal alteration of silicates, especially the feldspars. In the opinion of A. F. Rogers, it is in all probability a late hydrothermal mineral. Sericite also occurs as a constituent of schists, phyllites, and slates.

Hydromuscovite. For a description of hydromuscovite, see page 413.

LEPIDOLITE

$LiKAl_2(OH,F)_2(Si_2O_5)_2$ Monoclinic

$$n_\alpha = 1.560$$
$$n_\beta = 1.598$$
$$n_\gamma = 1.605$$
$$2V = 40° \pm : Opt. (-)$$

Color. Colorless in thin sections.

Form. Lepidolite usually occurs in thick tabular or short prismatic pseudohexagonal crystals.

Cleavage. Perfect in one direction {001}.

Relief. Fair, $n >$ balsam.

Birefringence. Strong, $n_\gamma - n_\alpha = 0.045$; hence interference colors range up to the middle of the third order. Sections parallel to the cleavage (including cleavage flakes) have weak double refraction $n_\gamma - n_\beta = 0.007$).

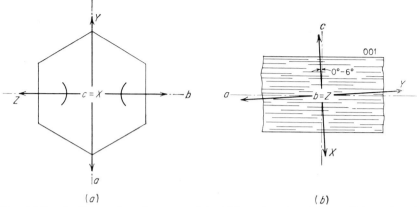

(a)   (b)

FIG. 16-8 a,b. Orientation diagrams of lepidolite. Sections (a) parallel to (001) and (b) parallel to (010).

FIG. 16-9. (×20) Lepidolite cut parallel to cleavage in a plagioclase matrix. (× nicols.)

Extinction. The extinction angle measured against the cleavage traces varies from zero up to a maximum of 6° or 7°.

Orientation. The direction of the cleavage trace is always the slower ray.

Twinning. Twinning is common according to the mica law [twin-plane = {110}], the composition face being {001}. Sometimes there are penetration twins.

Interference Figure. The figure is biaxial negative with a moderate axial angle, usually about 40°. Dispersion, $r > v$ weak.

Distinguishing Features. Lepidolite is very similar to muscovite in its optical properties but has a larger extinction angle. It may be necessary to use some non-optical test to distinguish them. (Lepidolite is easily fusible and gives a lithium flame.)

Related Minerals. Zinnwaldite is a lithium-iron mica also found in tin-stone veins and granite pegmatites.

Occurrence. Lepidolite occurs in granite pegmatites, in some high-temperature veins, and occasionally in granites. The usual associates are tourmaline (especially elbaite), albite, topaz, beryl, spodumene, and quartz.

PHLOGOPITE

$KMg_3Al(OH)Si_4O_{10}$ Monoclinic
$\angle\beta = 90° \pm$

$$n_\alpha = 1.551 \text{ to } 1.562$$
$$n_\beta = 1.598 \text{ to } 1.606$$
$$n_\gamma = 1.598 \text{ to } 1.606$$
$$2V = 0° \text{ to } 10°; \text{ Opt. } (-)$$
$$b = \beta \text{ or } Y$$

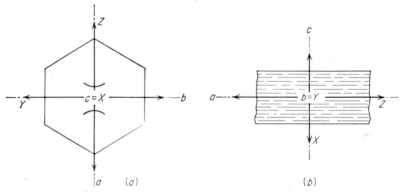

FIG. 16-10 *a,b*. Orientation diagrams of phlogopite.

Color. Pale brown to colorless in thin sections. Slightly pleochroic.

Form. Phlogopite is found in six-sided thick tabular to short prismatic crystals.

Cleavage. In one direction {001} as with the other micas.

Relief. Fair, $n >$ balsam.

Birefringence. Strong, $n_\gamma - n_\alpha = 0.044$ to 0.047; the maximum interference color is about the middle of the third order. Sections parallel to {001}, which include cleavage flakes, have very weak birefringence since $n_\gamma - n_\beta$ is very small ($0.000x$).

Extinction. Extinction is usually parallel to the cleavage, but sometimes the extinction angle is as much as 5°.

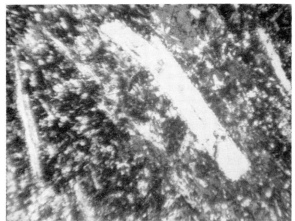

FIG. 16-11. (×30) Elongated sections of phlogopite cut through tabular crystals. (× nicols.)

FIG. 16-12. (×10) Scattered crystals of phlogopite in limestone. (× nicols.)

Orientation. The cleavage traces are parallel to the slower ray.

Twinning. Though often present, is not conspicuous. It may be recognized by differences in interference colors of adjacent parts of a crystal as well as by extinction angles.

Interference Figure. Basal sections, which also include cleavage flakes, give a negative interference figure that is either biaxial with a very small angle or practically uniaxial. Dispersion, $r > n$ weak.

Distinguishing Features. Phlogopite is distinguished from biotite by lighter color and weaker absorption. Colorless phlogopite is much like muscovite but may be distinguished by its smaller axial angle.

Occurrence. The characteristic occurrence of phlogopite is in metamorphic limestones. The common associates are chondrodite, spinel, and forsterite. It is also found in a few igneous rocks such as peridotites, derived from serpentines, and leucite-bearing rocks.

BIOTITE

$K_2(Mg,Fe)_2(OH)_2(AlSi_3O_{10})$ Monoclinic

$$\angle\beta = 90°$$

$$n_\alpha = 1.541 \text{ to } 1.579$$
$$n_\beta = 1.574 \text{ to } 1.638$$
$$n_\gamma = 1.574 \text{ to } 1.638$$
$$2V = 0° \text{ to } 25°; \text{ Opt. } (-)$$
$$b = \beta \text{ or } Y, c \wedge \alpha \text{ or } X = 3° \pm$$

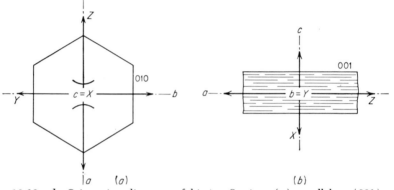

Fig. 16-13 *a,b*. Orientation diagrams of biotite. Sections (*a*) parallel to (001) and (*b*) parallel to (010).

Color. Brown, yellowish brown, reddish brown, olive green, or green in thin sections. Pleochroic. The absorption is stronger when the cleavage traces are parallel to the vibration plane of the lower nicol.

Form. Common in euhedral six-sided crystals that are usually tabular in habit; also in lamellar aggregates. The plates are sometimes bent.

Inclusions. Inclusions of such minerals as zircon surrounded by pleochroic halos are fairly common in biotite.

Cleavage. Perfect in one direction {001}. Sections cut parallel to {001} do not show any cleavage. In schistose rocks these sections predominate.

Relief. Fair, $n >$ balsam.

Birefringence. Strong, $n_\gamma - n_\alpha = 0.033$ to 0.059; interference colors range up to second-order red, but the color of the mineral may mask the interference color. The birefringence of sections parallel to {001} is practically nil since $n_\gamma - n_\beta = 0.000x$.

Extinction. Usually parallel to the cleavage traces, but the extinction angle may be as much as 3° in some sections. Bent plates have wavy ex-

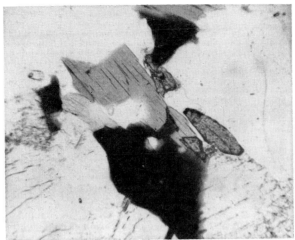

FIG. 16-14. (×30) Biotite in positions of illumination (gray crystal showing cleavage) and absorption (black) associated with zircon (high relief).

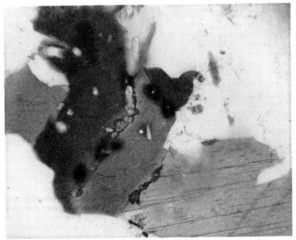

FIG. 16-15. (×30) Biotite showing halos around minute radioactive cores.

tinction. Near the extinction position a peculiar crinkly appearance is usually noticed in biotite.

Orientation. The direction of the cleavage traces is always the slower ray.

Twinning. Twinning according to the mica law [twin-plane = {110}] may be present.

Interference Figure. Sections parallel to {001}, including cleavage flakes, give a negative biaxial figure with a very small axial angle. The axial plane is usually parallel to {010}, but is normal to {010} in one variety (anomite). Dispersion, $r > v$ or $r < v$ weak.

Distinguishing Features. Biotite is distinguished from phlogopite by its darker color and stronger absorption. From ordinary brown hornblende it is distinguished by the smaller extinction angle and difference in cleavage. Lamprobolite also has the typical amphibole cleavage. Tourmaline has strong absorption when elongation of the crystals is normal to the vibration plane of the lower nicol.

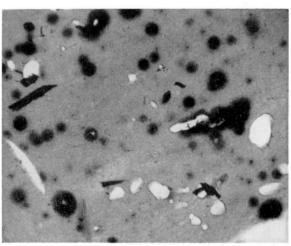

FIG. 16-16. (×30) Halos in biotite caused by alpha-particle bombardment from small zircon crystals containing radioactive impurities.

Related Minerals. Lepidomelane resembles biotite but has higher indices and larger axial angle. Manganophyll is a manganian biotite found in metamorphic dolomite at Långban, Sweden.

Alteration. Biotite is often more or less altered to chlorite. It may also alter to vermiculite. In the opinion of E. W. Galliher, detrital biotite is the source of practically all glauconite.

Occurrence. Biotite is a widely distributed and common mineral. It occurs in igneous rocks of nearly all types. It is also a prominent constituent of schists and gneisses and may be found in contact-metamorphic zones. Biotite is common in detrital sediments. It is often bleached or otherwise altered.

Chlorite Group

The micaceous mineral group, *chlorite*, covers a range of chemical modifications with corresponding optical variation. This form of mica occurs most frequently in flake-like crystals with anomalous birefringence and greenish pleochroism. Hey (1954) in a survey of the literature indicates 24 chlorite species with varying degrees of validity. Studies of

chromian chlorite by D. L. Lapham (1957) suggest a generalized fundamental division of the chlorite group as follows:

CHLORITE GROUP°

Corundophilite	Mg 5.3 $Al_1(Si_{2.3}Al_{1.7})O_{10}(OH)_8$
Prochlorite	Mg 5.1 $Al_1(Si_{2.6}Al_{1.4})O_{10}(OH)_8$
Clinochlore	Mg 5.0 $Al_1(Si_{3.0}Al_{1.0})O_{10}(OH)_8$
Penninite	Mg 4.9 $Al_1(Si_{3.2}Al_{0.8})O_{10}(OH)_8$

* Fe-chlorite (substitution > 4 per cent FeO or Fe_2O_3 for Mg)
  Cr-chlorite (substitution < 2 per cent Cr_2O_3 for Mg or Al)
  Kotschubeite (Tetrahedral Cr > 2 per cent Cr_2O_3)
  Kammererite (Octahedral Cr > 2 per cent Cr_2O_3)

FIG. 16-17. (×30) Chlorite formed along the border of a quartz mass.

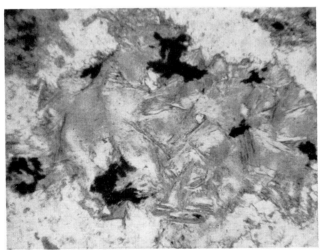

FIG. 16-18. (×30) An aggregate of chlorite crystals associated with magnetite.

Fig. 16-19. (×30) Flaky chlorite crystals in interlocking aggregate. (× nicols.)

In terms of occurrence four representative chlorites are considered, prochlorite, clinochlore, penninite, and the Fe-chlorite widely known as chamosite, All are probably monoclinic and exhibit distinct cleavage parallel to (001). Although green prevails, lavender, pink, or purple may predominate for higher chromian chlorites.

The term orthochlorite has been applied to the group of chlorites low in iron and leptochlorite to the high iron group.

PROCHLORITE

(Ripidolite)   Monoclinic

$$n_\alpha = 1.588 \text{ to } 1.658$$
$$n_\beta = 1.589 \text{ to } 1.667$$
$$n_\gamma = 1.599 \text{ to } 1.667$$
$$2V = 0° \text{ to } 30°; \text{ Opt. } (+)$$

Color. Green or greenish in thin sections. Pleochroism weak.

Form. Prochlorite usually occurs in scaly masses. It is also frequently found in vermicular crystals with hexagonal cross sections and in fan-shaped crystal aggregates.

Cleavage. In one direction parallel to {001} as in the other chlorites.

Relief. Fair to moderately high, $n >$ balsam.

Birefringence. Usually weak but varies from very weak to rather weak, $n_\gamma - n_\alpha = 0.001$ to 0.011.

Extinction. Parallel to almost parallel.

Orientation. Cleavage traces are parallel to the faster ray.

Interference Figure. The interference figure is usually difficult to obtain. When found, it is usually biaxial positive with a very small axial angle, often practically uniaxial. The axial plane is parallel to {010}. Dispersion, $r < v$.

Distinguishing Features. Prochlorite is distinguished from clinochlore and pennine by higher indices of refraction.

Occurrence. Prochlorite is the principal constituent of some chlorite schists often accompanied by magnetite. It also is found as an alteration product of other silicates. A characteristic occurrence of prochlorite is in quartz veins with adularia, albite, sphene, etc.

CLINOCHLORE

$Mg_5(Al,Fe)(OH)_8(Al,Si)_4O_{10}$ Monoclinic
         $\angle\beta = 89°40'$

$$n_\alpha = 1.571 \text{ to } 1.588$$
$$n_\beta = 1.571 \text{ to } 1.588$$
$$n_\gamma = 1.576 \text{ to } 1.597$$
$$2V = 0° \text{ to } 50°; \text{ Opt. } (+)$$
$$b = \beta \text{ or } Y, c \wedge \gamma \text{ or } Z = 2° \text{ to } 9°$$

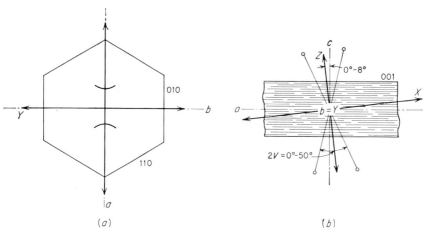

(a)   (b)

FIG. 16-20 a,b. Orientation diagram of clinochlore. Sections (a) parallel to (001) and (b) parallel to (010).

Color. Colorless to green in thin sections. Pleochroic with absorption: α or X and β or $Y > \gamma$ or Z.

Form. The crystal habit varies from thin to thick tabular with pseudo-hexagonal outlines. Crystals are often bent.

Cleavage. Perfect in one direction parallel to {001}.

Relief. Fair, $n >$ balsam.

Birefringence. Weak to rather weak, $n_\gamma - n_\alpha = 0.004$ to 0.011.

Extinction. The maximum extinction angle measured from cleavage traces varies from 2° to 9°. Basal sections are practically isotropic.

Orientation. Crystals showing cleavage are usually length-fast.

Twinning. Polysynthetic twinning is common, according to the mica law.

Interference Figure. The interference figure is biaxial positive with a variable axial angle. The axial plane is {010}. Dispersion, $r < v$.

Distinguishing Features. Clinochlore is distinguished from other chlorites by the oblique extinction and from pennine by greater birefringence and distinctly biaxial character.

Related Minerals. Leuchtenbergite is an iron-free chlorite that is colorless in thin sections. Kotschubeite is a chromian clinochlore frequently associated with chromite.

Occurrence. Clinochlore occurs in chlorite schists and in other metamorphic rocks. Common associates are talc, antigorite, chondrodite, and phlogopite. It is also an alteration product of other silicates.

PENNINITE (PENNINE)

$Mg_5(Al,Fe)(OH)_8(Al,Si)_4O_{10}$ Monoclinic

$$n_\alpha = 1.575 \text{ to } 1.582$$
$$n_\beta = 1.576 \text{ to } 1.582$$
$$n_\gamma = 1.576 \text{ to } 1.583$$
$$2V = 0° \text{ to } 20°; \text{ Opt. } (+) \text{ or } (-)$$

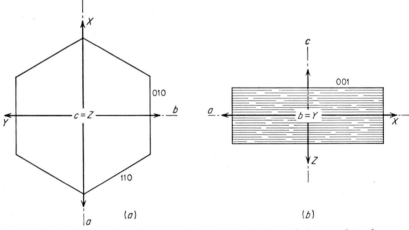

FIG. 16-21 *a,b*. Orientation diagrams of penninite. Sections (*a*) normal to the *c*-axis and (*b*) parallel to (010).

Color. Green or greenish in thin sections. Pleochroic from green to nearly colorless: occasionally from green to brownish red.

Form. Penninite usually occurs in six-sided crystals of thick tabular habit.

Cleavage. Perfect in one direction parallel to {001}.

Relief. Fair, $n >$ balsam.

Birefringence. Very weak, $n_\gamma - n_\alpha = 0.001$ to 0.004; the interference color is often an anomalous "Berlin blue," a color not found on the interference color chart.

Extinction. Parallel or almost parallel to cleavage traces and to crystal outlines.

Orientation. The cleavage traces are parallel to either the faster or slower ray.

Twinning. Twinning parallel to {001} with (001) as the composition face is so characteristic that this mode of twinning is known as the *pennine law*. Since the extinction is practically parallel this twinning is not easily recognized in thin sections.

Interference Figure. The interference figure is biaxial with such a small axial angle that it appears to be uniaxial. The optical sign is usually positive, but sometimes it is negative. The axial plane is usually parallel to {010}.

Distinguishing Features. Penninite is distinguished from most of the other chlorites by parallel extinction, very small axial angle, and anomalous interference colors. The indices of refraction are lower than those of prochlorite.

Related Minerals. Kämmererite is a chromian penninite very similar to kotschubeite. Pseudophite is a compact tough variety of penninite. It is one of the pseudojades known as "Styrian jade."

Occurrence. Penninite usually occurs as an alteration product of other silicates such as garnet. The most typical specimens are found in seams and cavities.

CHAMOSITE

$Fe_3^{II}Al_2Si_2O_{10}.3H_2O$ Monoclinic(?)

$$n \text{ ca.} = 1.635$$
$$2V \text{ small}; \text{Opt.} (-)$$

Color. Green, greenish gray, gray, pale brown to almost colorless in thin sections. Some sections show slight pleochroism.

Form. Usually oolitic with pseudospherulitic structure (concentric instead of fibrous elements). Subhedral crystals of thick tabular habit are occasionally found. The ooliths often have a portion of a chamosite crystal as a nucleus. Chamosite is sometimes massive with aggregate structure.

Cleavage. In one direction, but not as perfect as in the micas. The ooliths often show concentric parting.

Relief. Moderate, $n >$ balsam. The index of refraction is in the neighborhood of 1.635.

Birefringence. Nil to weak, up to about 0.007 to 0.008. Interference colors are not appreciably anomalous.

Orientation. Both cleavage traces and the concentric layers of ooliths are length-slow.

Distinguishing Features. Chamosite is distinguished from the other chlorites by higher index of refraction and from glauconite by lower birefringence. Chamosite often resembles oolitic collophane, but the presence of chamosite crystals and the slightly higher index of refraction will usually distinguish it.

Related Minerals. The chlorites, delessite and thuringite, are similar to chamosite, but the former occurs in true spherulites in amygdaloidal rocks and the latter in schists. Greenalite, an iron silicate occurring in amorphous granules in cherts of the Lake Superior region, also resembles chamosite.

Occurrence. Chamosite is a prominent constituent of oolitic sedimentary iron ores that are prominent in the Jurassic of England, where they are usually known as *ironstones* and are commercially important low-grade ores. According to Hallimond, they are for the most part of marine origin, but some are probably fresh water. The usual associates of chamosite are siderite, calcite, collophane, pyrite, and various detrital minerals.

These chamositic ores are also found in Scotland, Lorraine, southern Sweden, Bohemia, and Newfoundland.

Brittle Mica Group

Micaceous minerals without the flexibility of chlorite, lacking the alkali content of biotite, and frequently containing calcium in place of magnesium constitute the brittle mica group. The minerals stilpnomelane, clintonite, margarite, chloritoid, and ottrelite belong to this group. Stilpnomelane and chloritoid are common minerals.

STILPNOMELANE

$H_2(Mg,Fe)Al_2SiO_7$ Monoclinic?

$$n_\alpha = 1.612 \text{ to } 1.634$$
$$n_\beta = n_\gamma = 1.700 \text{ to } 1.745$$
$$2V = \text{ca. } 0°$$

Color. Brown and yellow to green. Pleochroic with Y and $Z > X$.

Form. Often found in micaceous masses, but it may occur in isolated crystals.

Cleavage. Perfect parallel to (001).

Relief. Moderate to high, $n > $ balsam.

Birefringence. Moderate to strong, $n_\gamma - n_\alpha = 0.030$ to 0.119. Basal plates are almost isotropic.

Extinction. Almost parallel.

Orientation. The angle between X and c is small.

Twinning. Polysynthetic twins after the mica law.

Interference Figure. Flakelike crystals are reported to give a uniaxial negative figure.

Distinguishing Features. The mineral resembles biotite and may be overlooked in field examination. The pseudo-uniaxial interference figure and higher index of refraction are distinctive. Pleochroism is ordinarily more colorful than pleochroism of biotite.

Related Minerals. Stilpnomelane is related to the other members of the brittle mica group.

Occurrence. Stilpnomelane has been found in quartz-adularia pegmatite veins, in nepheline-syenite pegmatites, and probably occurs as an introduced mineral formed as a hydrothermal alteration product.

CHLORITOID

$H_2(Fe,Mg,Mn)Al_2SiO_7$ (Ottrelite)   Monoclinic

$$n_\alpha = 1.715 \text{ to } 1.724$$
$$n_\beta = 1.719 \text{ to } 1.726$$
$$n_\gamma = 1.731 \text{ to } 1.737$$
$$2V = 36° \text{ to } 63°; \text{ Opt. } (+)$$
$$b = \beta \text{ or } Y, c \wedge \gamma \text{ or } Z = +3° \text{ to } +21°$$

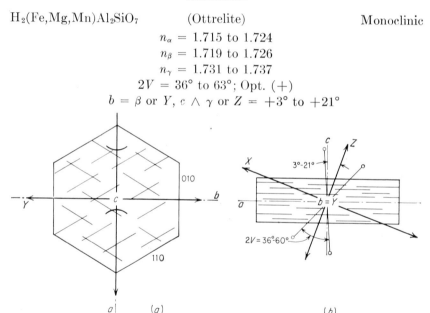

o (a)   (b)

FIG. 16-22 a,b. Orientation diagrams of chloritoid. Sections (a) normal to the c-axis and (b) parallel to (010).

Color. Green, greenish gray to colorless. Usually more or less pleochroic.

Form. Chloritoid, one of the group known as *brittle micas*, commonly occurs in pseudohexagonal tabular crystals. Inclusions are often present. It often shows a kind of "hourglass" structure.

Cleavage. Perfect in one direction {001} and imperfect parallel to {110}.

Relief. High, $n >$ balsam.

Birefringence. Weak to moderate, $n_\gamma - n_\alpha = 0.013$ to 0.016. Basal plates are practically isotropic.

Extinction. Almost parallel up to ca. $20°$.

Orientation. The crystals are length-fast.

Twinning. Polysynthetic twins after the mica law are very common.

Interference Figure. The figure is biaxial positive with a moderate to rather large axial angle. The axial plane is {010}. Dispersion, $r > v$ or $r < v$.

Fig. 16-23. ($\times 10$) Chloritoid forming a metacryst in phyllite. ($\times$ nicols.)

Distinguishing Features. Chloritoid somewhat resembles some of the chlorites, but the relief is much higher and the cleavage less perfect.

Related Minerals. Ottrelite, usually treated as a variety of chloritoid, is considered by Mèlon to be a distinctive mineral.

Occurrence. Chloritoid occurs in metamorphic rocks such as mica schists and phyllites as metacrysts.

TALC

$Mg_3(OH)_2(Si_2O_5)_2$ Monoclinic
$\angle \beta = (?)$

$$n_\alpha = 1.538 \text{ to } 1.545$$
$$n_\beta = 1.575 \text{ to } 1.590$$
$$n_\gamma = 1.575 \text{ to } 1.590$$
$$2V = 6° \text{ to } 30°; \text{ Opt. } (-)$$
$$a = \beta \text{ or } Y, b = \gamma \text{ or } Z, c = \alpha \text{ or } X$$

Color. Colorless in thin sections.

Form. Talc occurs in coarse to fine platy or fibrous aggregates that often have a more or less parallel arrangement. Shreds and plates are often bent. Euhedral crystals of talc are unknown.

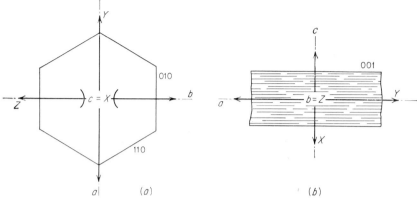

$a|$ (a) (b)

Fig. 16-24 a,b. Orientation diagrams of talc. Sections parallel to (a) (001) and (b) (010).

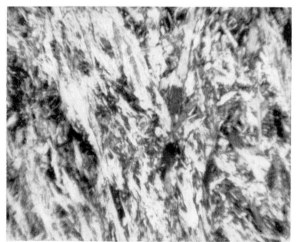

Fig. 16-25. ($\times 10$) A section cut through a foliated mass of talc crystals. ($\times$ nicols.)

Cleavage. Perfect in one direction {001}.

Relief. Fair, $n >$ balsam.

Birefringence. Very strong, $n_\gamma - n_\alpha = 0.030$ to 0.050; the maximum interference colors are upper third order. Sections parallel to the cleavage give very low first-order gray colors since $n_\gamma - n_\beta$ is almost nil ($0.000x$).

Extinction. The extinction is parallel to the cleavage traces in most sections; in a few sections the extinction is $2°$ or $3°$; hence talc is probably monoclinic.

Orientation. Cleavage traces and shreds are length-slow as in muscovite.

Interference Figure. Cleavage flakes give a biaxial negative figure with a small axial angle. Dispersion, $r > v$ distinct.

Distinguishing Features. Talc greatly resembles muscovite and pyrophyllite, but may often be distinguished by the smaller axial angle provided an interference figure can be obtained.

It may be necessary to make a chemical or microchemical test in order to prove the identity of talc. The association with other magnesium minerals indicates the presence of talc rather than muscovite or sericite.

Occurrence. Talc is the principal constituent of talc schists and soapstones. It is often a hydrothermal mineral formed at the expense of antigorite and tremolite in shear zones of serpentines. Dolomite and magnesite are frequent associates.

PYROPHYLLITE

$Al_2(OH)_2Si_4O_{10}$ Monoclinic(?)

$$n_\alpha = 1.552$$
$$n_\beta = 1.588$$
$$n_\gamma = 1.600$$
$$2V = 53° \text{ to } 60°; \text{ Opt. } (-)$$
$$a = \gamma \text{ or } Z, b = \beta \text{ or } Y, c = \alpha \text{ or } X$$

Color. Colorless in thin sections.

Form. Pyrophyllite occurs in subhedral crystals that are tabular parallel to {010} and much elongated. The crystals are usually curved and distorted. A radial structure is common. It also occurs in fine aggregates.

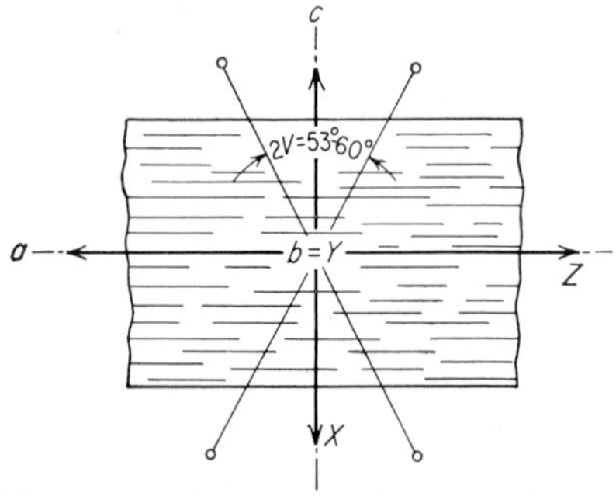

Fig. 16-26. Orientation diagram of pyrophyllite. Section parallel to (010).

Cleavage. Perfect in one direction {001}.

Relief. Rather low to moderate, $n >$ balsam.

Birefringence. Strong, $n_\gamma - n_\alpha = 0.048$; the maximum interference color is upper third order. Sections parallel to the cleavage give gray or first-order colors since $n_\gamma - n_\beta = 0.012$.

Extinction. Parallel or almost parallel to cleavage traces and parallel to the elongate sections.

Orientation. Cleavage traces are parallel to the slower ray. Elongate sections not showing cleavage are length-slow.

Twinning. Twinning like that found in the micas is present but is not well defined.

Interference Figure. Sections parallel to {001} or cleavage flakes give a biaxial negative figure with a rather large axial angle. The axial angle is parallel to {010} or the length of the crystals.

FIG. 16-27. (×10) A radial aggregate of pyrophyllite crystals. (× nicols.)

Distinguishing Features. Pyrophyllite usually has a peculiar elongate tabular habit. Muscovite and talc greatly resemble pyrophyllite. Talc has a much smaller axial angle. Microcrystalline pyrophyllite is very difficult to distinguish from sericite or talc by optical means; it may be necessary to make chemical or microchemical tests.

Occurrence. Pyrophyllite occurs in metamorphic rocks and has often developed as a hydrothermal alteration product. Common associates are andalusite, sillimanite, kyanite, lazulite, and alunite.

The Clay Minerals

These minerals are widely distributed in sedimentary rocks, may be found in veins, and occur as alteration products of igneous and metamorphic rocks. The most common clay minerals belong to the kaolin, montmorillonite, palygorskite, and hydromica groups. All are finely crystalline or metacolloidal and occur in flakelike or dense aggregates of varying types.

The kaolin group includes the minerals kaolinite, anauxite, dickite, nacrite, halloysite, hydrohalloysite, and allophane. Of these, kaolinite, dickite, and nacrite have the same composition ($Al_2O_3.2SiO_2.2H_2O$) but differ optically and also in internal structure, as shown by X-ray diffraction. Anauxite ($Al_2O_3.3SiO_2.2H_2O$) differs slightly from kaolinite both structurally and optically. Halloysite ($Al_2O_3.2SiO_2.2H_2O$) and hydrated halloysite ($Al_2O_3.2SiO_2.4H_2O$) differ somewhat optically and also structurally. Allophane is a solidified gel ($Al_2O_3.xSiO_2.nH_2O$) with an index of refraction lower than the indices of the other minerals of the group.

Kaolinite, the most common kaolin, occurs in large quantities, both residual and as a transported mineral in the white clays of the south-eastern United States. It is frequently formed by the decomposition *in situ* of rocks containing feldspars. Dickite, although less common, is better crystallized and may occur in pseudohexagonal plates. It is commonly formed by hydrothermal solutions in veins or dikes and occasionally occurs associated with sulfides in ore deposits. Halloysite is found as a porcelain-like mass or fine white powder in shales and sandstones and as a replacement of limestone. It may occur independently but is frequently associated with kaolinite, alunite, and various forms of hydrous aluminum oxides.

Montmorillonite is a widely distributed clay mineral. It occurs as an alteration product of volcanic ash and tuff. The rock bentonite, common in the western United States, is composed largely of montmorillonite. Montmorillonite is also found in minor amounts as an alteration product in pegmatite dikes. The montmorillonite group consists of montmorillonite $[(Mg,Ca)O.Al_2O_3.5SiO_2.nH_2O]$, nontronite $[(Al,Fe)_2O_3.3SiO_2.nH_2O]$, and saponite $(2MgO.3SiO_2.nH_2O)$.

Palygorskite, a clay mineral from a mining district in the Ural Mountains, Russia, was named by Ssaftschenkow in 1862. Fersman later defined the palygorskite minerals. The minerals in this group now recognized include pilolite, lassallite, and attapulgite. Attapulgite, common in Florida and southern Georgia and found at Mormiron, France, is the essential constituent of most fullers earth. Sepiolite yields a tubular structure in electron micrographs and in dehydration resembles attapulgite (Martin-Vivaldi and Cano-Ruiz, 1955).

Hydromica (or illite) represents a poorly defined group intermediate between muscovite and montmorillonite. It is likely to occur in shale or other argillaceous beds where it may be associated with kaolinite or montmorillonite and mixed with fine detrital fragments of other minerals. The general formula $(OH)_4K_\gamma(Al_4Fe_4Mg_4Mg_6)(Si_{8-\gamma}Al_\gamma)O_{20}(\gamma = 1$ to $1.5)$ suggested by Grim[1] indicates the complex chemical character of hydromica.

The significant optical properties of the clay minerals may be conveniently outlined for the four groups from the standpoint of microscopic observation: (1) The kaolin group is characterized by weak birefringence and indices of refraction approximating those of quartz. (2) The montmorillonite group has a comparatively high birefringence but indices of refraction for the most part lower than Canada balsam. (3) Palygorskite resembles montmorillonite in thin section but has a higher index of refraction and shows more abundant mass extinction. (4) The hydromica

---

[1] The name *illite* has been applied to this group, but it is possible that *hydromuscovite*, as described by A. Johnstone [*Quar. J. Geol. Soc. London,* **45:** 363 (1889)] merits priority.

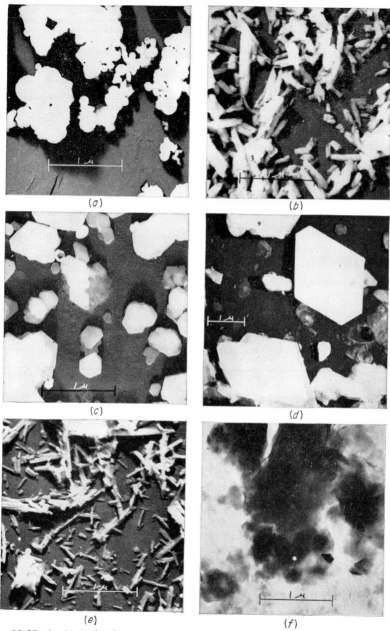

Fig. 16-28. (×16,000) Electron micrographs of clay minerals showing features not disclosed at magnifications possible with the polarizing microscope. (*American Petroleum Institute: Reference Clay Minerals.*) (*a*) Allophane showing spherical forms; (*b*) tubular forms of halloysite; (*c*) pseudohexagonal plates of kaolinite; (*d*) (×8,000) crystals of dickite; (*e*) rodlike forms of attapulgite; (*f*) rods and tubular forms of sepiolite.

CLAY MINERALS

	Chemical composition	Crystal system	n_α	n_β	n_γ	$n_\gamma - n_\alpha$
Kaolin group						
Kaolinite	$Al_2O_3.2SiO_2.2H_2O$	Triclinic	1.561	1.565	1.566	0.005
(Anauxite)	$Al_2O_3.3 \pm SiO_2.2H_2O$	Triclinic		(see kaolinite)		
Dickite	$Al_2O_3.2SiO_2.2H_2O$	Monoclinic	1.560	1.562	1.566	0.006
Nacrite	$Al_2O_3.2SiO_2.2H_2O$	Monoclinic	1.557	1.562	1.563	0.006
Halloysite	$Al_2O_3.2 + SiO_2.2 \pm H_2O$	Aggregates		$n = 1.549\text{-}1.561$		0.001
Hydrohalloysite (Endellite)	$Al_2O_3.2 \pm SiO_2.4 \pm H_2O$	Aggregates		$n = 1.526\text{-}1.542$		
Allophane	$Al_2O_3.xSiO_2.nH_2O$	Amorphous		$n = 1.47\text{-}1.49$		
Montmorillonite group						
Montmorillonite	$(Mg,Ca)O.Al_2O_3.5SiO_2.nH_2O$	Monoclinic	1.492	....	1.513	0.021
(Beidellite)	$Al_2O_3.3SiO_2.nH_2O$	Monoclinic	1.517	....	1.549	0.032
Nontronite	$Fe_2O_3.3SiO_2.nH_2O$	Monoclinic	1.580	....	1.615	0.035
Saponite	$2MgO.3SiO_2.nH_2O$	Monoclinic	1.479-1.490	1.510-1.525	1.511-1.527	0.032-0.037
Hectorite						
Hydromica group						
Hydromuscovite (Illite)	$KAl_2(OH)_2[AlSi_3(O,OH)_{10}]$	Monoclinic	1.535-1.57	....	1.565-1.605	0.030-0.035
Palygorskite group						
Palygorskite (Attapulgite)	$2MgO.3SiO_2.4H_2O$ to $Al_2O_3.5SiO_2.6H_2O$	Monoclinic	1.510	....	1.533	0.023
Sepiolite	$2MgO.3SiO_2.nH_2O$	Monoclinic	1.490-1.506	....	1.505-1.526	0.015-0.020

group is characterized by a comparatively high birefringence with indices of refraction above Canada balsam.

Potash-bearing clay, probably hydromica, is frequently found as an alteration product of old volcanic ash, particularly in the Ordovician of the eastern United States, or at times as a gouge clay in ore deposits.

A strong artificial illumination is advisable in determining the birefringence of the clay minerals. A summary of the optical properties of the more important clay minerals based upon determinations either by C. S. Ross or R. E. Grim is given in the foregoing tabulation.

The most important clay minerals exhibit distinguishing features in thin sections. In general, however, these minerals present problems in identification best solved by coordinated optical, X-ray, thermal, and chemical methods. Electron micrographs of some clay minerals are also significant.

KAOLINITE

$Al_2O_3.2SiO_2.2H_2O$ Triclinic

$$n_\alpha = 1.561$$
$$n_\beta = 1.565$$
$$n_\gamma = 1.566$$

$2V$ variable; Opt. $(-)$

$b = \gamma$ or Z, $c \wedge \alpha$ or $X = 1°$ to $3\frac{1}{2}°$

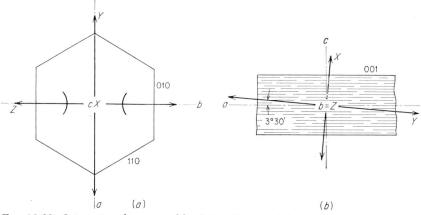

Fig. 16-29. Orientation diagrams of kaolinite. Sections (a) normal to the c-axis and (b) parallel to (010).

Color. Colorless to pale yellow.

Form. Kaolinite occurs in fine mosaiclike masses of crystals, in veinlets replacing feldspars and other minerals, and in scalelike individuals. Occasionally small plates show accordionlike outlines.

Cleavage. Perfect in one direction parallel to {001}.

Relief. Low, $n >$ balsam.

Birefringence. Weak, $n_\gamma - n_\alpha = 0.005$. In normal sections kaolinite gives gray and white interference colors.

Extinction. The angle of extinction on (010) against the base is 1° to 3½°.

Orientation. The cleavage traces and crystals are length-slow.

Twinning. Minute crystals of kaolinite do not appear to show twinning.

Interference Figure. Kaolinite is ordinarily too fine-grained to give an interference figure. The axial plane is normal to {010} and nearly parallel to {100}.

Distinguishing Features. It is distinguished by low relief and weak birefringence. From dickite it is distinguished largely by its smaller extinction angle.

Occurrence. Kaolinite is found as a weathering product of igneous and metamorphic rocks produced particularly by the decomposition of feldspars. It is a prominent clay mineral in sedimentary beds. At times it may be a product of hydrothermal alteration associated with mineral deposits.

DICKITE

$Al_2O_3.2SiO_2.2H_2O$ Monoclinic

$n_\alpha = 1.560$

$n_\beta = 1.562$

$n_\gamma = 1.566$

$2V = 52°$ to $80°$; Opt. $(+)$

$b = Z, c \wedge X = 15°$ to $20°$

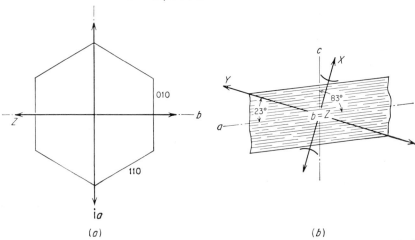

(a)   (b)

FIG. 16-30. Orientation diagrams of dickite. Sections (a) normal to the c-axis and (b) parallel to (010).

Color. Colorless to pale yellow.

Form. Dickite occurs in small pseudohexagonal flakelike crystals.

Cleavage. Perfect in one direction parallel to {001}.

Relief. Low, $n >$ balsam.

Birefringence. Weak, $n_\gamma - n_\alpha = 0.006$; the maximum interference colors are middle first order.

Extinction. Angle of extinction on {010} against base varies from 15° to 20°.

Orientation. The cleavage traces and crystals are length-slow.

Twinning. No apparent twinning.

Interference Figure. Ordinary thin sections yield poor interference figures or none at all. The axial plane is normal to {010}. Dispersion, $r < v$.

Distinguishing Features. Dickite is distinguished from kaolinite by slightly higher birefringence, larger crystals, and a larger extinction angle.

Fig. 16-31. (×30) Scattered dickite crystals on a microscope slide. (× nicols.)

Occurrence. The mineral is commonly found associated with metallic minerals in ore deposits. It is usually produced by hydrothermal action and may occur as a replacement of quartz in quartzite.

HALLOYSITE

$Al_2O_3.2SiO_2.2H_2O$ Aggregates
(Crystal system
unknown)

$n = 1.549$ to 1.561

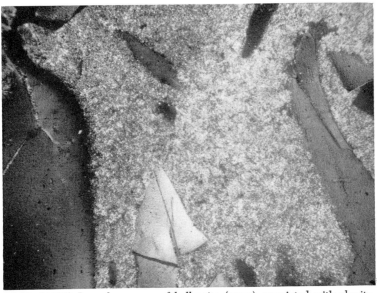

FIG. 16-32. (×15) Irregular masses of halloysite (gray) associated with alunite (salt and pepper texture). (× nicols.)

Color. Colorless.

Form. Halloysite occurs in extremely fine-grained or colloform masses and commonly shows shatter cracks.

Relief. Low, n slightly $>$ balsam.

Birefringence. Very weak, almost isotropic.

Distinguishing Features. Halloysite is distinguished by extremely weak birefringence, an index of refraction almost equal to balsam and shatter cracks. It is commonly associated with other clay minerals.

Occurrence. The mineral occurs in altered areas in limestone associated with diaspore, alunite, or gibbsite; in clay beds associated with kaolinite; and probably in extremely weathered portions of some shales.

Hydrohalloysite. X-ray study shows that two forms of halloysite exist: a more hydrous form, $Al_2O_3.2SiO_2.4H_2O$, known as *endellite* or *hydrohalloysite;* a less hydrous type, $Al_2O_3.2SiO_2.2H_2O$, which is halloysite. The more hydrous form is found in mine workings under the influence of groundwater. It changes to the less hydrous form on standing in dry atmosphere.

MONTMORILLONITE

$(Mg,Ca).Al_2O_3.5SiO_2.nH_2O$ Monoclinic

$$n_\alpha = 1.492$$
$$n_\beta = n_\gamma = 1.513$$
$$2V = 10° \text{ to } 25°; \text{ Opt. } (-)$$

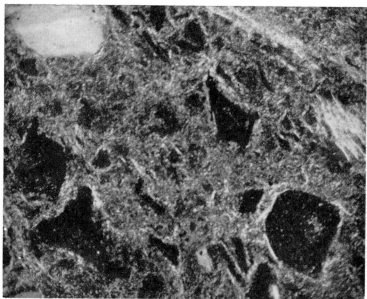

Fig. 16-33. ($\times 15$) Montmorillonite, more or less altered glass shards, and feldspar fragments in bentonite. ($\times$ nicols.)

Color. Pale pink, greenish, or colorless.

Form. Massive, claylike microcrystalline aggregates in the shape of shards. Nearly always in extremely fine scalelike crystals. Crystals of this type have been described by E. T. Wherry as a one-dimensional colloid since they are usually so thin.

Relief. Rather low, $n <$ balsam.

Birefringence. Moderate, $n_\gamma - n_\alpha = 0.021$. Although the birefringence is moderate, the crystals are usually so thin that interference colors in thin sections seldom go above the second order.

Interference Figure. Individual crystals are usually so small and thin that figures cannot be obtained.

Distinguishing Features. The most characteristic feature of montmorillonite is microcrystalline aggregates in the shape of shards.

Occurrence. Montmorillonite is the chief constituent of bentonite, which is altered volcanic ash. It is a common constituent of shale where it may be associated with hydromuscovite. Occasionally it occurs as an alteration material in pegmatite dikes. Montmorillonite is one of the early alteration minerals formed in wall rock bordering mineral deposits.

HYDROMUSCOVITE

(Hydromica)

(Illite)

$KAl_2(OH)_2[AlSi_3(O,OH)_{10}]$ Monoclinic(?)

$$n_\alpha = 1.535 \text{ to } 1.570$$
$$n_\gamma = 1.565 \text{ to } 1.605$$
$$2V \text{ small}; \text{ Opt. } (-)$$
$$\alpha \text{ or } X = \perp \text{ plane of } a \text{ and } c.$$

FIG. 16-34. Kaolinite prisms with intergrown hydromuscovite plates. (*After* S. G. *Galpin*, 1912.)

Color. Colorless to yellowish brown.

Form. Hydromuscovite is found in irregular matted flakes that may be intercalated with flakes of montmorillonite or kaolinite.

Relief. Low, $n >$ balsam.

Birefringence. Rather strong, $n_\gamma - n_\alpha = 0.030$ to 0.035, but the small, thin crystals may not yield colors above the second order.

Distinguishing Features. Hydromuscovite occurs in matted small flakes resembling kaolinite and montmorillonite but is distinguished from montmorillonite by higher indices of refraction and from kaolinite by a higher birefringence. It is distinguished from muscovite by a lower axial angle. Various polymorphs of mica and interlayer mixtures of hydromuscovite and montmorillonite require X-ray identification.

Occurrence. Hydromuscovite is a widespread constituent of shale or soil. It forms during the alteration of feldspathic minerals, biotite, muscovite, and other constituents.

PALYGORSKITE

$2MgO.3SiO_2.4H_2O$ Monoclinic(?)

to

$Al_2O_3.5SiO_2.6H_2O$

$$n_\alpha = 1.510$$
$$n_\gamma = 1.533$$

Color. Colorless to pale yellow or green.

Form. Found in compact fine aggregates.

Relief. Low, $n <$ balsam.

Birefringence. Moderate, $n_\gamma - n_\alpha = 0.023$.

Extinction. Matted aggregates often tend to show a more or less uniform mass extinction in thin section.

Distinguishing Features. Resembles montmorillonite in thin section. Electron micrographs exhibit a striking rodlike structure.

Occurrence. Widespread in fullers earth deposits of Georgia and Florida, where the name *attapulgite* has been used. Originally found in the Ural Mountains of Russia. Found in France, Scotland, and Australia. It is also reported to form by hydrothermal action in "mountain leather."

SEPIOLITE

$2MgO.3SiO_2.nH_2O$ Monoclinic

$$n_\alpha = 1.490 \text{ to } 1.503$$
$$n_\gamma = 1.505 \text{ to } 1.526$$
$$2V = 40° \text{ to } 60°; \text{ Opt. } (-)$$

Color. Colorless to gray.

Form. Frequently fibrous and in aggregates.

Relief. Low, $n <$ balsam.

Birefringence. Rather strong, $n_\gamma - n_\alpha = 0.015 \text{ to } 0.020$.

Extinction. Approximately parallel with positive elongation (length-slow).

Distinguishing Features. Occurs in fibrous aggregates with curved and matted fiber groups.

Occurrence. Found in a contact metamorphic veinlike mass associated with intrusives in Yavapi County, Arizona. Considered by some to be, at times, a constituent of clay.

Serpentine Group

Serpentinite is a rock type of widespread occurrence in which hydrous magnesian silicate minerals belonging to the serpentine group are abundant. The usage which considers serpentinite as a rock name follows the pattern by which rock names such as quartzite, pyroxenite, and amphibolite are derived.

The serpentine mineral group consists of the two minerals antigorite and chrysotile which occur independently or as natural mixtures in various proportions (Nagy and Faust, 1956). The general formula $Mg_6Si_4O_{10}(OH)_8$ applies to both; however, Mg may be replaced by Fe,

 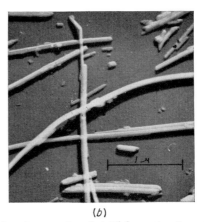

(a)   (b)

FIG. 16-35. ($\times 16,000$) Electron micrographs of serpentine. (a) Flaky antigorite and fibrous chrysotile and (b) tubular chrysotile and flaky antigorite (*American Petroleum Institute: Reference Clay Minerals*).

Ni, or Mn to form *ferro, nickel,* or *manganese chrysotile,* and by similar replacement *ferro, nickel,* or *manganese antigorite* may be formed.

The name serpophite was proposed by Lodochnikow (1933) as a combination of serp and ophite to apply to a compact nearly isotropic mineraloid of the serpentine group. It corresponds in part to serpentine, used as a mineral name by Selfridge. The lizardite of Whittaker and Zussman, if the conclusions of Nagy and Faust apply, is probably also in part this submicroscopic material.

The members of the serpentine group occur for the most part in crystalline units so small that discrete forms are not observed without the electron microscope. Chrysotile is best defined and occurs in long flexible tubular or rodlike forms. Antigorite exhibits a flat, flaky, or lathlike habit. Patterns of serpentine minerals observed with the polarizing microscope are aggregate effects due to crystals which range in dimensions within a fraction of one micron.

ANTIGORITE

$H_4Mg_3Si_2O_9$ Orthorhombic

$$n_\alpha = 1.555 \text{ to } 1.564$$
$$n_\beta = 1.562 \text{ to } 1.573$$
$$n_\gamma = 1.562 \text{ to } 1.573$$
$$2V = 20° \text{ to } 90°; \text{ Opt. } (-)$$
$$a = \beta \text{ or } Y, \, b = \alpha \text{ or } X, \, c = \gamma \text{ or } Z$$

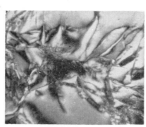

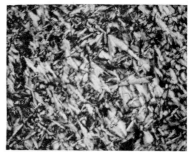

FIG. 16-36.   FIG. 16-37.

FIG. 16-36. Orientation diagram of antigorite. Section parallel to (010).
FIG. 16-37. (×15) Antigorite in serpentine. (× nicols.)

Color. Colorless to pale green in thin sections.

Form. Antigorite occurs in anhedral crystals or aggregates of fibro-lamellar structure. It often occurs as pseudomorphs after pyroxene (bastite), olivine, etc.

Relief. Rather low, $n >$ balsam.

Birefringence. Weak, $n_\gamma - n_\alpha = 0.007$ to 0.009; the maximum interference color is first-order yellow. This yellow is slightly anomalous since it has a greenish tinge.

Extinction. Parallel.

Orientation. The crystals are length-slow.

Interference Figure. The figure is biaxial negative with variable axial angle. The axial plane is {100}. Dispersion, $r > v$ weak.

Distinguishing Features. Chrysotile is distinguished from its dimorph antigorite by the fine fibrous structure. Antigorite usually shows aggregate structure and is in practically all cases an alteration product of some other silicate mineral. Serpophite has lower birefringence than antigorite and shows little or no form or structure.

Occurrence. Antigorite is the main constituent of serpentine, a metamorphic rock. It has been formed from olivine, enstatite, augite, etc., by

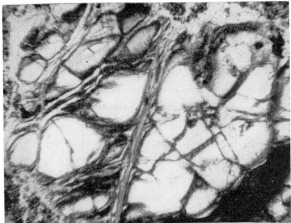

FIG. 16-38. (×30) Olivine cut and surrounded by serpentine. (× nicols.)

FIG. 16-39. (×30) Texture in serpentine accentuated by interference colors. (× nicols.)

hydrothermal alteration. Common associates are chrysotile, talc, magnetite, chromite, and picotite.

CHRYSOTILE

$H_4Mg_3Si_2O_9$ Orthorhombic

$$n_\alpha = 1.493 \text{ to } 1.546$$
$$n_\beta = 1.504 \text{ to } 1.550$$
$$n_\gamma = 1.517 \text{ to } 1.557$$
$$2V = 0° \text{ to } 50°; \text{ Opt. } (+)$$

Color. Colorless in thin sections.

Form. Chrysotile occurs in cross-fiber veinlets (Figure 8-13).

Relief. Low, n slightly greater than balsam.

Birefringence. Moderate, $n_\gamma - n_\alpha = 0.011$ to 0.014; the maximum interference color is bright yellow of the first order.

Extinction. Parallel.

Orientation. The fibers are length-slow.

Distinguishing Features. The other forms of asbestos (tremolite, anthophyllite, and crocidolite) all have higher indices of refraction than chrysotile. Tremolite has oblique extinction.

Occurrence. Chrysotile occurs in veinlets in serpentinite.

PREHNITE

$H_2Ca_2Al_2(SiO_4)_3$ Orthorhombic

$$n_\alpha = 1.615 \text{ to } 1.635$$
$$n_\beta = 1.624 \text{ to } 1.642$$
$$n_\gamma = 1.645 \text{ to } 1.665$$
$$2V \text{ variable; Opt. } (+)$$
$$a = \alpha \text{ or } X, \; b = \beta \text{ or } Y, \; c = \gamma \text{ or } Z$$

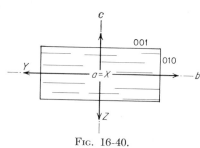 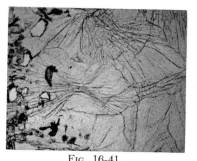

FIG. 16-40.   FIG. 16-41.

FIG. 16-40. Orientation diagram of prehnite. Section parallel to (100).
FIG. 16-41. ($\times 12$) Prehnite showing "bow-tie" structure.

Color. Colorless in thin sections.

Form. Prehnite usually occurs in aggregates that are often sheaflike and approach spherulites. What may be called *bow-tie* structure is characteristic (Figure 16-41). Crystals are mostly tabular parallel to {001}.

Cleavage. Good in one direction {001}.

Relief. Fairly high, $n >$ balsam.

Birefringence. Moderate to rather strong, $n_\gamma - n_\alpha = 0.020$ to 0.033; the maximum interference color varies from low to upper second order. Anomalous interference colors are found in some varieties.

Extinction. Parallel to the cleavage. The extinction is often wavy on account of the structure.

Orientation. The cleavage traces are parallel to the fast ray.

Twinning. Fine polysynthetic twinning in two directions at right angles is found in some sections.

Interference Figure. Prehnite gives a positive biaxial figure, but the axial angle is variable even in the same specimen. The axial plane is {010}. Dispersion, $r > v$ weak.

Distinguishing Features. Lawsonite in some occurrences is like prehnite, but the birefringence of lawsonite is considerably lower and the indices of refraction somewhat higher.

Occurrence. Prehnite is a secondary mineral in cavities and seams of various igneous rocks. It is a prominent mineral in amygdaloidal rocks of the Lake Superior copper ores. It is sometimes found in veins. Associated minerals are quartz, calcite, datolite, and zeolites.

GLAUCONITE

$KMg(Fe,Al)(SiO_3)_6.3H_2O$ Monoclinic(?)

$$n_\alpha = 1.590 \text{ to } 1.612$$
$$n_\beta = 1.609 \text{ to } 1.643$$
$$n_\gamma = 1.610 \text{ to } 1.644$$
$$2V = 16° \text{ to } 30°; \text{ Opt. } (-)$$
$$\alpha \text{ or } X \text{ ca. } \perp \{001\}$$

Color. Green, yellow-green, or olive-green in thin sections. Pleochroic from yellow to green.

Form. Glauconite occurs in grains or pellets that are in part aggregates of minute crystals and in part single crystals. Euhedral crystals have not been observed. The grains are often casts of foraminiferal tests.

Cleavage. Perfect in one direction {001}.

Relief. Moderate, $n >$ balsam.

Birefringence. Moderate to rather strong, $n_\gamma - n_\alpha = 0.020$ to 0.032; the highest interference colors are second-order colors, but they are masked by the color of the mineral. Many specimens show aggregate polarization.

FIG. 16-42. (×50) Glauconite (dark) in arkose.

Extinction. The extinction with reference to cleavage traces is practically parallel, but angles of 2° or 3° have been recorded.

Orientation. The cleavage traces are length-slow as in the micas.

Interference Figure. Cleavage flakes give a biaxial negative figure with a small axial angle, but the figure is difficult to obtain on account of the small size of the crystals. Dispersion, $r > v$.

Distinguishing Features. Glauconite much resembles some of the lepto-chlorites such as chamosite, but the latter has a higher index of refraction and weaker birefringence. Chamosite usually has an oolitic structure lacking in glauconite.

Alteration. Glauconite is sometimes altered to limonite.

Occurrence. Glauconite occurs in sands, sandstones, and limestones. It is especially abundant in the loosely consolidated sandstone known as *greensand,* which is prominent in the Cretaceous of New Jersey. A common associate is collophane.

Origin. Glauconite is the product of interstitial sedimentation. Glauconite may be the result of the alteration of detrital biotite. The addition of iron to a clay mineral in a marine environment is also possible.

MINERALOIDS

The term *mineraloid* is given to the mineral-like constituents of rocks that are too indefinite in chemical composition or in physical properties to be included in the list of minerals. The most common and abundant mineraloid is naturally occurring glass or volcanic glass, which is widespread and often of geological importance. Obsidian, perlite, pitchstone, pumice, etc., are petrographic terms, but glass as a whole may be treated as a mineraloid.

Palagonite, an alteration product of fragmental basaltic glass formerly classed as a mineral, is probably a mineraloid.

Hydrocarbons also may be treated as mineraloids.

Certain minerals shown by X-ray studies to yield diffraction lines, but at the same time optically isotropic, such as cliachite, collophane, or opal, are included in this group.

VOLCANIC GLASS

$SiO_2, Al_2O_3, Fe_2O_3, FeO, MgO,$ Amorphous
$CaO, Na_2O, K_2O, H_2O,$ etc.   (Mineraloid)

$$n = 1.48 \text{ to } 1.61$$

Color. Colorless to gray or reddish in thin sections.

Form. Usually massive, sometimes vesicular, perlitic, etc. Often contains spherulites of orthoclase, microlites, crystallites, microphenocrysts, and phenocrysts.

Cleavage. Absent, but it may show perlitic parting.

Relief. Low to moderate, n usually less than balsam but sometimes greater. The index of refraction increases as the silica decreases.

Birefringence. Usually nil, but some varieties show weak birefringence that is due to strain.

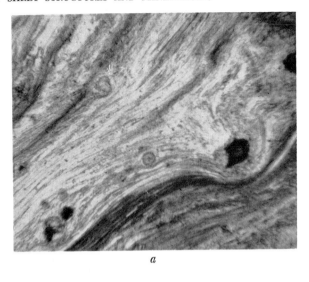

a

b

FIG. 16-43. Volcanic glass and associated features as shown in thin sections (×10). (*a*) Banding caused by flowage; (*b*) acicular crystallites in glass; (*c*) feldspar spherulites (× nicols); (*d*) extinction crosses in spherulites (× nicols); (*e*) perlitic texture and crystallites; (*f*) perlitic texture.

Distinguishing Features. Opal may be mistaken for glass, but the refractive index of opal is distinctly lower.

Alteration. Volcanic glass is often more or less devitrified (see Figure 16-43). The alteration products are usually rather indefinite, but sometimes feldspars, tridymite, cristobalite, or montmorillonite are the result

c

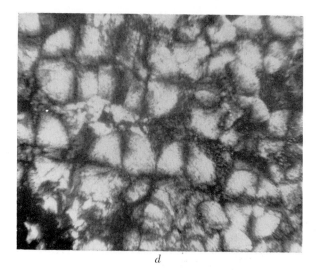

d

of devitrification. Palagonite is always the result of alteration of glass fragments.

Occurrence. Glass often occurs as an independent igneous rock such as obsidian, pumice, perlite, or pitchstone. Most volcanic glass corresponds to rhyolite in composition. Glass is also found as a narrow selvage

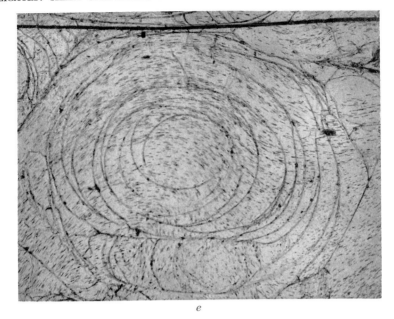

e

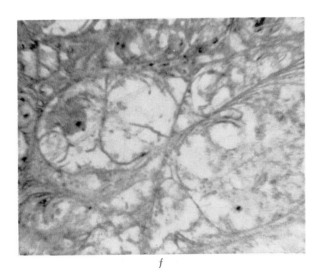

f

to basalt dikes. This variety is known as *tachylyte*. Glass is a prominent constituent of vitrophyre and occurs in the groundmass of many volcanic rocks.

Silica glass has been described under the name *lechatelierite* (see page 247).

PALAGONITE

$SiO_2, Al_2O_3, Fe_2O_3FeO, MgO,$ Amorphous
CaO, H_2O (Mineraloid)
(Altered Glass)

$$n = 1.47 \text{ to } 1.63$$

Color. Usually yellow to yellowish brown but also brown and greenish in thin sections.

Form. Palagonite is found as a rim or zone around glass fragments or in massive form. It often shows an apparent oolitic structure that is due to the filling of microvesicles.

Relief. Low to medium, n either less or greater than balsam.

Birefringence. Nil to very weak. Palagonite is a hydrogel, and the weak birefringence sometimes noted is probably due to strain.

Distinguishing Features. Palagonite resembles opal, collophane, and volcanic glass. The index of refraction is too high for opal and nearly always too low for collophane. It is distinguished from glass by the high water content.

Alteration. The palagonite formed from basaltic breccia fragments at Roseburg, Ore., has, according to A. C. Waters, been altered to chlorite.

Occurrence. Palagonite is found in palagonite tuffs and palagonite rock. It is formed by the hydration of fragmental basaltic glass. The glass fragments are in whole or in part converted into the palagonite. Associates besides glass are calcite, zeolites, chlorite, pyroxene, olivine, and plagioclase (the last three are relict minerals from the original glass).

REFERENCES

Mica Group

Foster, M. D.: Correlation of dioctahedral potassium micas on the basis of their charge relations, *U.S. Geol. Survey Bull.* 1036-D, pp. 57–67, 1956.

Heinrich, E. W., and A. A. Levinson: Studies in the Mica Group; Polymorphism among the High-Silica Sericites, *Am. Mineralogist,* vol. 40, pp. 983–995, 1955.

Levinson, A. A.: Studies in the Mica Group; Polymorphism among Illites and Hydrous Micas, *Am. Mineralogist,* vol. 40, pp. 41–49, 1955.

Smith, J. V., and H. S. Yoder: Experimental and Theoretical Studies of the Mica Polymorphs, *Mineral. Mag.,* vol. 31, pp. 209–235, 1956.

Yoder, H. S.: Synthetic and Natural Muscovites, *Geochim. et Cosmochim. Acta,* vol. 8, pp. 225–280, 1955.

Chlorite Group

Brindley, G. W., K. Robinson: The Chlorite Minerals. X-ray Identification and Structures of Clay Minerals, *Mineralog. Soc.,* London, pp. 173–198, 1951.

Hey, Max H.: A New Review of the Chlorites, *Mineral. Mag.,* vol. 30, pp. 277–292, 1954.

Lapham, Davis M.: Structural and Chemical Variation in Chromium Chlorite, *Am. Mineralogist*, vol. 43, pp. 921–956, 1958.

Winchell, A. N.: Chlorite as a Polycomponent System, *Am. J. Sci.*, vol. 2, pp. 283–300, 1926.

———: A Third Study of Chlorite. *Am. Mineralogist*, vol. 21, pp. 642–651, 1936.

———: Additional Notes on Chlorite, *Am. Mineralogist*, vol. 13, pp. 161–170, 1928.

Clay Mineral Group

Brindley, G. W.: X-ray Identification and Crystal Structures of Clay Minerals, Clay Minerals Group, *Mineralog. Soc.*, London, 1951.

Committee on Clay Minerals: Clays and clay minerals, Conferences 2, 3, and 4, *Nat. Research Council*, Washington, D.C., 1954, 1955, 1956.

Correns, C. W., and H. Piller: Mikroskopie der feinkörnigen Silikatminerale, Part 1: Mikroskopie der Gesteine; "Handbuch der Mikroskopie in der Technik," vol. 4, Umschau Verlag, Frankfurt, 1955.

Grim, R. E.: "Clay Mineralogy," McGraw-Hill Book Company, Inc., New York, 1953.

Keller, W. D.: "The Principles of Chemical Weathering," Lucas Brothers Publishers, Columbia, Mo., 1955.

Kerr, P. F. et al.: Reference Clay Minerals, *Am. Petrol. Inst. Res. Proj.* 49, New York, 1950.

Serpentine Group

Gruner, J. W.: Notes on the Structure of Serpentines, *Am. Mineralogist*, vol. 22, p. 103, 1937.

Kalousek, G. L., and L. E. Muttart: Studies on the Chrysotile and Antigorite Components of Serpentine, *Am. Mineralogist*, vol. 42, pp. 1–22, 1957.

Lodochnikov, W. N.: Serpentines and Serpentinites and the Petrological Problems Connected with them, *Problems Soviet Geol.*, vol. 2, pp. 145–150, 1933.

Nagy, B., and G. T. Faust: Serpentines: Natural Mixtures of Chrysotile and Antigorite, *Am. Mineralogist*, vol. 41, pp. 817–838, 1956.

Selfridge, G. C.: An X-ray and Optical Investigation of the Serpentine Minerals, *Am. Mineralogist*, vol. 21, pp. 463–503, 1936.

Whittaker, E. J. W., and J. Zussman: The Characterization of Serpentine Minerals by X-ray Diffraction, *Mineral. Mag.*, vol. 31, pp. 107–126, 1956.

Zussman, J., and G. W. Brindley: Electron Diffraction Studies of the Serpentine Minerals, *Am. Mineral.*, vol. 42, pp. 133–153, 1957.

Index

427